PROBLEMS AND SOLUTIONS IN LOGIC DESIGN

PROBLEMS AND SOLUTIONS IN LOGIC DESIGN

By

D. ZISSOS

Professor of Computing Science
and
Adjunct Professor of
Electrical Engineering
University of Calgary

with contributions by

F. G. DUNCAN

Reader in Computer Science
University of Bristol

and

J. C. BATHORY

University of Calgary

SECOND EDITION

OXFORD UNIVERSITY PRESS 1979

Oxford University Press, Walton Street, Oxford OX2 6DP

OXFORD LONDON GLASGOW
NEW YORK TORONTO MELBOURNE WELLINGTON
KUALA LUMPUR SINGAPORE JAKARTA HONG KONG TOKYO
DELHI BOMBAY CALCUTTA MADRAS KARACHI
NAIROBI DAR ES SALAAM CAPE TOWN

Casebound ISBN 0 19 859362 7
Paperback ISBN 0 19 859359 7

Printed in Great Britain
by Richard Clay (The Chaucer Press) Ltd.,
Bungay, Suffolk.

Preface

The function of a logic circuit, as indeed of any circuit, is to accept input signals and to generate output signals that bear a definite relationship to the input signals. Previously, logic circuits were designed empirically using informal techniques. Engineering constraints, such as fan-in restrictions and gate-speed tolerances, were not generally taken into account until the implementation or development stage.

The development of the sequential equations in 1969 made possible the specification of clear-cut step-by-step design procedures in which realistic circuit constraints are taken into account at the design level. These procedures, which require no engineering or specialist knowledge, consist essentially of (i) flow-charting the desired I/O signal relationship to be established by the circuit; (ii) writing down a set of simple equations; and (iii) drawing the circuit. The three stages are analogous to flow charting, writing the software statements, and executing a computer program. All our circuits work!

An important feature is that the documentation is inherent in the design. The use of state diagrams and sequential equations eliminates the possibility of confusion existing in verbal statements.

The book has been written with the following classes of reader in mind: the teacher with little experience in logic design who wants a reliable guide to the essentials of the subject; the experienced teacher who wants to deal with topics in depth; the examiner who wants a library of questions graded in complexity; the student, who is provided with a self-pacing set of exercises with solutions to refer to; the manager, who needs a working knowledge of logic design in order to appraise the hardware of digital systems; and the engineer, who has simple has clear-cut procedures to meet his needs both economically and reliably.

Thanks are due to Betty Cline and Marilyn Croot of the University of Calgary for their enthusiasm in preparing the text and illustrations.

Calgary D. Zissos

Contents

1. BASIC CONCEPTS IN LOGIC DESIGN 1
   - 1.1 Introduction 1
   - 1.2 The design philosophy 1
   - 1.3 Classification of logic circuits 1
   - 1.4 Gates and gate configurations 3
   - 1.5 State diagrams 7
   - 1.6 State variables 9
   - 1.7 Dummy states 9
   - 1.8 Unused states 11
   - 1.9 State tables 12
   - 1.10 State reduction 12
   - 1.11 'Don't care' conditions 15
   - 1.12 Causes of circuit misoperation 15
   - 1.13 Sequential equations 19
   - 1.14 The $33\frac{1}{3}$ per cent property 21
   - 1.15 Race hazards 22
   - 1.16 Multiplexor circuits 28

2. UNCLOCKED SEQUENTIAL CIRCUITS 35
   - 2.1 Introduction 35
   - 2.2 The design steps 35
   - 2.3 Problems and solutions 37

3. CLOCKED SEQUENTIAL CIRCUITS 82
   - 3.1 Introduction 82
   - 3.2 Clocked flip-flops 82
   - 3.3 The design steps 83
   - 3.4 Shift register arrangements 86
   - 3.5 Cyclic circuits 87
   - 3.6 Problems and solutions 90

4. PULSE-DRIVEN CIRCUITS 115
   - 4.1 Introduction 115
   - 4.2 Pulse-driven circuits 115
   - 4.3 The design steps 117
   - 4.4 Multi-mode sequential circuits 121
   - 4.5 Problems and solutions 123

5. COUNTERS 134
   - 5.1 Introduction 134
   - 5.2 Codes 134

5.3 The design steps 136
5.4 Synchronous 'up' binary counters (maximum length) 136
5.5 Synchronous 'down' binary counters (maximum length) 139
5.6 Synchronous 'up' Gray counters (maximum length) 140
5.7 Synchronous 'down' Gray counters (maximum length) 143
5.8 Up/down control 144
5.9 Synchronous 'up/down' binary counters 146
5.10 Synchronous 'up/down' Gray counters 146
5.11 Asynchronous (ripple-through) binary counters 146
5.12 Resettable counters 149
5.13 Decade counters 151
5.14 B-c-d counters 153
5.15 Johnson counters 154
5.16 Problems and solutions 154

6. COMBINATION CIRCUITS 170
6.1 Introduction 170
6.2 The merging table 172
6.3 Problems and solutions 176

APPENDIX 1. BOOLEAN ALGEBRA 194
A1.1 Basic concepts 194
A1.2 Boolean theorems 195
A1.3 Boolean reduction 199
A1.4 Boolean minimization 204
A1.5 Minterm and maxterm expressions 212
A1.6 The Karnaugh map 213
A1.7 Problems and answers 218

INDEX 221

1 *Basic Concepts in Logic Design*

In this chapter the basic concepts used in the design of logic circuits are discussed in detail and the adopted design philosophy is outlined. Detailed design procedures are developed.

All sequential circuits implemented using these procedures are inherently hazard-free when implemented with gates of plus or minus $33\frac{1}{3}$ per cent maximum speed variation, and always work.

1.1 INTRODUCTION

Up to 1969, when the Boolean sequential equations were developed, the design of sequential circuits was achieved through an empirical choice of unrelated informal techniques paying little attention to engineering constraints until, in most cases, the implementation stage. The advent of the sequential equations has made possible the development of clear-cut step-by-step design procedures in which realistic circuit constraints are taken into account at the design level. No engineering or other specialist knowledge is necessary to use these design procedures.

1.2 THE DESIGN PHILOSOPHY

The design philosophy adopted is one that allows the emphasis to be placed on optimal rather than minimal design. This is to enable the non-specialist, such as the student, the user with no specialist knowledge of 'electronics', and the less experienced designer, to produce sound and economical designs, while at the same time providing the means whereby the specialist designer may improve his technique in dealing with more sophisticated assemblies involving such devices as ROMs, RAMs, microprocessors, and so on.

The primary design objective is to produce sound and reliable circuits which are meaningful not only to the designer but also to the user.

1.3 CLASSIFICATION OF LOGIC CIRCUITS

Logic circuits are classified into two groups (see Figure 1.1), *combinational* and *sequential.*

A combinational circuit is one whose output is a function of its input signals, whereas a sequential circuit is one whose output is determined by the order in which the input signals are applied. Sequential circuits are sometimes said to have a sense of history. An everyday example of a combinational circuit is a domestic lighting circuit controlled by an ordinary tumbler switch. If the switch is up the light is on, and if the switch is down the light is off. A lighting circuit controlled by a cord-pull on the other hand is sequential, for the effect of pulling the cord depends on the current state of the circuit. If the light is on, a pull turns it off, and if the light is off, a pull turns it on.

Sequential circuits in turn are classified as:

(i) event-driven,
(ii) clock-driven, and
(iii) pulse-driven.

The above three categories of circuits are also referred to as *unclocked*, *clocked*, and *pulsed*, respectively.

Event-driven (unclocked) sequential circuits respond directly to changes in their input signals, in contrast to clock-driven circuits, whose operation is synchronized with the application of clock pulses, between which no changes of state can occur. Event-driven circuits can therefore operate at speeds which are limited only by the response time of their components, in contrast to the clock-driven circuits whose speed of operation is determined by the clock frequency, which must be low enough to accommodate the slowest circuit response. On the other hand, as we shall see in Chapters 2 and 3, clock-driven circuits are easier to design and implement, particularly when the number of input and output signals involved is large and/or their relationship is complex, as, for example, in microprocessor systems.

When the input signals are non-overlapping pulses, simplicity of design and fast circuit response can be readily accommodated by circuits implemented with T flip-flops (TFFs) and gates, as we show in Chapter 4. We shall refer to these circuits as *pulse-driven circuits.*

If a sequential circuit returns to its initial state after a specified number of changes in the input stage, we refer to it as *cyclic circuit*; otherwise it is classified as a *non-cyclic circuit. Counters* are cyclic circuits whose output in a specified binary code gives the number of changes of the input signal or the number of the input pulses received since the circuit was in its initial state. Counters in turn are classified as *synchronous* or *asynchronous* (ripple-through), see Fig. 1.1. Their functional characteristics and suitable design procedures are discussed in Chapter 5.

Sequential circuits can be described

(i) *verbally*, by means of word statements,
(ii) *diagrammatically*, by means of state diagrams,
(iii) *tabularly*, by means of state tables, and
(iv) *algebraically*, by means of Boolean statements, loosely referred to as sequential equations.

Although these methods are described in detail later in this chapter, their main features are outlined below.

Generally speaking, verbal statements are subject to misinterpretation

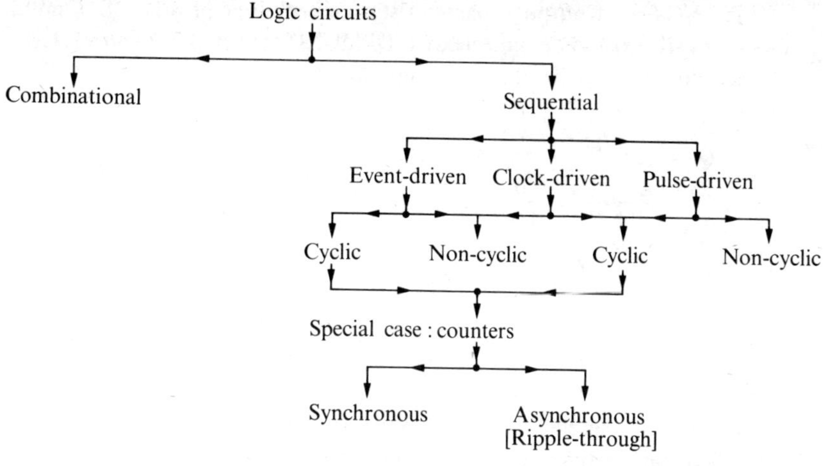

FIG. 1.1

and they may have to be translated into a different language, which in itself can result in further ambiguities. State diagrams are completely free of ambiguities and they emphasize the operational features of the circuit. No language or specialist knowledge is required. This is a useful factor when exporting systems, as their operation and circuit features can be understood with minimum knowledge of English, or of the language used by the exporting organization. State tables are used primarily in the design stage for reducing the size of the circuit, when such a reduction is possible. Sequential equations were recently developed (by Duncan and Zissos) and allow all engineering constraints, such as gate fan-in and fan-out restrictions, and gate minimality, to be met realistically before the circuit is implemented.

1.4 GATES AND GATE CONFIGURATIONS

There exists nowadays a great variety of i.c. (integrated circuit) chips, which can accommodate combinations of logic elements ranging from a few gates to complex logic circuits, such as the m.p.u. of a microprocessor. Clearly, the designer has the option of implementing a logic system using several types of i.c. chips with a view to reducing the chip count and/or the wiring. The reader's attention, however, is drawn to the fact that in such cases great care must be exercised to avoid race-hazards, which may cause the circuit to misoperate. Race-hazards and their suppression are discussed in Section 1.15. On the other hand, circuits which are implemented using AND, OR, and INVERTER gates (and flip-flops in the case of sequential circuits), or only NAND gates, or only NOR gates, can be made to be hazard-free, as stated at the beginning of the book and as will be proved in Section 1.14.

The I/O (input/output) characteristics of each type of gate and of multiplexors (MUXs) and demultiplexors (DEMUXs) are listed in Figure 1.2. By direct reference to this Figure, we obtain:

$$
\begin{aligned}
P &= AB \\
Q &= A + B \\
R &= \overline{AB} = \overline{A} + \overline{B} \\
S &= \overline{A + B} = \overline{A}\cdot\overline{B} \\
T &= \overline{ABC} = \overline{A} + \overline{B} + \overline{C} \\
U &= \overline{A + B + C} = \overline{A}\,\overline{B}\,\overline{C} \\
V &= \overline{A} \\
W &= \overline{B}\overline{A}a + \overline{B}Ab + B\overline{A}c + BAd, \text{ and} \\
K &= \overline{B}\overline{A}a,\ L = \overline{B}Aa,\ M = B\overline{A}a, \text{ and } N = BAa
\end{aligned}
$$

Circuits composed entirely of NAND or entirely of NOR gates are generally more economical and convenient to use than circuits using AND, OR, and INVERTER gates. We shall therefore concentrate on the design of all-NAND or all-NOR circuits. As the design of a NOR circuit is the same as that of a NAND circuit for the dual function, we shall confine our attention to NAND gates. For example, to implement the NOR circuit of a Boolean function we derive the NAND circuit of the dual function and replace the NAND gates in our solution by NOR gates. This is illustrated at the end of the next section.

NAND circuits

A NAND gate generates the OR function of its input signals in their inverted form. For example, the output of a NAND gate driven by signals A and $\overline{B}$ is $\overline{A\cdot\overline{B}}$, which expands to $\overline{A} + B$. Two levels of NAND gates generate a two-level sum-of-products expression, as shown in Figure 1.3. In general n levels of NAND gates generate an n-level sum-of-products expression. We use symbol g_n to denote the output of the gate whose number in Figure 1.3 is n.

Reference to Figure 1.3 shows the one-to-one relationship that exists between a sum-of-products expression and its NAND implementation. The reader's attention is drawn to the fact that the implementation of a minimal sum-of-products expression does not necessarily result in a minimal circuit. For example, the implementation of the minimal expression $A\overline{B} + \overline{A}B$ requires 5 gates (fourth circuit in Figure 1.3), whereas the NAND circuit implementing is non-minimal form $A(\overline{A} + \overline{B}) + (\overline{A} + \overline{B})B$ requires one gate less (fifth circuit in Figure 1.3). The derivation of the correct form of a Boolean expression for minimal circuit implementation is discussed in Chapter 6. The last two circuit diagrams in Figure 1.3 show NAND implementations of a MUX and of a DEMUX.

NOR circuits

As we explained earlier, because of the dual property that exists between

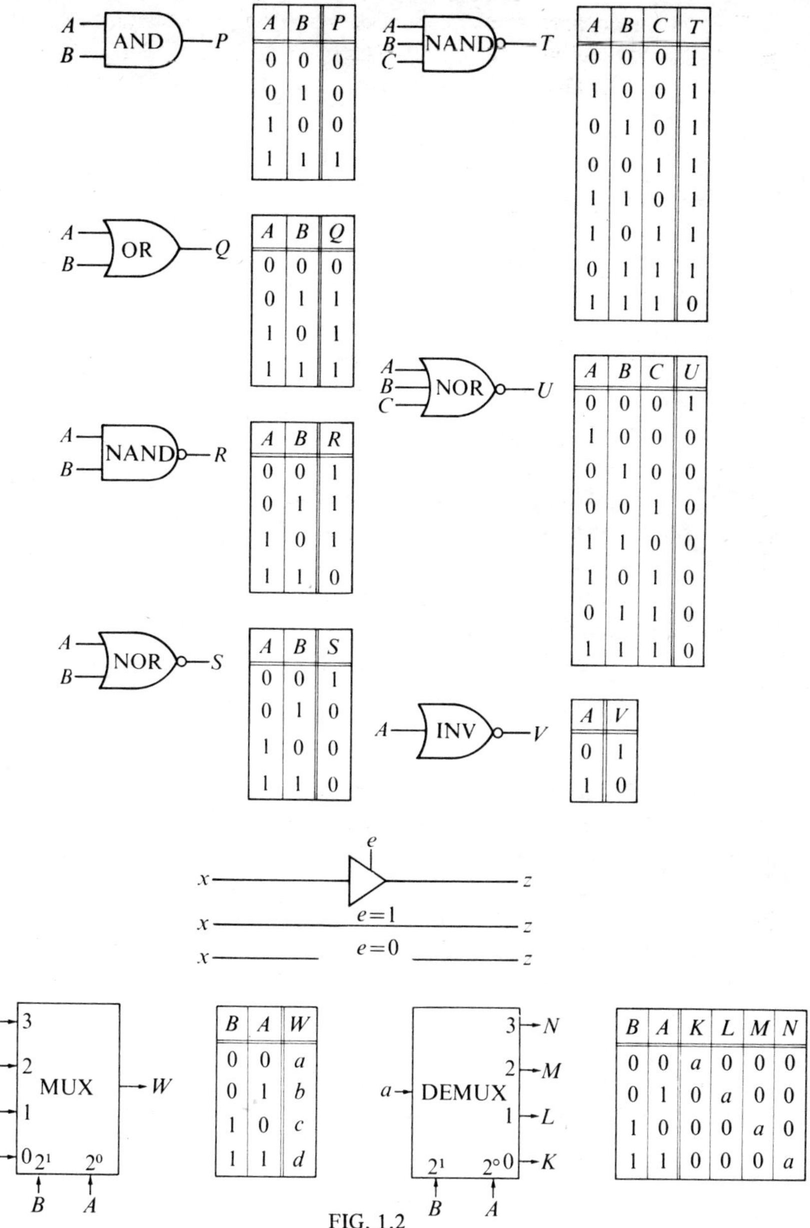

A	B	P
0	0	0
0	1	0
1	0	0
1	1	1

A	B	Q
0	0	0
0	1	1
1	0	1
1	1	1

A	B	R
0	0	1
0	1	1
1	0	1
1	1	0

A	B	S
0	0	1
0	1	0
1	0	0
1	1	0

A	B	C	T
0	0	0	1
1	0	0	1
0	1	0	1
0	0	1	1
1	1	0	1
1	0	1	1
0	1	1	1
1	1	1	0

A	B	C	U
0	0	0	1
1	0	0	0
0	1	0	0
0	0	1	0
1	1	0	0
1	0	1	0
0	1	1	0
1	1	1	0

A	V
0	1
1	0

B	A	W
0	0	*a*
0	1	*b*
1	0	*c*
1	1	*d*

B	A	K	L	M	N
0	0	*a*	0	0	0
0	1	0	*a*	0	0
1	0	0	0	*a*	0
1	1	0	0	0	*a*

FIG. 1.2

NOR and NAND gates, it follows that if a given configuration of NAND gates generates a function, the same configuration of NOR gates will generate the dual of the signal. For example, if the NAND gates in Figure 1.3 were replaced by NOR gates the outputs of the first six circuits would be

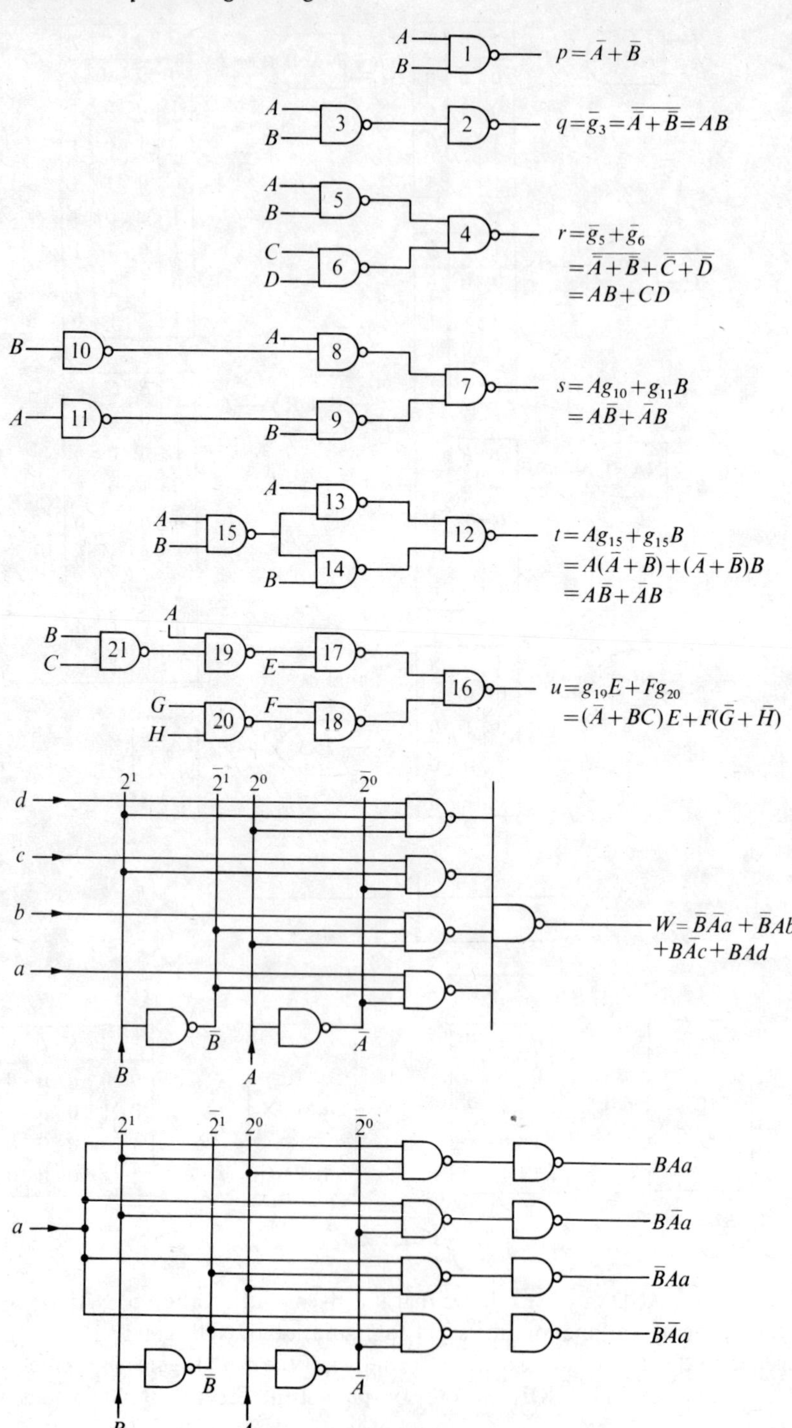
A
B
1
$p=\bar{A}+\bar{B}$
A
B
3
2
$q=\bar{g}_3=\overline{\bar{A}+\bar{B}}=AB$
A
B
5
C
D
6
4
$r=\bar{g}_5+\bar{g}_6$
$=\overline{\bar{A}+\bar{B}}+\overline{\bar{C}+\bar{D}}$
$=AB+CD$
B
10
A
8
A
11
B
9
7
$s=Ag_{10}+g_{11}B$
$=A\bar{B}+\bar{A}B$
A
13
A
B
15
B
14
12
$t=Ag_{15}+g_{15}B$
$=A(\bar{A}+\bar{B})+(\bar{A}+\bar{B})B$
$=A\bar{B}+\bar{A}B$
A
B
C
21
19
17
E
G
H
20
F
18
16
$u=g_{19}E+Fg_{20}$
$=(\bar{A}+BC)E+F(\bar{G}+\bar{H})$
2^1
$\bar{2}^1$
2^0
$\bar{2}^0$
d
c
b
a
$\bar{B}$
$\bar{A}$
B
A
$W=\bar{B}\bar{A}a+\bar{B}Ab$
$+B\bar{A}c+BAd$
2^1
$\bar{2}^1$
2^0
$\bar{2}^0$
a
BAa
$B\bar{A}a$
$\bar{B}Aa$
$\bar{B}\bar{A}a$
$\bar{B}$
$\bar{A}$
B
A

FIG. 1.3.

$\overline{A}\overline{B}$, $A+B$, $(A+B)(C+D)$, $(A+\overline{B})(\overline{A}+B)$,
$(A+\overline{B})(\overline{A}+B)$, $[\overline{A}(B+C)+E][F+\overline{G}\overline{H}]$.

Tristates

Tristates were developed in 1969 by H. Mine and others at Kyoto University. Each gate has one input, one output, and one enable terminal, as shown in Figure 1.2. When $e=1$ the gate behaves like a short circuit, that is, the output follows the input $z=x$. When $e=0$ the gate is tristated, that is, it behaves like an open circuit.

MUX circuits

The block diagrams and truth tables of a 4 to 1 multiplexor (MUX) and a 1 to 4 demultiplexor (DEMUX) are shown in Figure 1.2.

The implementation of circuits using MUXs and DEMUXs is discussed in Section 1.16.

1.5 STATE DIAGRAMS

In a state diagram nodes represent states and lines linking nodes inter-state transitions. The direction of a transition is shown by an arrow pointing to the destination state. The signal condition that initiates the transition is indicated by its Boolean function inserted either above or below the line. For example, $S0 \bullet\!\xrightarrow{X\overline{Y}}\!\bullet\, S1$ indicates that the circuit moves from state $S0$ to $S1$ when $X\overline{Y}=1$, i.e. when $X=1$ and $Y=0$.

State diagrams can be used to describe both the external and internal operations of sequential circuits. In the first case we refer to them as *external-state diagrams* and in the second case as *internal-state diagrams.* The external- and internal-state diagrams of a circuit that allows the activation of a switch X in Figure 1.4(a) to operate in turn two lights, $L1$ and $L2$, are shown in Figure 1.4(b) and (c). Variables X_n and X_{n+1} are used to indicate the nth and $(n+1)$th activation of the switch. Note that

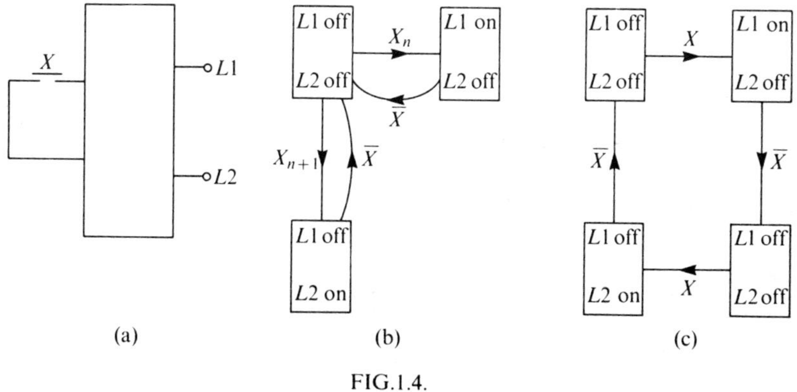

FIG.1.4.

the external-state diagram closely resembles a flow chart, which as in the case of programming can be drawn with very little, if any, regard for its implementation.

There are no hard-and-fast rules that can be used to develop internal-state diagrams. Since such diagrams describe the internal operation of a machine, the designer usually makes arbitrary choices depending on past experience, his understanding of the problem, availability of components, etc., which can lead to different but equivalent results. This is often a source of concern to newcomers (particularly to students) when they compare their own apparently clumsy internal-state diagrams with more

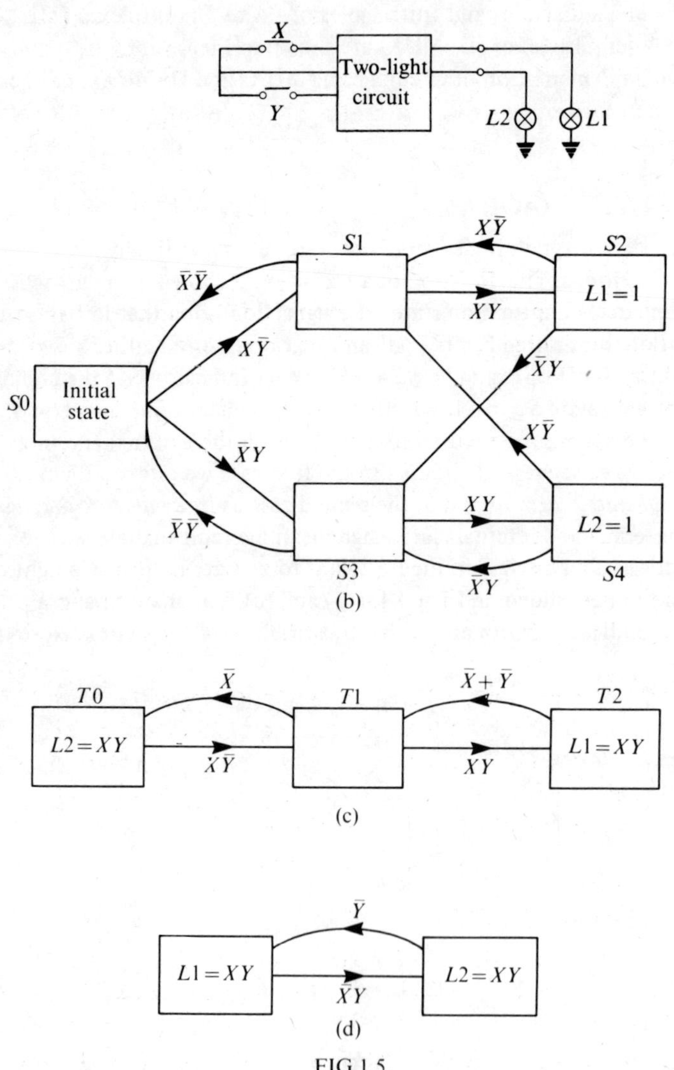

(b)

(c)

(d)

FIG.1.5.

refined versions developed by experienced designers or their instructors. In such cases, one should aim for accuracy of performance rather than elegance of design bearing in mind that the latter will be acquired with practice.

The following example is used to illustrate typical variations in the internal-state diagrams of a relatively simple light circuit in Figure 1.5. The function of the circuit is to turn lamp $L1$ on when the two switches X and Y are activated in that order, and lamp $L2$ on when the switches are activated in the reverse order. Three different but correct versions of the internal operation of the required circuit are shown in (b), (c), and (d).

Most persons attempting this problem would probably derive internal state diagram (b). A more experienced designer might derive (c), and very few, if indeed any, would arrive at (d) the first time round. As we shall see later the circuit implementation of (d) is the simplest. Before we discuss methods of reducing state diagrams (b) and (c) to (d), the reader's attention is drawn to the fact that at each internal state the circuit outputs must be clearly specified.

1.6 STATE VARIABLES

The circuit implementation of a given state diagram consists of defining each state by a unique combination of logic signals called *state variables* or *secondary signals.* Clearly one state variable, A, defines two states, one by $A = 0$ and the other by $A = 1$. Two state variables define four states, each state corresponding to a combination of their values 00, 01, 11, and 10. In general n variables define 2^n states.

For example the four states $S0$, $S1$, $S2$, and $S3$ in Figure 1.4(c) can be defined by $AB = 00, 01, 11, 10$. In allocating secondary signals to states in unclocked circuits one must ensure that each circuit transition involves a change in the value of a single signal only. The reason for this restriction is described later in Section 1.12. This restriction does not apply to clocked circuits.

The most convenient method of allocating secondary signals in unclocked circuits is with the aid of the *race-free diagrams*, illustrated in Figure 1.6 for up to 16 states. All states that differ in one variable only are linked by a dotted line. Therefore, races between secondary signals are automatically avoided if each circuit transition lies on a race-free line.

1.7 DUMMY STATES

There are certain patterns of internal-state diagrams that cannot be assigned race-free codes. Such a pattern is shown in Figure 1.7(a). Clearly if the state codes for $S0$, $S1$, and $S2$ are 00, 01, and 11 respectively, the direct transition from state $S2$ to state $S0$ cannot be implemented, as this

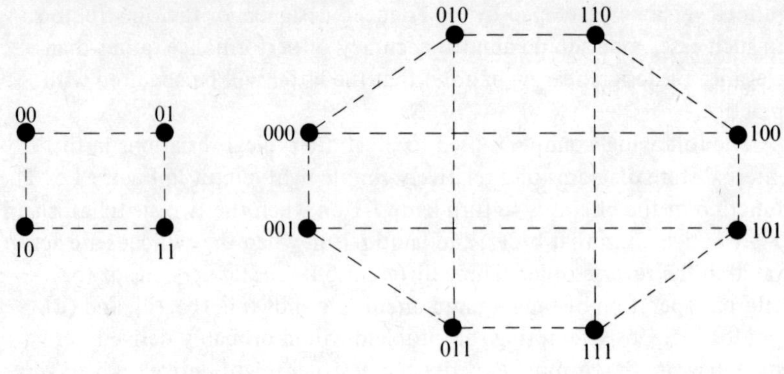

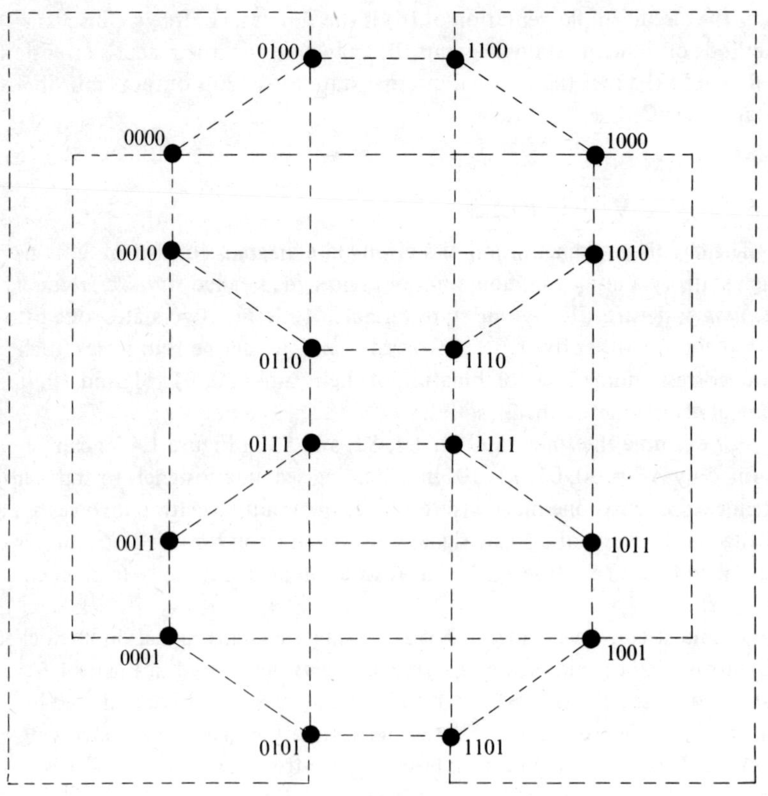

FIG. 1.6.

would involve the simultaneous change in the value of two signals A and B from 11 to 00. In cases like this the offending direct link can be replaced by a number of race-free links.

One method of implementing this is to introduce a dummy state, $S3$ in our example. This replaces line $S2 - S0$ by race-free links $S2 - S3$ and

*S*3 - *S*0. The *S*3 - *S*0 transition is unconditional, i.e. once the circuit assumes state *S*3 it moves automatically to state *S*0. In terms of the state variables this ensures that signal *B* is first turned off, which in turn turns signal *A* off.

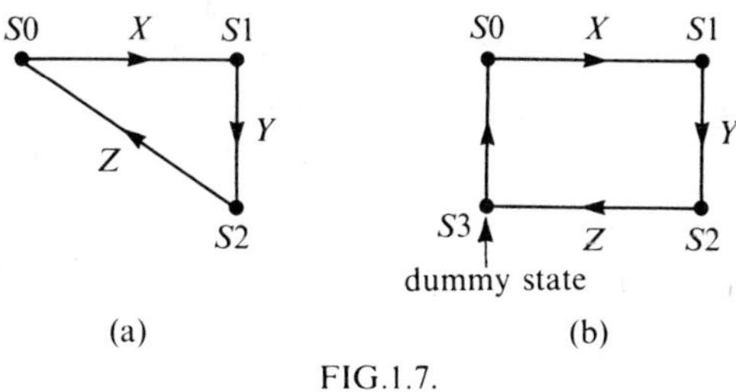

FIG.1.7.

1.8 UNUSED STATES

If the number of states to be implemented is *N*, where $2^{n-1} < N < 2^n$, there will be clearly $2^n - N$ *unused* or *redundant states.* In the case of a six-state diagram, there will be two unused state - see Figure 1.8. Although theoretically one can assume that a circuit does not move into a redundant state, such a possibility cannot be excluded in practice. For example when the circuit is in state *S*3 a noise signal could turn signal *B* off, which would cause the circuit to assume redundant state *S*7. If such a circuit is inter-clocked with other circuits in a system, moving into state *S*7 will get it out of step with the other circuits with consequences of varying degrees.

The designer is therefore strongly advised to take such a possibility into account at the design level and predetermine the desired action. For example if the above circuit going out of step can jam a production line, a possible action would be to use signal $A\overline{B}$ (defining the two unused states) to turn

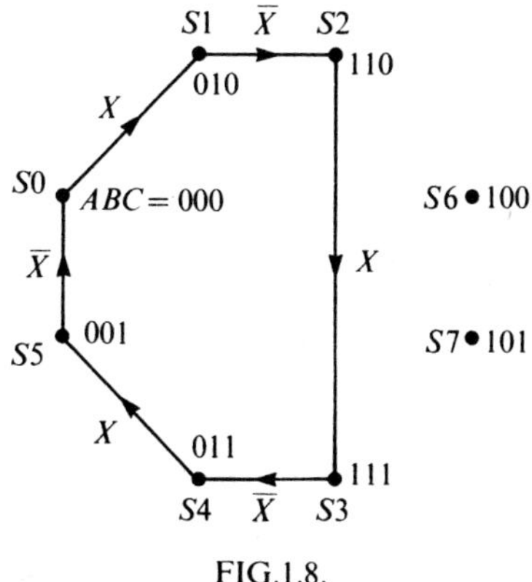

FIG.1.8.

off all the machines that have to be stopped and trip an alarm. Clearly the exact action can only be defined in reference to specific systems, but it must be done at the design level and with safety foremost in mind.

In summary, no state diagram containing other than 2^n states must be implemented. Referring to our light circuit in Figure 1.5, only state diagram (d) can be implemented directly. The implementation of (c) and (b) would require the addition of one and three states respectively. The question now arises as to whether one can reduce the number of states to 2^n. Specifically, can the state diagrams in Figure 1.5(b) and (c) be reduced to the two state diagram in Figure 1.5(d). Under certain conditions it is possible to do so using Caldwell's state reduction steps. As this method is based on merging rows in state tables, before we discuss the steps it is necessary to describe the state tables.

1.9 STATE TABLES

The operation of a logic circuit can be displayed on a table, the *state table.* Such a table has as many rows as states and as many columns as combinations of input signals (input states). Each row corresponds to a state in the diagram, and each column to an input state. The rows and columns are headed by labels representing the corresponding inputs and states. In each square we enter the circuit destination, i.e. the next state that the circuit assumes when it is in a state represented by the row heading and the input signals are those specified by the column heading.* If the designer does not wish to specify the next state to be assumed (see §1.11) under certain circuit conditions, he can leave the entry in the corresponding square blank. As in the case of state diagrams in each square we must specify the circuit outputs, unless it is a blank square. Clearly, if the circuit destination is the same as its current state, the circuit is stable – in such cases it is the convention to circle the entries.

The state tables corresponding to Figure 1.5(b) and 1.8 are shown in Figure 1.9(a) and (b) respectively.

1.10 STATE REDUCTION

The process of combining the rows of a state table is made in accordance with the following rules.

1. Two or more rows may be merged when either of the following two conditions is met. (a) The state numbers and the circuit outputs appearing in corresponding columns of each row are alike, or if the

* In the case of clocked circuits, we omit the clock signals from our state tables since it has already been specified that circuit changes can only be initiated by clock pulses – see Chapter 3.

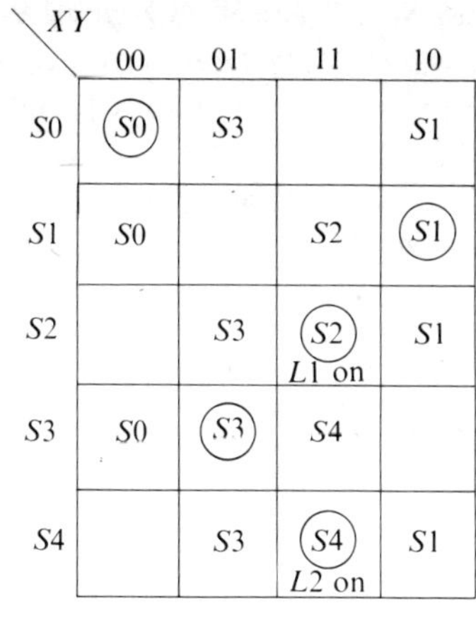

XY	00	01	11	10
S0	(S0)	S3		S1
S1	S0		S2	(S1)
S2		S3	(S2) L1 on	S1
S3	S0	(S3)	S4	
S4		S3	(S4) L2 on	S1

(a)

X	0	1
S0	(S0)	S1
S1	S2	(S1)
S2	(S2)	S3
S3	S4	(S3)
S4	(S4)	S5
S5	S0	(S5) Z=1

(b)

FIG.1.9.

entry in one or both of the rows is blank. (b) The uncircled entries and the circled outputs appearing in corresponding columns of each row are alike, or if the entry in one or both rows is blank.

2. When circled and uncircled entries of the same state numbers are to be combined, the resulting entry is circled. Thus the two rows

3	(5)		
3	5	6	(8)

combine into

3	(5)	6	(8)

Note that a change from state 5 to state 8 now involves a change of the input state only. When a row S_m is merged with a row S_n we shall denote the new row by S_{mn}.

When circled entries merge the resultant entry is circled. For example

3_0	$(5)_1$		7_1
3_0	$(8)_1$	6_ϕ	7_1

combine into

3_0	$(58)_1$	6_ϕ	7_1

– see state reduction problem 24 in next chapter.

Using these rules we can merge rows $S0$, $S1$, and $S2$ in Figure 1.9(a) into row $S012$ and rows $S3$ and $S4$ into row $S34$, as shown in Figure 1.10(a). The corresponding state diagram is shown in Figure 1.10(b). Note that it is identical to the state diagram in Figure 1.5(d).

No merging of rows is possible in Figure 1.9(b), since no two rows have the same entries in corresponding columns.

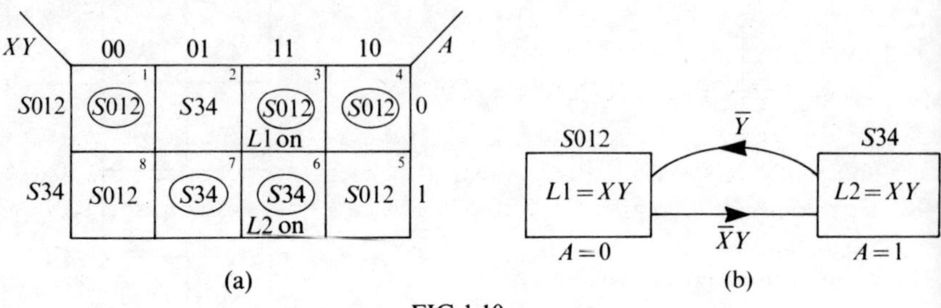

FIG.1.10

The reader is advised to apply the reduction steps to the state diagram in Figure 1.5(c) - the results in summary form are shown in Figure 1.11.

At first sight no merging is possible. However, both entries in squares 9 and 10 can be replaced by $T0$, which generates the correct conditions for merging states $T1$ and $T2$. The equivalent state diagram is shown in Figure 1.11(c).

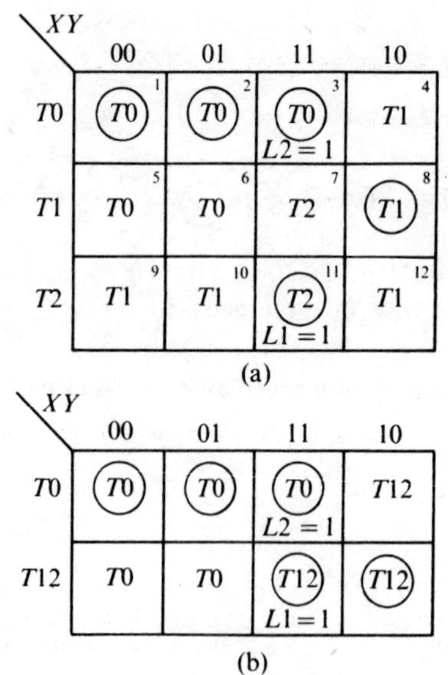

FIG.1.11

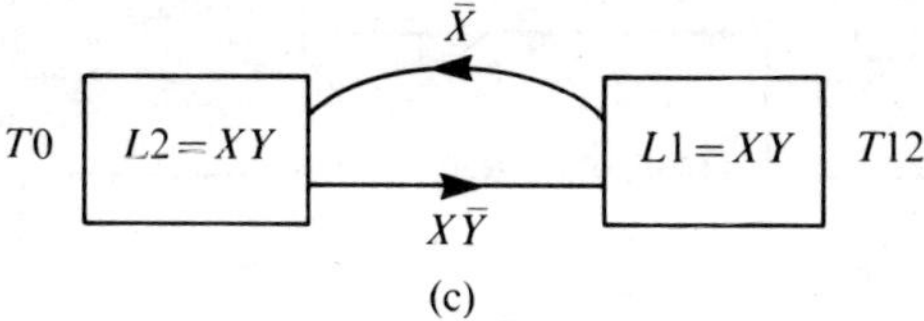

(c)

FIG.1.11 (continued)

1.11 'DON'T CARE' CONDITIONS

'Don't care' conditions are circuit conditions for which the designer has chosen not to specify the response of the circuit, on the assumption that they do not arise in practice. Unused states in a state diagram are a typical example.

Boolean expressions defining 'don't care' conditions can be used as optional products to reduce the circuit equations and hence the complexity of the circuit.

The assumption that certain circuit conditions do not arise in practice is valid only for normal operation. Since one cannot exclude the possibility of abnormal conditions occurring in real life, the designer is strongly advised not to leave undefined the response of circuits under such conditions. In other words, there are no circuit conditions for which the responsible designer can afford not to care. The reader is therefore strongly advised against the mathematically convenient use of 'don't care circuit conditions.

1.12 CAUSES OF CIRCUIT MISOPERATION

Circuit misoperation is said to occur when the circuit assumes an internal state other than the one intended. For example, if on leaving state $S0$ in Figure 1.12 with $X = Y = 1$ it assumes a state other than $S3$, circuit misoperation occurs. Excluding component failure, the causes of circuit misoperation in unclocked circuits are:

1. races between primary signals,
2. races between secondary signals, and
3. races between primary and secondary signals.

We shall examine each of the three causes in turn and suggest solutions in each case.

Races between primary signals

Consider the implementation of the circuit shown in Figure 1.12. It is required to operate three lamps, $L1$, $L2$, and $L3$, according to the following specifications.

1. Lamp $L1$ is to turn on when both input switches are operated, but only if switch X is operated before switch Y.

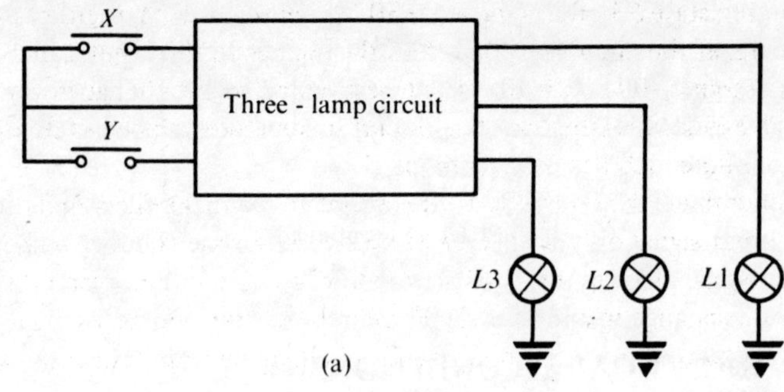

(a)

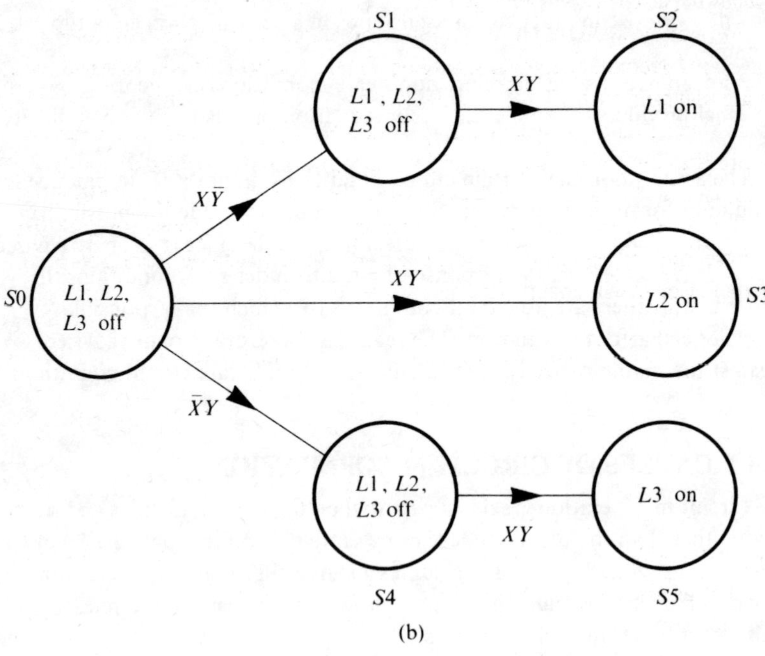

(b)

FIG. 1.12

2. Lamp $L2$ is to turn on when both input switches are operated simultaneously.
3. Lamp $L3$ is to turn on when both switches are operated, but only if switch Y is operated before switch X.

Now in practice a logic circuit, and indeed any type of circuit, responds with different speeds to changes in the input signals. Therefore the response time of our circuit to a change in the input signal X must be assumed to be different from the response time to a change in the input signal Y.

The effect of this fact in our example is as follows. When we operate the two input switches X and Y simultaneously, instead of our circuit assuming state $S3$ on leaving state $S0$ in Figure 1.12(b), it either assumes state $S2$, if the circuit responded to the change in the input signal X first or it assumes state $S5$ if the circuit responded to the change in the input signal Y first. In either case the circuit misoperates, since a state other than the one intended has been assumed.

Since there is no remedy to this problem we make the stipulation that one input signal only is allowed to change at a time. That is, before an input signal changes, we shall assume that the circuit has responded to the previous change in an input signal. Should we not in practice be able to prevent two or more input signals from changing simultaneously, we would use staticisors.

Races between secondary signals

We will now discuss how circuit misoperation can result from races involving secondary signals. Consider Figure 1.13(a). This is the internal state diagram of the T flip-flop, where the coding of the internal states is such that circuit transitions $S0$ to $S1$ and $S2$ to $S3$ involve the change of more than one secondary signal. Let us first consider the transition from $S0$ to $S1$. This involves the change of secondary signals A and B from 0,0 to 1,1. Now in practice because of variations in the response times of the two secondary signals to the change in the input signal X from 0 to 1, either A or B will change first.

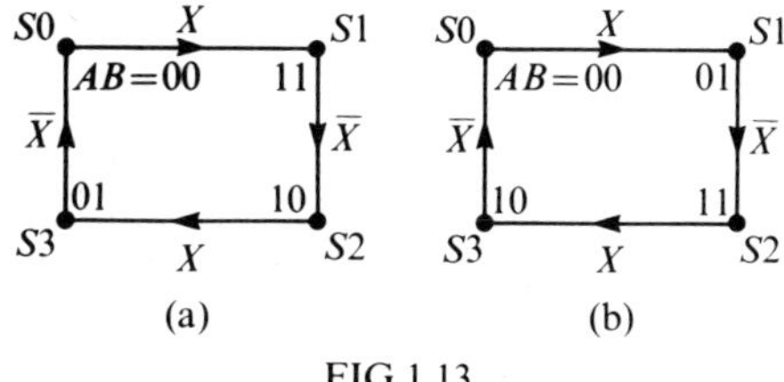

FIG.1.13.

Let us assume that A changes first. This means that the switching sequence of the secondary signals A and B is

$$00 \qquad 10 \qquad 11,$$

which are the binary codes for states $S0$, $S2$, and $S1$ respectively in Figure 1.13(a). The implication of this is that the circuit when it leaves $S0$ first assumes state $S2$. From state $S2$, because $X = 1$, the circuit is directed to state $S3$, which is stable for $X = 1$. This clearly results in circuit misoperation, since on leaving state $S0$ the circuit assumes state $S3$ instead of state $S1$.

Let us assume next that signal B changes faster than signal A. In this case the switching sequence of the secondary signals A and B is

$$00 \qquad 01 \qquad 11,$$

which are the binary codes of the states $S0$, $S3$, and $S1$ respectively in

Figure 1.13(a). That is, the circuit on leaving state $S0$ first assumes state $S3$, from which no further transitions are initiated with $X = 1$. Since the circuit assumes the wrong state (state $S3$ instead of state $S1$), clearly circuit misoperation again results.

The solution to this problem is to ensure that each circuit transition involves the change of a single secondary signal only as in Figure 1.13(b). The most convenient way of implementing this solution is with the aid of the race-free diagrams shown in Figure 1.6. See also Section 1.6.

Races between primary and secondary signals

Let us consider the circuit implementation of Figure 1.13(b) in its block schematic form - its NAND circuit implementation is derived in the next section. We designate, for reference purposes, letters *a* and *b* to the two circuit sections that generate the secondary signals A and B - see Figure 1.14. We shall assume that signal X drives circuit *a* in its inverted form and circuit *b* in its uninverted form.

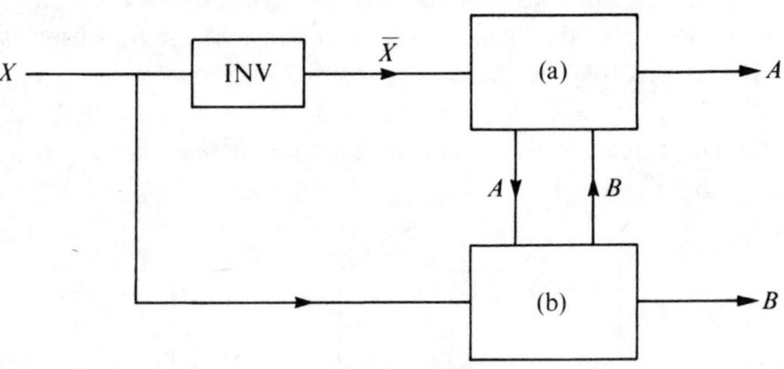

FIG. 1.14

Let us consider the $S0$ to $S1$ circuit transition in Figure 1.13(b). This transition will take place in the time it takes to turn on secondary signal B - let us denote this time by *ts*. Let us next denote the time it takes for the inverter in Figure 1.14 to respond to a change in X by *tp*.

Now if $tp > ts$ the following sequence of events takes place.

1. Signal B changes to 1 causing the circuit to assume state $S1$ at *ts*.
2. On assuming state $S1$ the conditions for turning signal A on are generated - viz. $\overline{X} = 1$ and $B = 1$.
3. Secondary signal A turns on causing the circuit to move to state $S2$.
4. On assuming state $S2$, the circuit moves to state $S3$ since $X = 1$.

If $tp < ts$ on assuming state $S1$ the input signal to circuit section *a* has already changed ($\overline{X} = 0$), resulting in a stable circuit condition.

Unlike in the previous two cases, in this case elimination of primary to secondary signal races cannot be achieved, since a change in a secondary signal is caused by a change in the primary signal. Therefore, to avoid circuit misoperation we simply ensure that $tp \leqslant ts$.

It follows that no circuit misoperation will occur if we ensure that the maximum delay associated with an input signal, *tp* max, is less than the minimum delay associated with a secondary signal *ts* min -

$$\frac{tp \max}{ts \min} < 1 \tag{1.1}$$

1.13 SEQUENTIAL EQUATIONS

Having defined the internal operation of an unclocked sequential circuit by means of a state diagram and having assigned suitable binary codes to the states, we proceed to derive Boolean expressions for the secondary and output signals. The secondary signals are expressed algebraically by means of Boolean statements, analogous to programming statements of the form $n = n + 1$. These Boolean statements are loosely referred to as *sequential equations.*

There are two basic forms of sequential equations. In the case of a secondary signal A, these are:

$$A = \Sigma \text{ turn-on sets of } A + A \cdot (\Sigma \overline{\text{turn-off sets of } A}) \tag{1.2}$$

$$A = (\Sigma \text{ turn-on sets of } A + A)(\Sigma \overline{\text{turn-off sets of } A}), \tag{1.3}$$

the terms having meanings as follows:

Turn-on set of a secondary signal is a set of Boolean variables, which when equal to 1, cause the secondary signal to turn on (i.e. assume the value of 1). By analogy,

Turn-off set of a secondary signal is a set of Boolean variables which when equal to 1, cause the secondary signal to turn off (i.e. assume the value of 0).

Equation 1.2 is used when the design is to be implemented with NAND gates and equation 1.3 when it is to be implemented with NOR gates. We therefore refer to them as NAND and NOR sequential equations respectively.

The turn-on and turn-off sets of secondary signals are derived directly from the state diagram. For example, by direct reference to Figure 1.13(b), we obtain:

$$\begin{aligned} \text{Turn-on set of } A &= B\overline{X} & \qquad \text{Turn-on set of } B &= \overline{A}X \\ \text{Turn-off set of } A &= \overline{B}\overline{X} & \qquad \text{Turn-off set of } B &= AX. \end{aligned}$$

Substituting these values in equation 1.2, we obtain the circuit's NAND equations.

$$\begin{aligned} A &= B\overline{X} + A(B + X) \\ B &= \overline{A}X + B(\overline{A} + \overline{X}). \end{aligned}$$

Similarly when we substitute these values in equation 1.3, we obtain the circuit's NOR equations:

$$A = (B\overline{X} + A)(B + X)$$
$$B = (\overline{A}X + B)(\overline{A} + \overline{X}).$$

Their NAND and NOR implementations are shown in Figure 1.15(a) and (b).

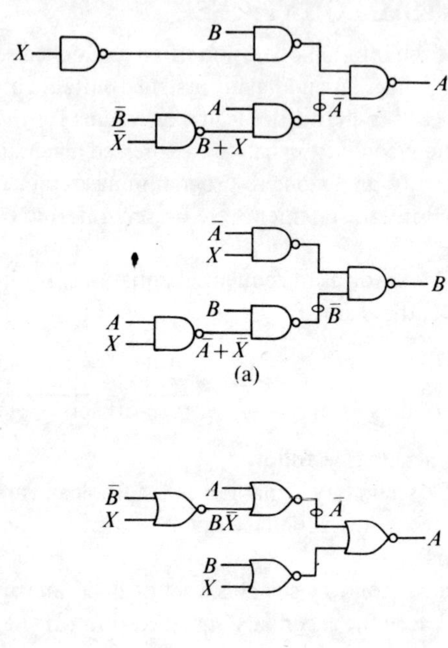

FIG.1.15

The NAND sequential equations of the six-state diagram in Figure 1.8 are

$$A = B\overline{C}\overline{X} + A(\overline{B} + \overline{C} + X)$$
$$B = \overline{A}\overline{C}X + B(A + \overline{C} + \overline{X})$$
$$C = ABX + C(A + B + X).$$

Since the optional product BC defining the two unused states $S6$ and $S7$ has not been used, the circuit will automatically lock should it assume one of these states.

The general form of a NAND sequential equation with s and r as turn-on and turn-off sets is

$$A = s + A\bar{r}. \qquad (1.4)$$

Its NAND implementation is shown in Figure 1.16.

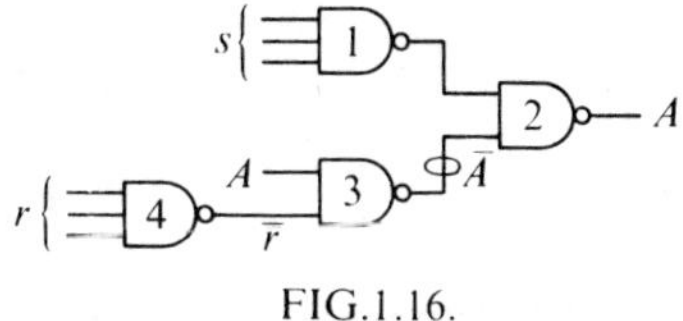

FIG.1.16.

Inverting both sides of equation 1.4, we obtain

$$\begin{aligned} \bar{A} &= \bar{s}(\bar{A} + r) \\ &= \bar{s}\bar{A} + \bar{s}r. \qquad (1.5) \end{aligned}$$

Now $sr = 0$, since s and r cannot equal 1 simultaneously. Similarly $s\bar{A} = 0$, since when $s = 1, A$ is turned on, i.e. $A = 1$. Adding sr and $s\bar{A}$ to equation 1.5 we obtain

$$\begin{aligned} \bar{A} &= \bar{s}\bar{A} + \bar{s}r + sr + s\bar{A} \\ &= \bar{A}(s + \bar{s}) + r(s + \bar{s}) \\ &= \bar{A} + r \\ &= \text{output of gate 3, in Figure 1.16.} \end{aligned}$$

This is not a surprising result since gates 2 and 3 being connected back-to-back form a conventional SRFF (set-reset flip-flop).

1.14 THE $33\frac{1}{3}$ PER CENT PROPERTY

It was stated at the beginning of the chapter that all our sequential circuits are hazard-free when implemented with gates whose maximum speed tolerance is $\pm 33\frac{1}{3}$ per cent. If for example, the nominal propagation time of a gate is $10n$ secs, the fastest gate can be switched in $6.7n$ secs and the slowest in $13.3n$ secs without the circuit misoperating.

The justification of this statement is as follows:

The maximum delay by which a primary signal in primitive sequential circuits can be delayed is 1 gate delay, tg, when it has to be invited. Allowing x per cent variation due to production spread, loading, etc., tp max $= tg(1 + x)$.

The minimum delay associated with a secondary signal is $2tg$, since at least two levels of switching are involved – see equations 1.2 and 1.3. Allowing x per cent variation, ts min $= 2tg(1 - x)$.

Substituting these values in equation 1.1, we obtain:

$$\frac{tg(1+x)}{2tg(1-x)} \leqslant 1 \text{ for no misoperation}$$

$$1+x \leqslant 2(1-x)$$

$$3x \leqslant 1$$

$x \leqslant \frac{1}{3}$ - *the required proof.*

The reader should note that the $33\frac{1}{3}$ per cent property applies to circuits implementing sequential equations in their primitive form - i.e. equation 1.2 or equation 1.3. Algebraic manipulating of the primitive sequential equations will clearly upset the relative delays of the primary and secondary signals and therefore invalidate the $\pm 33\frac{1}{3}$ per cent property. Although processing of sequential equations is possible, it is not advised. The interested reader is referred to *Logic Design Algorithms* by D. Zissos, Oxford University Press (1972). The $33\frac{1}{3}$ per cent figure represents a theoretical maximum - in practice it can be increased considerably by taking into account the filtering effect of the switching elements and also on statistical grounds of the probability of two of the fastest gates in a circuit racing the slowest gate in a critical.

1.15 RACE HAZARDS

Race hazards are circuit transients, which under certain changes of an input signal in a circuit with certain delays, can occur at the output of a gate. In Figure 6.1 we show how such a signal spike can be generated.

In this section we shall discuss briefly the nature of race hazards, how they can effect the operation of a circuit and how they can be detected and corrected. For a more detailed study of race hazards the interested reader is referred to *Logic Dèsign Algorithms* by D. Zissos, Oxford University Press (1972).

There is in general a time delay between the arrival of an input signal to a gate and the change in the output signal of that gate. We shall use the symbol *tg* to denote the signal delay caused by a gate. For the time being we shall assume that the gate delay *tg* is the same for all gates in a circuit.

In Figure 1.17 we show how the changes of the output of an inverter, $\overline{A}$, lag behind the changes of its input signal A. Note that at each change there is a period *tg* during which the output of the inverter is the same as its input, that is $A = \overline{A} = 0$ or 1. Algebraically, this may be expressed as follows.

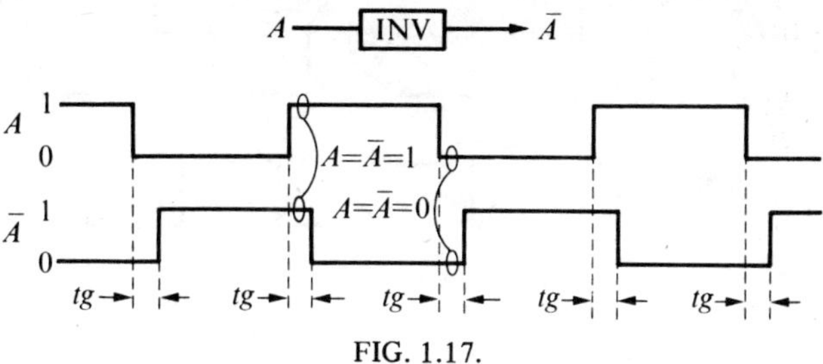

FIG. 1.17.

In a theoretical circuit with no signal delays ($tg = 0$), all signals follow exactly the laws of Boolean algebra and, in particular, $A + \bar{A} = 1$ and $A . \bar{A} = 0$ at all times. In a practical circuit with signal delays ($tg > 0$), the signals still follow the laws of Boolean algebra, with one important exception. During transitional periods in which A changes, signals A and $\bar{A}$ cannot be assumed to be the complement of each other, that is they cannot be assumed to satisfy the Boolean relations $A + \bar{A} = 1$ and $A . \bar{A} = 0$. However, these relations are satisfied at all other times and they are not affected by changes in other signals.

In discussing the design of logic circuits, we shall assume that an input signal is available in its true form only and that we shall therefore use an inverter to generate its complement. This assumption is based on the practical consideration that it is much simpler and cheaper in a system to run a single wire to a given point and use an inverter at its end, rather than run two wires carrying a signal in its true form and a signal in its inverted form. It, therefore, follows that there is always a relative delay between changes in a signal A and corresponding changes in its complement $\bar{A}$.

If A and $\bar{A}$ are used as inputs to a gate, their relative delay manifests itself in the form of 'signal spikes' at the output, as indicated in Figure 1.18.

Let us consider the NAND gate more closely. There is a spike when the output originally 0 changes to 1 before the other input has changed from 1 to 0; but there is no spike when the input originally 1 changes to 0 before the other input is changed from 0 to 1. We can express this in another way. If the change of an input from 0 to 1 takes place at time $t01$, and the change of the other input from 1 to 0 takes place at time $t10$, then there is a spike in the output of the NAND gate whenever $t01/t10 < 1$. The ratio $t01/t10$ we define as the *delay ratio.* From Figure 1.18 it can be seen that this is also the case for the AND gate; for the OR and NOR gates the spike occurs whenever $t01/t10 > 1$.

These results, and the form of the spikes, are summarized in Figure 1.19.

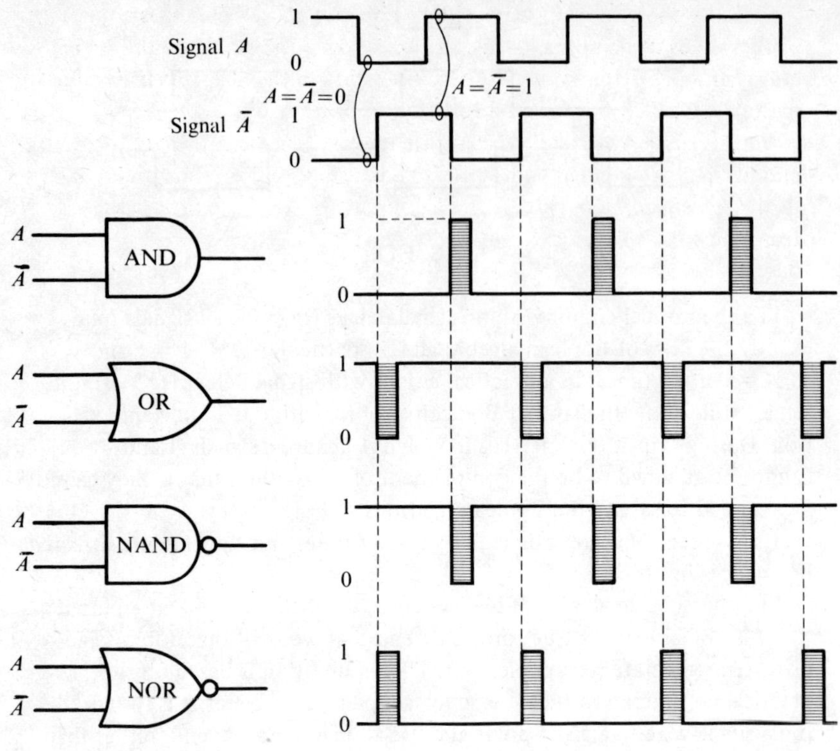

FIG. 1.18.

Type of gate	Delay ratio, $\frac{t\ 01}{t\ 10}$	Gate output
AND	< 1	1 0
OR	> 1	1 0
NAND	< 1	1 0
NOR	> 1	1 0

FIG. 1.19.

Because the steady-state output of a combinational circuit is a function of the values of its input signals, the effect of race-hazards on their operation can only be temporary. The suppression of race-hazards in combinational circuits is discussed in Chapter 6.

In this section we shall concentrate on how race-hazards in sequential circuits can be detected and suppressed. Our method is based on the use of the *transition table* (Zissos and Copperwhite 1965) defined directly from the circuit diagram. Clearly, it is not advisable to use a probe to detect signal spikes in a given circuit, since its use may mask an existing spike or cause one to be generated by simply affecting the relative signal delays of the circuit.

Note that it is not necessary to analyze sequential circuits that have been designed and implemented using our step-by-step procedures, since all such circuits are automatically hazard-free when implemented with gates of maximum propagation tolerance of $\pm 33\frac{1}{3}$ *per cent.*

The transition table

This is a table in which we display the gate output signals, the signal delays, signal races, and race-hazards. In this section we show how it is derived and used by means of an example. For further examples the interested reader is referred to *Logic Design Algorithms* by D. Zissos, Oxford University Press (1972).

EXAMPLE

Determine the race-hazards present in the NAND circuit shown in Figure 1.20(a). Its internal state diagram is shown in Figure 1.20(b). Show how the circuit operation can be made hazard-free for maximum gate speed tolerances of $\pm 33\frac{1}{3}$ per cent.

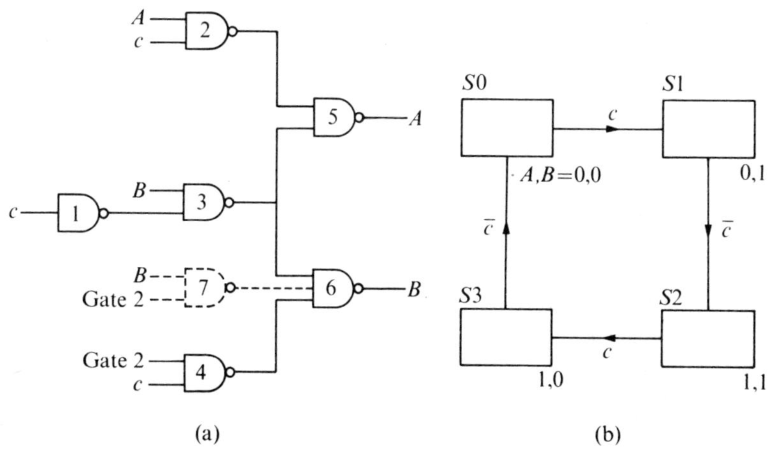

FIG. 1.20.

SOLUTION

To determine the display the race-hazards present in the given circuit, we proceed as follows.

We first express algebraically the output of each gate.

$$
\begin{aligned}
\text{Output of gate 1} &= \bar{c} \\
\text{Output of gate 2} &= \bar{A} + \bar{c} \\
\text{Output of gate 3} &= \bar{B} + c \\
\text{Output of gate 4} &= \overline{g2} + \bar{c} = Ac + \bar{c} = A + \bar{c} \\
\text{Output of gate 5} &= A \\
\text{Output of gate 6} &= B.
\end{aligned}
$$

We next determine the gate outputs at each of the four stable states. We do so by simply substituting the values of A, B, and c in the above equations.

State S0

$c = 0, A = 0$, and $B = 0$. Therefore,

$$
\begin{aligned}
\text{Output of gate 1} &= \bar{c} = \bar{0} = 1 \\
\text{Output of gate 2} &= \bar{A} + \bar{c} = \bar{0} + \bar{0} = 1 + 1 = 1 \\
\text{Output of gate 3} &= \bar{B} + c = \bar{0} + 0 = 1 + 0 = 1 \\
\text{Output of gate 4} &= A + c = 0 + \bar{0} = 0 + 1 = 1 \\
\text{Output of gate 5} &= A = 0 \\
\text{Output of gate 6} &= B = 0.
\end{aligned}
$$

State S1

$c = 1, A = 0$, and $B = 1$. Therefore,

$$
\begin{aligned}
\text{Output of gate 1} &= \bar{c} = \bar{1} = 0 \\
\text{Output of gate 2} &= \bar{A} + \bar{c} = \bar{0} + \bar{1} = 1 + 0 = 1 \\
\text{Output of gate 3} &= \bar{B} + c = \bar{1} + 1 = 0 + 1 = 1 \\
\text{Output of gate 4} &= A + \bar{c} = 0 + \bar{1} = 0 + 0 = 0 \\
\text{Output of gate 5} &= A = 0 \\
\text{Output of gate 6} &= B = 1.
\end{aligned}
$$

State S2

$c = 0, A = 1$, and $B = 1$. Therefore,

$$
\begin{aligned}
\text{Output of gate 1} &= \bar{c} = \bar{0} = 1 \\
\text{Output of gate 2} &= \bar{A} + \bar{c} = \bar{1} + \bar{0} = 0 + 1 = 1 \\
\text{Output of gate 3} &= \bar{B} + c = \bar{1} + 0 = 0 + 0 = 0 \\
\text{Output of gate 4} &= A + \bar{c} = 1 + \bar{0} = 1 + 1 = 1 \\
\text{Output of gate 5} &= A = 1 \\
\text{Output of gate 6} &= B = 1.
\end{aligned}
$$

State S3

$c = 1, A = 1$, and $B = 0$. Therefore,

$$\text{Output of gate 1} = \bar{c} = \bar{1} = 0$$
$$\text{Output of gate 2} = \bar{A} + \bar{c} = \bar{1} + \bar{1} = 0 + 0 = 0$$
$$\text{Output of gate 3} = \bar{B} + c = \bar{0} + 1 = 1 + 1 = 1$$
$$\text{Output of gate 4} = A + \bar{c} = 1 + \bar{1} = 1 + 0 = 1$$
$$\text{Output of gate 5} = A = 1$$
$$\text{Output of gate 6} = B = 0.$$

Circuit states	c	gate 1	gate 2	gate 3	gate 4	gate 5 (A)	gate 6 (B)	Critical races	Delay ratios	Maximum gate speed tolerance
S0	0	1	1	1	1	0	0			
S01		—		RH 301	—		=	RH 301	$\frac{2(tg)}{1(tg)} = 2$	$\pm 33\frac{1}{3}\%$
S1	1	0	1	1	0	0	1			
S12		—	RH 212	=	—	≡	RH 612	RH 612	$\frac{1(tg)}{2(tg)} = \frac{1}{2}$	Misoperation
S2	0	1	1	0	1	1	1			
S23		—	—	=	RH 423	RH 523		RH 523	$\frac{2(tg)}{1(tg)} = 2$	$\pm 33\frac{1}{3}\%$
S3	1	0	0	1	1	1	0			
S30		—	—		RH 430	=		RH 430	$\frac{1(tg)}{1(tl)} \leq \infty$	No limits
S0	0	1	1	1	1	0	0			

FIG. 1.21

These values are entered in the corresponding squares of the table in Figure 1.21.

Signal races at the input of a gate are determined by direct reference to the columns corresponding to each pair of its input signals. For example, in the case of gate 3 we proceed as follows. We select columns 1 and 6 in the transition table to determine races that may exist between its two inputs, that is between the outputs of gates 1 and 6. A race is revealed between the two signals during the *S*0–*S*1 transition, because the output of gate 1 changes from 1 to 0 and that of gate 6 from 0 to 1. We represent the existence of a race at the input of a gate by means of a pulse symbol on the diagram. For example, we enter a pulse symbol in column 3 and row *S*01 to display the signal race we have just discussed. We label this race hazard *RH*301 to indicate that there is a signal race at the input of gate 3 (indicated by the first digit of the subscript) during circuit transition *S*0 to *S*1 (indicated by the last two digits in the subscript). In the general case, a race at the input of gate *M* during transition *PQ* is labelled RH_{MPQ}. This process is carried out for each gate and the races marked on the transition table.

We next determine the criticality of each race. A race is critical if its outcome may result in a permanent circuit misoperation. Applying this criterion, RH_{301} is critical, because if it does occur it will turn secondary signal A on, causing permanent circuit misoperation. RH_{423} on the other hand is classified as non-critical, because its presence affects the output of gate 6, which is changing during this transition.

Having detected the critical races in the circuit, we next proceed to determine their *delay ratios.* By direct reference to the circuit we determine the sequence in which the gates are switched during each of the four circuit transitions.

Circuit transition $S0$–$S1$: gates 1 and 2
Circuit transition $S1$–$S2$: gates 1 and 4, 3, 5
Circuit transition $S2$–$S3$: gates 1 and 2, 3, 6
Circuit transition $S3$–$S0$: gates 1 and 2, 5.

Ignoring lead delays, we indicate the switching times in the transition table as gate delays. For example, we enter '–' in column 1 row $S01$ to indicate that gate 1 switches in one gate delay. '≡' in column 6 row $S23$ indicates that gate 6 switches three gate delays, after the change of the input signal.

Now in the case of NAND gates the condition for a race to affect the gate output (ignoring the filtering effect of the gate), arises when the delay ratio $t01/t10$ is greater than 1 (see Figure 1.19). The delay ratios associated with each critical race arc read directly from the transition table and noted in the appropriate column – in our case one before last. The corresponding gate tolerance that can be accommodated by the circuit configuration is read directly from Figure 1.17 and noted in the last column of the transition table. It is clear that our circuit can misoperate during the $S1$ to $S2$ circuit transition. To prevent circuit misoperation we use a blanking signal $K12$ defined by

$$\begin{aligned}\overline{K12} &= S1c + S1\bar{c} + S2\bar{c} \\ &= S1 + S2\bar{c} \\ &= \bar{A}B + AB\bar{c} \\ &= \bar{A}B + B\bar{c}.\end{aligned}$$

[A '0' input is required to maintain the output of a NAND gate at 1.]

Inverting, we obtain

$$\begin{aligned}K12 &= \bar{B} + Ac \\ &= \bar{B} + \overline{g2}.\end{aligned}$$

This signal is implemented by gate 7 in Figure 1.20.

1.16 MULTIPLEXOR CIRCUITS

In this section we shall outline methods for implementing combinational and event-driven logic circuits using MUXs and DEMUXs. The reader's attention is drawn to the fact that such circuits are not hazard-free although, with present-day i.c. chips, race hazards may well not reveal themselves. The transient performance of circuits using MUXs and DEMUXs is currently under investigation by Dr. G. S. Hope and the author.

The block diagrams and truth tables of a 4-to-1 MUX and of a 1-to-4 DEMUX are shown in Figure 1.2. NAND implementations of these two circuits are shown in Figure 1.3.

To implement a given Boolean function using MUXs, we proceed as follows.

1. We multiply out the given function,
2. We reduce the expression,
3. We express each product as a function of the select signals, variables A and B in Figure 1.2,
4. We reduce the expression using products that contain only select signals.

We shall demonstrate our steps by means of examples.

EXAMPLE 1:

Use 4-to-1 MUXs to implement the Boolean functions
(a) $f = A + B + C$,
(b) $g = A.B.C$, and
(c) $h = A.\overline{B} + \overline{A}.B$.

SOLUTION:

Choosing A and B as select signals, we obtain

(a)
$$\begin{aligned} f &= A + B + C \text{ (reduced)} \\ &= A(B+\overline{B}) + (A+\overline{A})B + (A+\overline{A})(B+\overline{B})C \\ &= AB + A\overline{B} + AB + \overline{A}B + \overline{A}\overline{B}C + A\overline{B}C + \overline{A}BC + AB \\ &= AB(1+c) + A\overline{B}(1+c) + \overline{A}B(1+c) + \overline{A}\overline{B}C \\ &= AB + A\overline{B} + \overline{A}B + \overline{A}\overline{B}C \\ &= \overline{B}\overline{A}C + \overline{B}A + B\overline{A} + BA \end{aligned}$$
– see Figure 1.22(a).

(b) $g = ABC$ (reduced).
This function is expressed in the 'correct form'. Therefore it can be implemented directly – see Figure 1.22(b).

(c) $f = A\overline{B} + \overline{A}B$ (reduced).
This function is also expressed in the 'correct' form, it is reduced and each of the two products contain A and B (our select signals). Therefore it can be implemented directly as shown in Figure 1.22(c). It can also be implemented using a 2-to-1 MUX as shown in Figure 1.22(d).

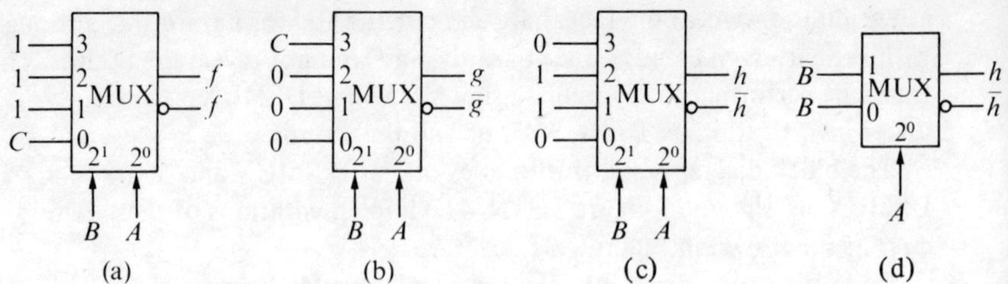

FIG. 1.22

EXAMPLE 2:

Use 4-to-1 MUXs to implement the Boolean function

(a) $w = AB + \bar{A}C + BC$

(b) $x = AB + \bar{A}C + (\bar{B} + \bar{C})D$

SOLUTION:

(a) Using A and B as select signals, we obtain

$$\begin{aligned} w &= AB + \bar{A}C + BC \\ &= AB + \bar{A}C \text{ (see theorem 2 in Appendix 1).} \\ &= AB + \bar{A}(B + \bar{B})C \\ &= AB + \bar{A}BC + \bar{A}\bar{B}C \\ &= \bar{B}\bar{A}C + B\bar{A}C + BA \text{ - see Figure 1.23(a).} \end{aligned}$$

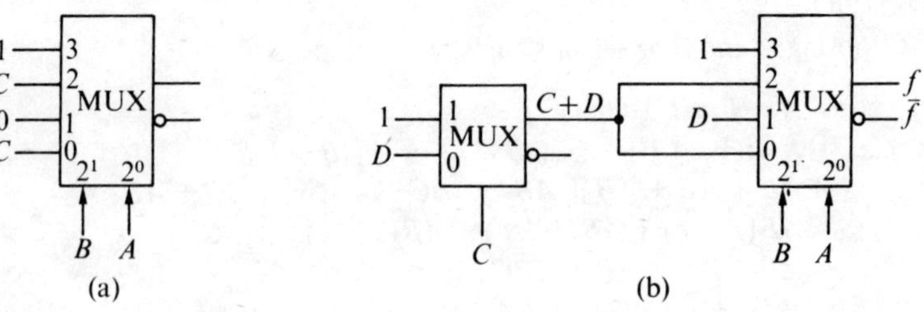

FIG. 1.23.

(b) Using A and B as select signals, we obtain

$$\begin{aligned} x &= AB + \bar{A}C + (\bar{B} + \bar{C})D \\ &= AB + \bar{A}C + \bar{B}D + \bar{C}D \end{aligned}$$

BC

CD

D —— replaces parent products $\bar{B}D$ and $\bar{C}D$.

Therefore, the reduced form of our expression is

$$f = AB + \bar{A}C + D.$$

We next express each product as a function of the select signals, arbitrarily chosen to be A and B.

$$\begin{aligned} f &= AB + \overline{A}(B + \overline{B})C + (A + \overline{A})(B + \overline{B})D \\ &= AB + \overline{A}BC + \overline{A}\overline{B}C + ABD + A\overline{B}D + \overline{A}BD + \overline{A}\overline{B}D \\ &= \overline{B}\overline{A}(C + D) + \overline{B}AD + B\overline{A}(C + D) + BA. \end{aligned}$$

The equivalent MUX implementation is shown in Figure 1.23(b).

EXAMPLE 3:

In this example we shall use MUXs to implement the drive circuitry for a seven-segment display, derived in problem 10 of Chapter 6.

SOLUTION:

We can solve this problem by referring either to the Karmaugh maps of the seven signals a, b, c, d, e, f, and g or to their Boolean equations, both of which are available - see Problem 10. Seven segment display in Chapter 6. We shall use the Karmaugh maps to derive the multiplexor equations of the seven signals.

By direct reference to these maps, which for ease of reference we reproduce in Figure 1.24, and using blank entries as optionals, we obtain

$$\begin{aligned} a &= \overline{B}\overline{A}\overline{C} + \overline{B}A(C + D) + B\overline{A} + BA, \\ b &= \overline{B}\overline{A} + \overline{B}A\overline{C} + B\overline{A}\overline{C} + BA, \\ c &= \overline{B}\overline{A} + \overline{B}A + B\overline{A}C + BA, \\ d &= \overline{B}\overline{A}\overline{C} + \overline{B}AC + B\overline{A} + BA\overline{C}, \\ e &= \overline{B}\overline{A}\overline{C} + B\overline{A}, \\ f &= \overline{B}\overline{A} + \overline{B}A(C + D) + B\overline{A}C, \text{ and} \\ g &= \overline{B}\overline{A}(C + D) + \overline{B}A(C + D) + B\overline{A} + BA\overline{C}. \end{aligned}$$

The corresponding MUX circuit is shown in Figure 1.25.

CD \ AB	00	01	11	10
00	1	1	1	0
01	1			1
11				
10	0	1	1	1

a

CD \ AB	00	01	11	10
00	1	0	1	1
01	1			1
11				
10	1	1	1	1

c

CD \ AB	00	01	11	10
00	1	1	1	1
01	1			1
11				
10	1	0	1	0

b

CD \ AB	00	01	11	10
00	1	1	1	0
01	1			0
11				
10	0	1	0	1

d

FIG. 1.24 (continued on p. 32)

CD \ AB	00	01	11	10
00	1	1	0	0
01	1			0
11				
10	0	1	0	0

e

CD \ AB	00	01	11	10
00	0	1	1	0
01	1			1
11				
10	1	1	0	1

g

CD \ AB	00	01	11	10
00	1	0	0	0
01	1			1
11				
10	1	1	0	1

f

FIG. 1.24 (continued)

EXAMPLE 4:

Use MUXs to implement the solution of the single fault detector derived in Problem 1 of Chapter 2.

SOLUTION:

Our starting points are the circuit equations derived in step 4 of the available solution. We repeat them below.

$$
\begin{aligned}
A &= Ba + A(B + \bar{a}),\\
B &= \bar{A}f + \bar{A}t + B(\bar{A} + f),\\
g &= \bar{B},\\
r &= B \text{ and}\\
b &= \bar{A}B + A\bar{B}.
\end{aligned}
$$

Multiplying out, we obtain

$$
\begin{aligned}
A &= Ba + AB + A\bar{a}\\
B &= \bar{A}f + \bar{A}t + \bar{A}B + Bf\\
g &= \bar{B}\\
r &= B\\
b &= \bar{A}B + A\bar{B}.
\end{aligned}
$$

We next reduce the expanded form of the equations

$$
\begin{aligned}
A &= Ba + AB + A\bar{a}\\
&= Ba + A\bar{a} \qquad \text{(See theorem 2 in Appendix 1.)}\\
B &= \bar{A}f + \bar{A}t + \bar{A}B + Bf\\
g &= \bar{B}\\
r &= B\\
b &= \bar{A}B + A\bar{B}.
\end{aligned}
$$

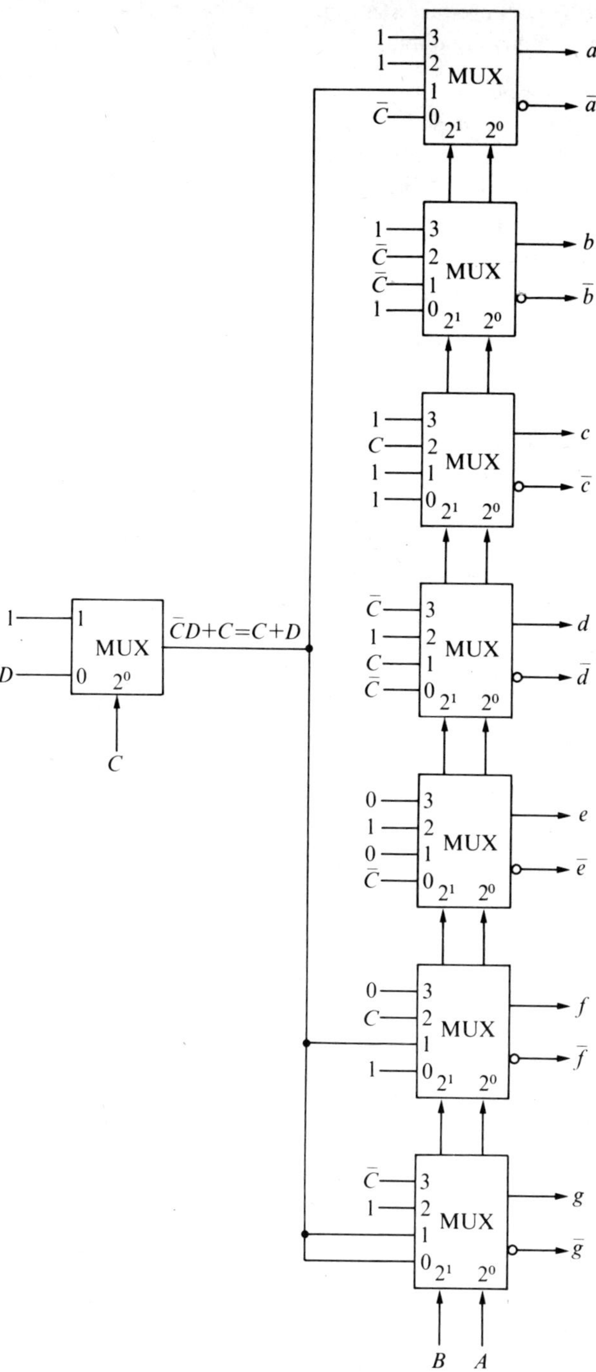
1
D
MUX
1
0
2^0
C
$\bar{C}D+C=C+D$
1
1
$\bar{C}$
3
2
1
0
MUX
2^1
2^0
a
$\bar{a}$
1
$\bar{C}$
$\bar{C}$
1
b
$\bar{b}$
1
C
1
1
c
$\bar{c}$
$\bar{C}$
1
C
$\bar{C}$
d
$\bar{d}$
0
1
0
$\bar{C}$
e
$\bar{e}$
0
C
1
f
$\bar{f}$
$\bar{C}$
1
g
$\bar{g}$
B
A

FIG. 1.25.

Expressing each product as a function of the select signals A and B (arbitrarily chosen), we obtain

$$\begin{aligned}
A &= Ba + A\bar{a} \\
&= (A + \bar{A})Ba + (B + \bar{B})A\bar{a} \\
&= ABa + \bar{A}Ba + AB\bar{a} + A\bar{B}\bar{a} \\
&= \bar{B}A\bar{a} + B\bar{A}a + BA.
\end{aligned}$$

$$\begin{aligned}
B &= \bar{A}f + \bar{A}t + \bar{A}B + Bf \\
&= \bar{A}(B + \bar{B})(f + t) + \bar{A}B + (A + \bar{A})Bf \\
&= \bar{A}\bar{B}(f + t) + \bar{A}B + ABf
\end{aligned}$$

$$\begin{aligned}
g &= \bar{B} \\
r &= B \\
b &= \bar{A}B + A\bar{B}.
\end{aligned}$$

The MUX implementation of the equations is shown in Figure 1.26.

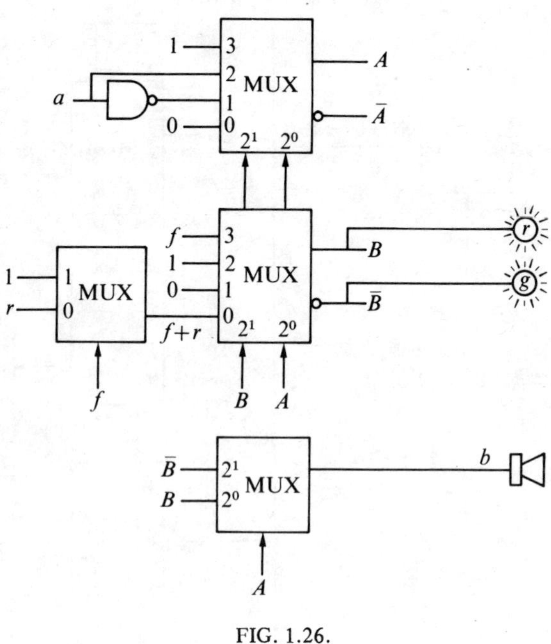

FIG. 1.26.

2 *Unclocked Sequential Circuits*

A four-step algorithm for the design of primitive NAND, NOR and relay AND/OR, OR/AND sequential circuits is described. Realistic circuit constraints are taken automatically into account by our design process. Twenty-three problems with fully worked out solutions are used to demonstrate the design steps.

2.1 INTRODUCTION

Our design process is accomplished in four steps, and meets the following design factors.

1. *Circuit reliability.* All circuits function correctly and reliably.
2. *Gate minimality.* Generally speaking not all our circuits will be minimal.
3. *Gate speed tolerance.* Variations of $\pm 33\frac{1}{3}$ per cent in the response times of gates are automatically met.
4. *Circuit maintainability.* Our circuits are easy to maintain.
5. *Design effort.* This is minimal.
6. *Documentation.* No additional documentation is needed.
7. *The design steps.* These are easy to apply. No specialist knowledge is necessary.
8. *Gate fan-in and fan-out restirctions.* These are met reliably though not elegantly.

2.2 THE DESIGN STEPS

The sequence in which the four design steps are executed is shown in Figure 2.1. A detailed description of each step is given.

Step 1 *I/O characteristics*

In this step we draw a block diagram to show the available input signals and the required output signals. We next use a state diagram to define the relationship which must be established by our circuit between the two sets of signals.

Step 2 *Internal characteristics*

In the second step the designer specifies the internal performance of the circuit. Although experience, intuition and foresight play an important part at this stage, the inexperienced designer should be primarily concerned

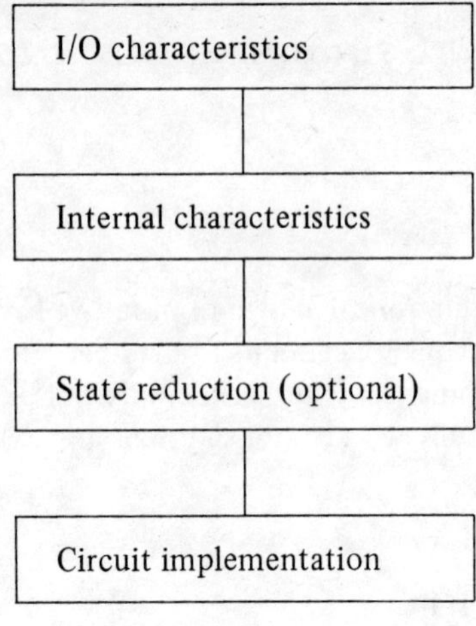

FIG. 2.1

that his specification of the internal circuit operation is complete and free of ambiguities. To this end he should avoid short cuts and use as many states as he finds necessary to give a complete and unambiguous specification of the circuit performance. The next step can be used to eliminate unwanted states.

STEP 3 *State reduction*

This step is optional and can be omitted. Its main purpose is to provide the designer with the means for reducing the number of internal states he used in step 2, if such a reduction is possible.

The circuit's state table (Section 1.9) is drawn and the state reduction steps (Section 1.10) are used to merge its rows.

Clearly to avoid redundant states we would only use this step to reduce the number of states to some power of 2. For example, whereas we would use it to reduce five states to four, we would not use it to reduce 4 states to 3.

Step 4 *Primitive circuit*

In this step, with the aid of a race-free diagram if necessary, we give each internal state a unique binary code. The coding must be such that no single circuit transition must involve the change of more than one secondary signal, as explained in Section 1.12.

From the coded state diagram we read the turn-on and turn-off sets of each secondary signal, which we then use to derive the circuit's primitive sequential equations. Expressions for the circuit output signals are also read directly from the state diagram. The implementation of these equations is the required circuit.

The reader's attention is drawn to the fact that the sequential equations must not be manipulated algebraically without a working knowledge of merging and signal substitution described in *Logic Design Algorithms* (Zissos, 1972).

2.3 PROBLEMS AND SOLUTIONS

Twenty-three problems and fully worked out solutions are used to illustrate the four design steps.

PROBLEM 1: *A Single Fault Detector*

Design a fault detector with the following terminal characteristics. The appearance of a fault signal *f* activates an alarm bell, turns a green light off and a red light on. The operator turns off the bell by pressing an acknowledge switch *a*. When the fault clears itself, the red light turns off, the green light turns on and the bell is automatically reactivated to attract the operator's attention. The bell is turned off when the operator presses the acknowledge button. A test button *t* is used to test the circuit.

SOLUTION

Step 1 *I/O characteristics*

The specified I/O characteristics are shown diagrammatically in Figures (a) and (b).

Step 2 *Internal characteristics*

Same as I/O characteristics.

Step 3 *State reduction*

Not attempted in order to maintain clarity of design.

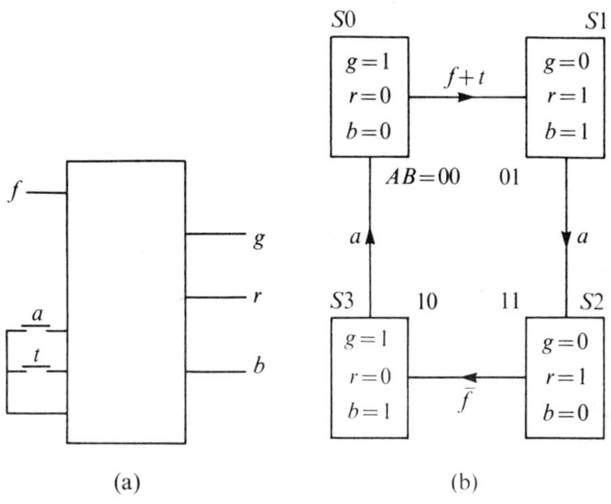

(a) (b)

Step 4 *Primitive circuit*

Suitable state codes are shown in Figure (b). By direct reference to this figure, we obtain:

$$\text{Turn-on set of } A = Ba \qquad \text{Turn-on set of } B = \overline{A}f + \overline{A}t$$
$$\text{Turn-off set of } A = \overline{B}a \qquad \text{Turn-off set of } B = A\overline{f}$$

Therefore, the NAND circuit equations are:

$$\begin{aligned} A &= Ba + A(B + \overline{a}) \\ B &= \overline{A}f + \overline{A}t + B(\overline{A} + f) \\ g &= \overline{A}\overline{B} + A\overline{B} = \overline{B} \\ r &= \overline{A}B + AB = B \\ b &= \overline{A}B + A\overline{B}. \end{aligned}$$

Their circuit implementation is shown in Figure (c).

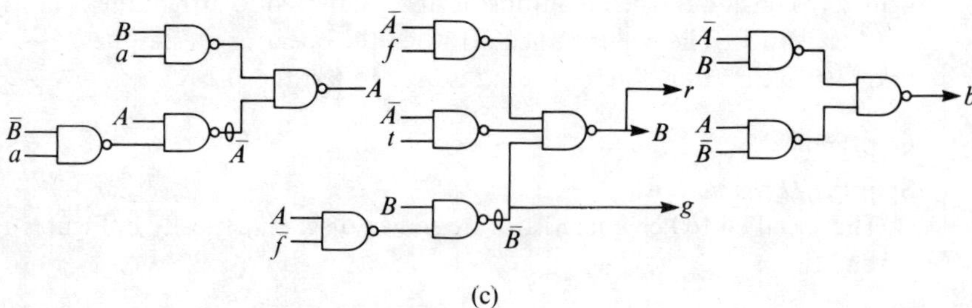

(c)

PROBLEM 2: *A Single Pump Controller*

Design a circuit to control the water pump in Figure (a) in the following manner. The pump is to turn on when the water goes below level 1 and is to remain on until it reaches level 2, at which point it turns off. The pump is to remain turned off until the water goes below level 1 again.

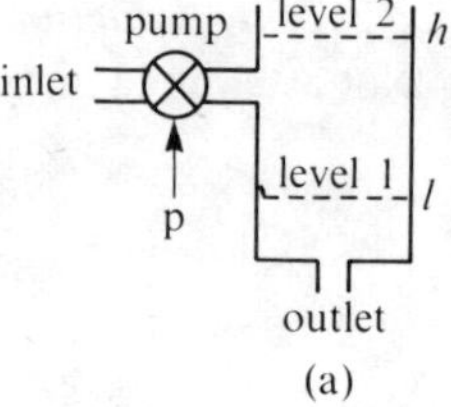

(a)

Two level detection signals, h and l, are provided. Signal $l = 1$ when the water is at or above level 1, otherwise $l = 0$. Similarly $h = 1$ when the water is at or above level 2, otherwise $h = 0$.

SOLUTION

Step 1 *I/O characteristics*

See Figures (b) and (c).

Step 2 *Internal characteristics*

A suitable state diagram is shown in Figure (d).

Step 3 *State reduction*

The state table corresponding to (d) is shown in (e). No state reduction is possible.

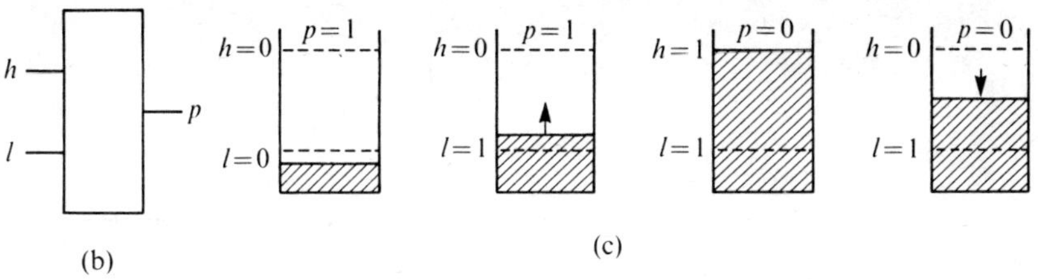

(b) (c)

Step 4 *Primitive circuit*

By direct reference to Figure (d), we obtain:

Turn-on set of $p = \bar{l}$
Turn-off set of $p = h$.

Therefore, the NAND circuit equations are

$$p = \bar{l} + p\bar{h}$$
$$\text{alarm} = h\bar{l}$$

The corresponding NAND circuit is shown in Figure (f).

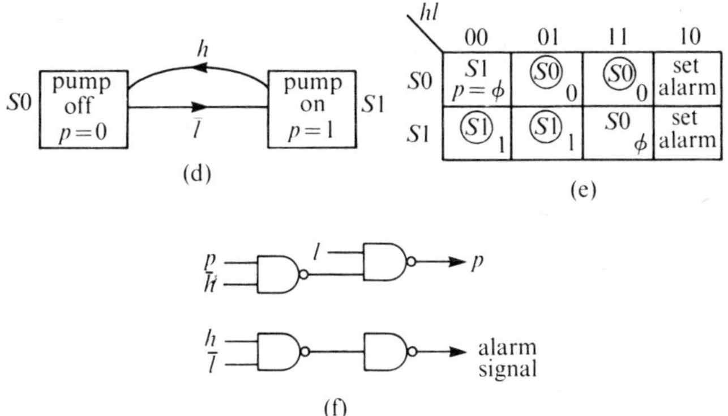

(d) (e) (f)

PROBLEM 3: *Railway crossing*

Design and implement a logic circuit that will operate a flashing light and a warning bell at the railway crossing shown in Figure (a) in the following manner.

The flashing light and bell are to turn on when a train enters either section 1 or section 3, and to turn off when the train leaves the intersection. Three signals p_1, p_2, and p_3 are generated when a train is in sections 1, 2, and 3 respectively.

SOLUTION:

Step 1 *External (I/O) characteristics*

The I/O signals are shown in Figure (b). Their relationship is as specified.

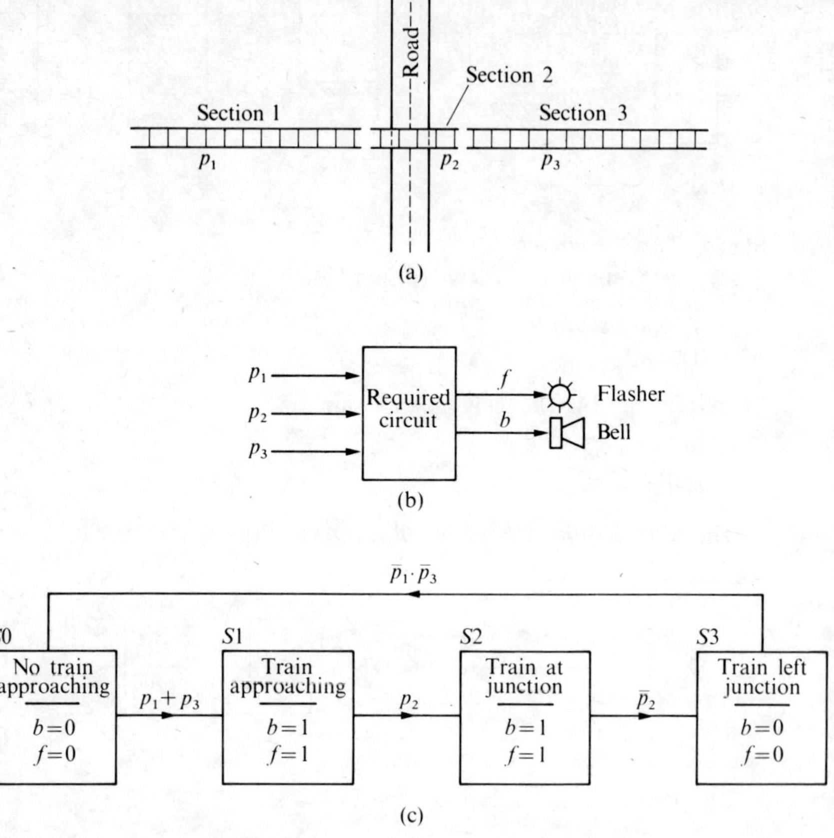

Step 2 *Internal characteristics*

The internal state diagram of a suitable circuit is shown in Figure (c). It operates in the following manner.

When no train is approaching it assumes state *S*0. When a train enters either section 1 or section 3 of the railway track, the circuit moves to state *S*1, turning the flasher and bell on. When the train enters the rail/road junction, our circuit moves to state *S*2. The bell and flasher remain on. When the tail end of the train leaves section 2, the circuit moves to state *S*3 turning the bell and flasher off. State *S*3 is maintained until the train leaves completely section 1 or section 3, at which point the circuit moves to state *S*0.

Step 3 *State reduction*

The equivalent state table is shown in Figure (d). Because the output devices (a flasher and a bell) do not respond to signals of short duration, during circuit transitions (indicated in our state table by uncircled entries) the designer has the option of defining the output signals, *f* and *b*, either as 0*s* or 1*s*, indicated by Ø.

$p_1p_2p_3$	000	010	110	100	101	111	011	001
S0	(S0) b,f=0,0			S1 ∅,∅				S1 ∅,∅
S1			S2 ∅,∅	(S1) 1,1			S2 ∅,∅	(S1) 1,1
S2		(S2) 1,1	(S2) 1,1	S3 ∅,∅		(S2) 1,1	(S2) 1,1	S3 ∅,∅
S3	S0 ∅,∅			(S3) 0,0				(S3) 0,0

(d)

$p_1p_2p_3$	000	010	110	100	101	111	011	001
S01	(S01) b,f=0,0		S23 ∅,∅=1,1	(S01) 1,1			S23 ∅,∅=1,1	(S01) 1,1
S23	S01 ∅,∅=0,0	(S23) 1,1	(S23) 1,1	(S23) 0,0		(S23) 1,1	(S23) 1,1	(S23) 0,0

(e)

In accordance with the state reduction rules, described in Section 10 of Chapter 1, row *S*0 can be combined with row *S*1, and row *S*2 with *S*3. The reduced state table is shown in Figure (e).

Reference to this table (Figure (e)) show that there exist four blank squares. These define abnormal situations. For example, the two squares in the fifth column from the left indicate that a train is in sections 1 and 3 of Figure (a) but not in section 2, a situation that clearly does not arise in practice. Because of the importance of safety to road users, the response of our circuit in these squares must be chosen with care. In our case we shall turn the flasher on and the bell off to indicate to the motorists that they should 'proceed with caution'. The entries to be inserted in the blank squares in Figure (e) are shown in Figure (f). The final form of the state table is shown in Figure (g).

An alarm can also be raised to alert the person or equipment that are

$p_1p_2p_3$	000	010	110	100	101	111	011	001
S01		(S01) b,f=0,1			(S01) 0,1	(S01) 0,1		
S23					(S23) 0,1			

(f)

$p_1p_2p_3$	000	010	110	100	101	111	011	001
$S01$	($S01$) $b,f=0,0$	($S01$) 0,1	$S23$ $\emptyset,\emptyset=1,1$	($S01$) 1,1	($S01$) 0,1	($S01$) 0,1	$S23$ $\emptyset,\emptyset=1,1$	($S01$) 1,1
$S23$	$S01$ $\emptyset,\emptyset=0,0$	($S23$) 1,1	($S23$) 1,1	($S23$) 0,0	($S23$) 0,1	($S23$) 1,1	($S23$) 1,1	($S23$) 0,0

(g)

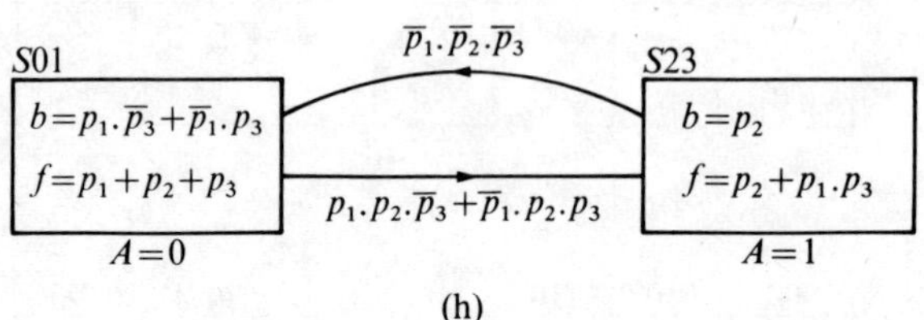

(h)

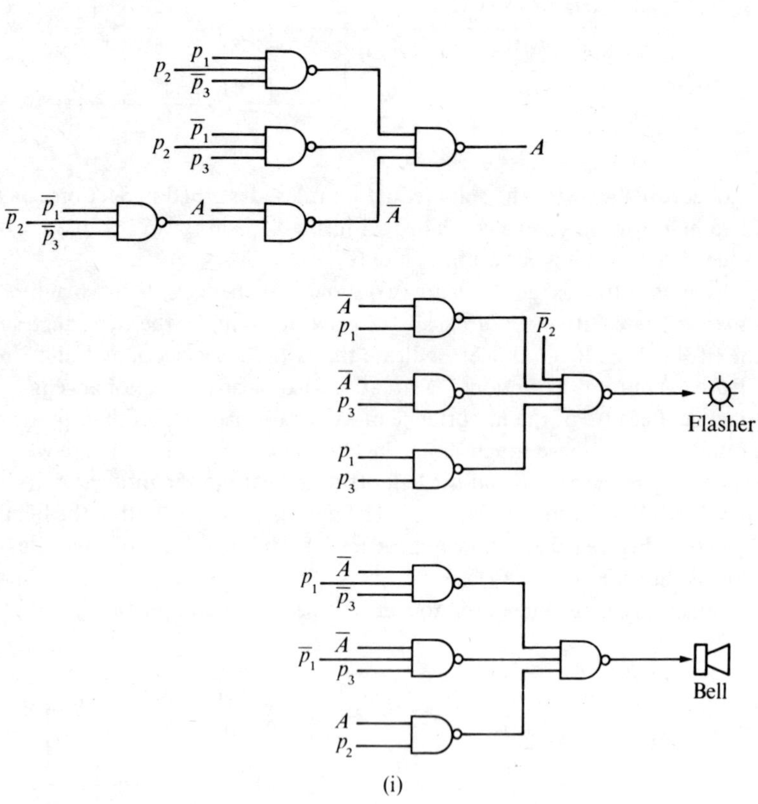

(i)

responsible for taking action in such situations. Its Boolean expression is

$$\begin{aligned}\text{alarm signal} &= S01\,.\,\bar{p}_1.p_2.\bar{p}_3+p_1.\bar{p}_2.p_3+S01\,.\,p_1.p_2.p_3\\ &= S01\,.\,\bar{p}_1.p_2.\bar{p}_3+p_1.\bar{p}_2.p_3+S01\,.\,p_1.p_3\end{aligned}$$

Step 4 *Primitive circuit*

The state diagram derived directly from the reduced state table is shown in Figure (h). By direct reference to it, we obtain

$$\begin{aligned}\text{Turn-on set of } A &= p_1.p_2.\bar{p}_3+\bar{p}_1.p_2.p_3\\ \text{Turn-off set of } A &= \bar{p}_1.\bar{p}_2.\bar{p}_3.\end{aligned}$$

Therefore the NAND circuit equations are

$$A = p_1.p_2.\bar{p}_3+\bar{p}_1.p_2.p_3+A\,.\,(p_1+p_2+p_3)$$

$$\begin{aligned}f &= S01\,.\,\overline{\bar{p}_1.\bar{p}_2.\bar{p}_3}+S23\,.\,p_2+S23\,.\,p_1.p_3\\ &= S01(p_1+p_2+p_3)+S23\,.\,p_2+S23\,.\,p_1.p_3\\ &= \bar{A}\,.(p_1+p_2+p_3)+A\,.\,p_2+A\,.\,p_1.p_3\\ &= p_2+\bar{A}\,.\,p_1+\bar{A}\,.\,p_3+A\,.\,p_1.p_3\\ &= p_2+\bar{A}\,.\,p_1+\bar{A}\,.\,p_3+p_1.p_3\end{aligned}$$

$$\begin{aligned}b &= S01\,(p_1.\bar{p}_2.\bar{p}_3+\bar{p}_1.\bar{p}_2.p_3+(p_1.p_2.\bar{p}_3)+(\bar{p}_1.p_2.p_3))\\ &\quad +S23\,.\,p_2\\ &= S01\,(p_1.\bar{p}_3+\bar{p}_1.p_3)+S23\,.\,p_2\\ &= A\,.\,p_1.\bar{p}_3+\bar{A}\,.\,\bar{p}_1.p_3+A\,.\,p_2.\end{aligned}$$

The equivalent NAND circuit is shown in Figure (i).

PROBLEM 4: *Long and short signals*

Design and implement a circuit that determines whether the duration of a signal on line g in Figure (a) is greater or less than t seconds. A pulse is to appear on terminal w in the first case and on terminal x in the second case, as shown in Figure (b).

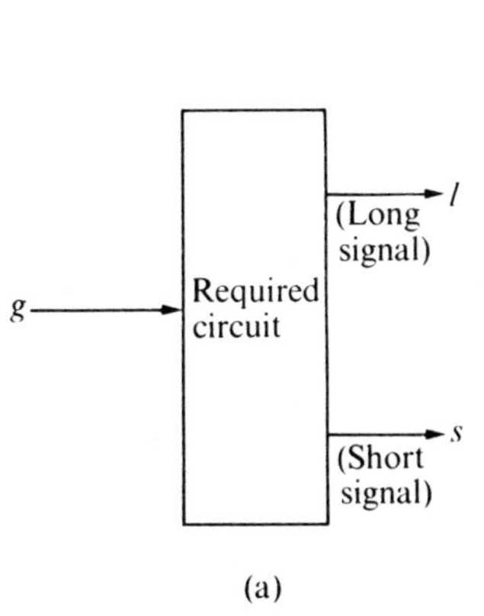

(a)

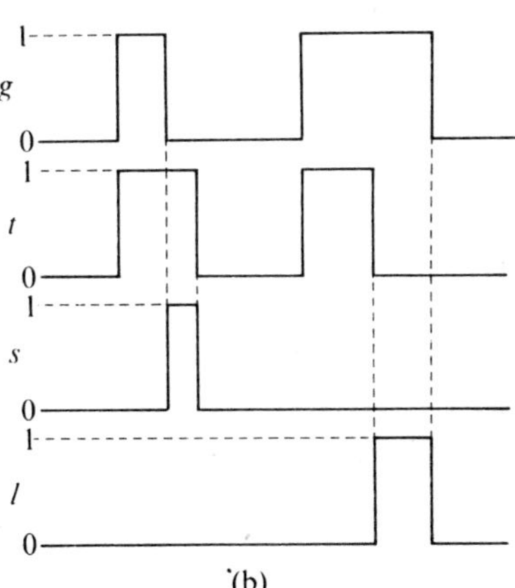

(b)

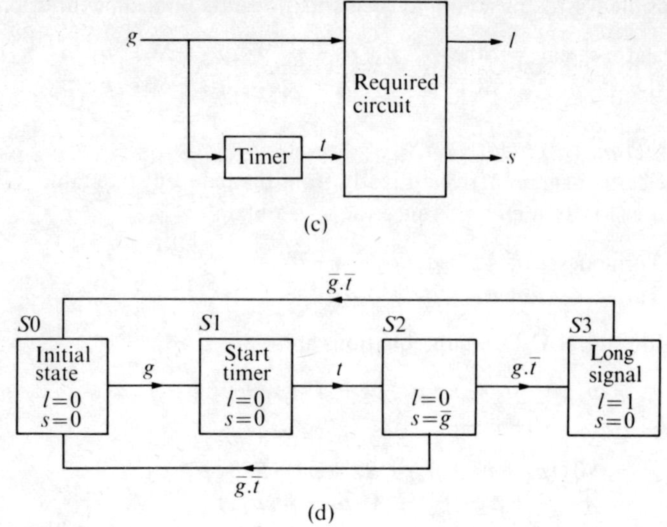

(d)

SOLUTION:

In our solution we shall use a timer, shown in Figure (c) to generate our time base of *t* seconds. A 0-to-1 transition on its input terminal generates a signal of *t* seconds duration at its output, as shown in Figure (b).

Step 1 *External (I/O) characteristics*

As specified in Figure (b).

Step 2 *Internal characteristics*

A suitable state diagram is shown in Figure (d). Its operation is self-explanatory.

Step 3 *State reduction*

The equivalent state table is shown in Figure (e).

gt	00	01	11	10
S0	(S0) $l,s=0,0$			S1 0,0
S1			S2 0,0	(S1) 0,0
S2	S0 0,Ø	(S2) 0,1	(S2) 0,0	S3 Ø,0
S3	S0 Ø,0			(S3) 1,0

(e)

In accordance with the state reduction rules, described in Section 10 of Chapter 1, rows $S0$ and $S2$ can be combined with rows $S1$ and $S3$ respectively. The reduced state table is shown in Figure (f).

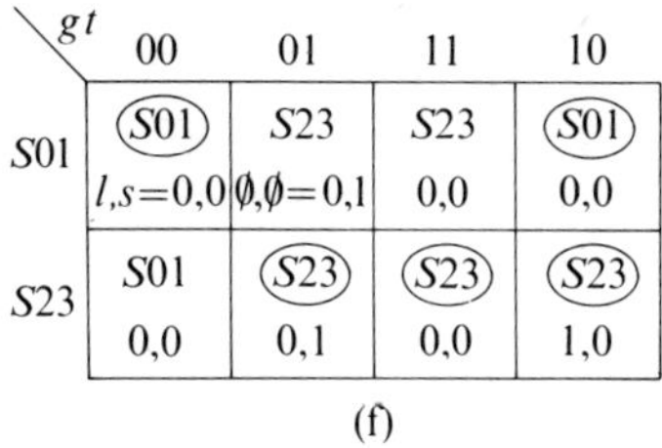

gt	00	01	11	10
$S01$	($S01$) $l,s=0,0$	$S23$ $\emptyset,\emptyset=0,1$	$S23$ 0,0	($S01$) 0,0
$S23$	$S01$ 0,0	($S23$) 0,1	($S23$) 0,0	($S23$) 1,0

(f)

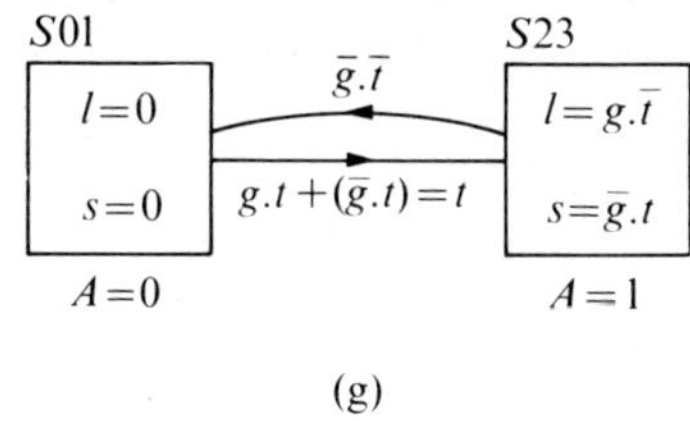

(g)

Step 4 *Primitive circuit*

The state diagram derived directly from the reduced state table is shown in Figure (g). When the circuit is in state $S01$, the Boolean product $\bar{g}.t$, specifying the blank square in Figure (g), can be used as an optional product. By direct reference to our state diagram, we obtain

$$\text{Turn-on set of } A = t$$
$$\text{Turn-off set of } A = \bar{g}.\bar{t} \xrightarrow{\text{Invert}} g + t.$$

Therefore, the circuit equations are

$$\begin{aligned} A &= t + A.(g+t) \\ &= t + A.g \end{aligned}$$

$$\begin{aligned} l &= S23.g.\bar{t} + [S01.\bar{g}.t] \\ &= A.g.\bar{t} + \bar{A}.\bar{g}.t \\ &= A.g.\bar{t}, \text{ and} \end{aligned}$$

$$\begin{aligned} s &= S23.\bar{g}.t + [S01.\bar{g}.t] \\ &= A.\bar{g}.t + \bar{A}.\bar{g}.t \\ &= \bar{g}.t. \end{aligned}$$

The equivalent NAND circuit is shown in Figure (h).

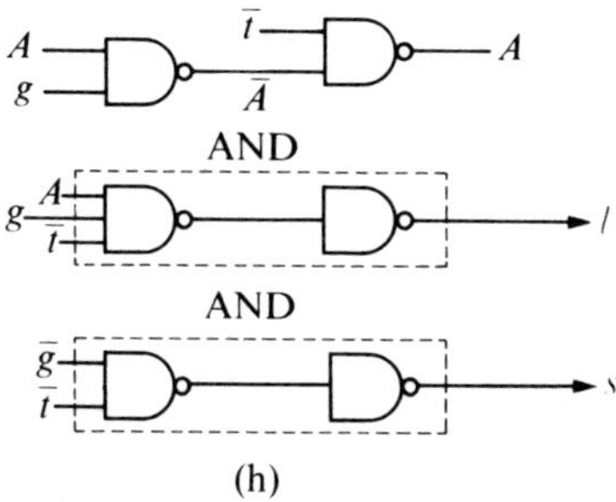

(h)

PROBLEM 5: *A Lamp Circuit*

A room has two doors and a single light fixture *L*. Two switches *X* and *Y* are mounted on the wall near each door to allow a person to turn the light on when he enters the room and turn it off when he leaves the room, regardless of which door he uses.

Design a suitable circuit.

SOLUTION

Step 1 *I/O characteristics*

The required I/O characteristics are shown in Figure (a).

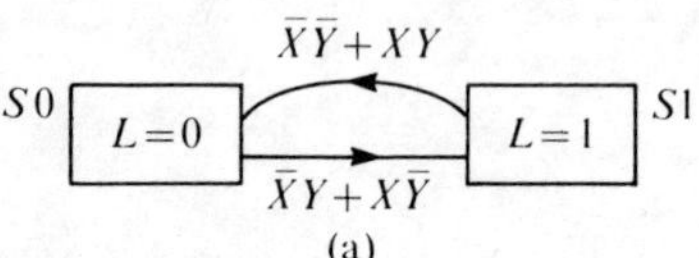

(a)

Step 2 *Internal characteristics*

Same as I/O characteristics.

Step 3 *State reduction*

State table (b) reduces to state table (c).

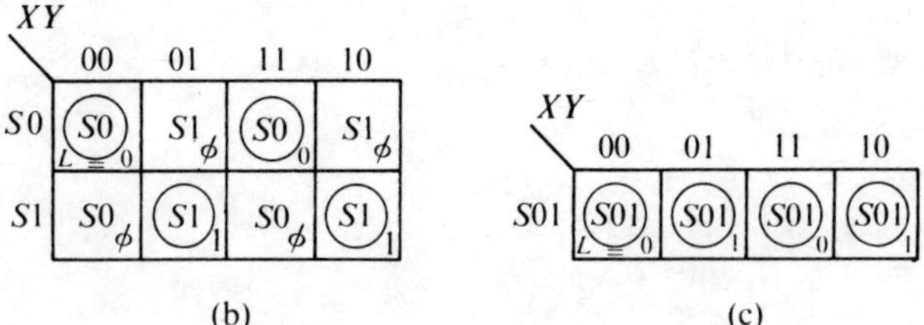

(b) (c)

Since the transition table reduces to one state, the required circuit is combinational. By direct reference to Figure (c), we obtain:

$$L = \bar{X}Y + X\bar{Y}.$$

Its relay circuit implementation is shown in Figure (d).

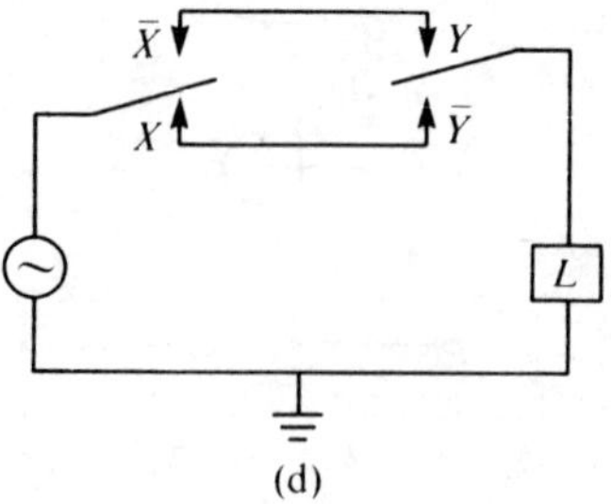

(d)

PROBLEM 6: *Control for a Jogging (Inching) Motor*

Design a control circuit to allow the operation of an electric motor, whose block diagram is shown in Figure (a), to be controlled by three pushbutton switches, *s*, *j*, and *h*, in the following manner.

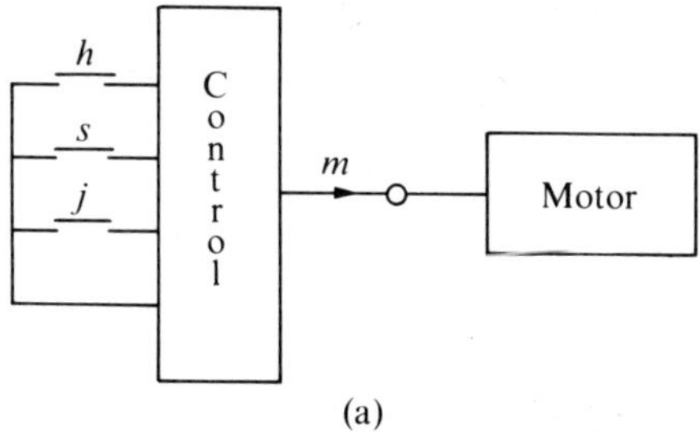

(a)

1. Activation of the start button, *s*, causes the motor to run and to remain running until the half switch is activated.
2. Pressing the 'jog' ('inching') button, *j*, causes the motor to run or to continue running for as long as the *j* button remains pressed. The motor stops when the *j* button is released.
3. Activation of the 'halt' button, *h*, is to stop the motor, irrespectively of the states of the other switches.

SOLUTION:

Step 1. *External (I/O) characteristics*

As stated.

Step 2. *Internal characteristics*

A suitable internal state diagram is shown in Figure (b).

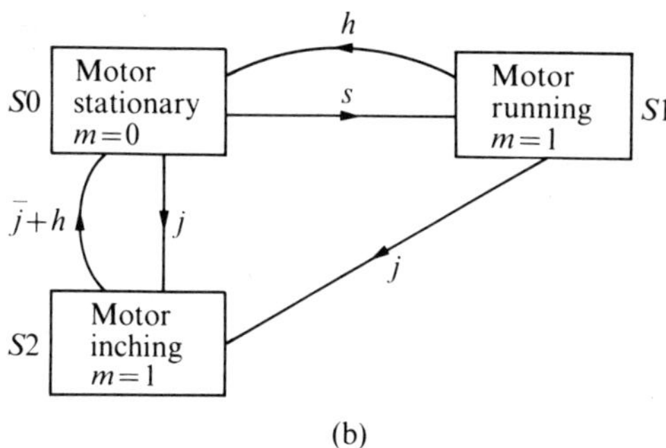

(b)

Step 3 *State reduction*

The equivalent state table is shown in Figure (c).

In accordance with the state reduction rules, described in Section 10 of Chapter 1, row *S*0 can be combined with row *S*2. The reduced state table is shown in Figure (d).

hsj	000	010	110	100	101	111	011	001
$S0$	($S0$) $m=0$	$S1$ $\emptyset$	($S0$) 0	($S0$) 0	($S0$) 0	($S0$) 0		$S2$ $\emptyset$
$S1$	($S1$) 1	($S1$) 1	$S0$ $\emptyset$	$S0$ $\emptyset$	$S0$ $\emptyset$	$S0$ $\emptyset$	$S2$ 1	$S2$ 1
$S2$	$S0$ $\emptyset$	$S1$ $\emptyset$	$S0$ $\emptyset$	$S0$ $\emptyset$	$S0$ $\emptyset$	$S0$ $\emptyset$	($S2$) 1	($S2$) 1

(c)

hsj	000	010	110	100	101	111	011	001
$S1$	($S1$) $m=1$	($S1$) 1	$S02$ $\emptyset=0$	$S02$ $\emptyset=0$	$S02$ $\emptyset=0$	$S02$ $\emptyset=0$	$S02$ 1	$S02$ $\emptyset=1$
$S02$	($S02$) 0	$S1$ $\emptyset$	($S02$) 0	($S02$) 0	($S02$) 0	($S02$) 0	($S02$) 1	($S02$) 1

(d)

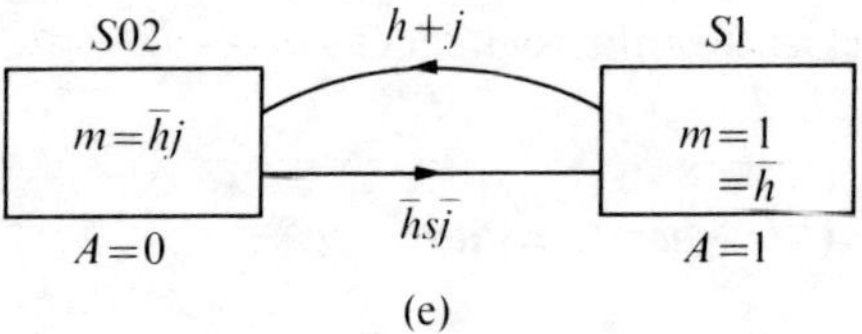

(e)

Step 4 *Primitive circuit*

The state diagram derived directly from the state table in Figure (d) is shown in Figure (e). For extra security, in state $S1$ we equate motor signal m to $\overline{h}$. This allows the motor to stop when push-button h is pressed, even if the circuit fails to move to state $S02$ from $S1$. By direct reference to the state diagram in Figure (e), we obtain

$$\text{Turn-on set of } A = \overline{h} \,.\, s \,.\, \overline{j}$$
$$\text{Turn-off set of } A = h + j \xrightarrow{\text{Invert}} \overline{h} \,.\, \overline{j}.$$

Therefore, the circuit equations are

$$\begin{aligned} A &= (\overline{h} \,.\, s \,.\, \overline{j} + A) \,.\, \overline{h} \,.\, \overline{j} \\ &= (s + A) \,.\, \overline{h} \,.\, \overline{j} \end{aligned}$$

$$\begin{aligned} m &= S02 \,.\, \overline{h} \,.\, j + S1 \,.\, \overline{h} \\ &= \overline{A} \,.\, \overline{h} \,.\, j + A \,.\, \overline{h} \\ &= \overline{h} \,.\, j + A \,.\, \overline{h} \\ &= \overline{h}(j + A). \end{aligned}$$

The corresponding relay circuit is shown in Figure (f).

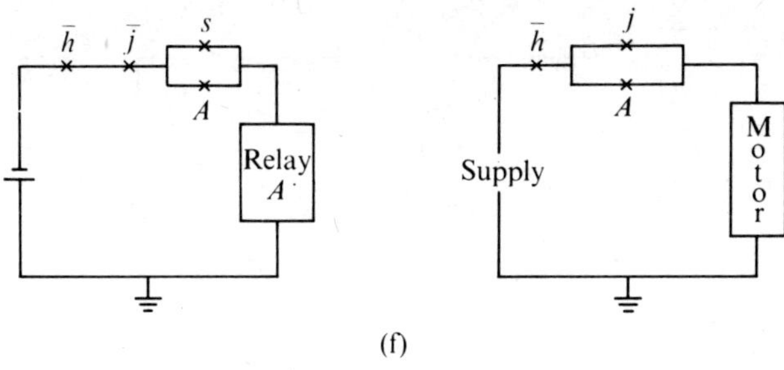

(f)

Note that in order that our circuit fails safe, we used the NOR form of the sequential equations. This, as we explained in Chapter 1, allows the turn-off set to override the turn-on set.

PROBLEM 7: *Motor Control*

The operation of an electric motor is to be controlled by the three push-buttons shown in Figure (a) in the following manner. The motor is to start by pressing push-button s, and to stop by pressing push-button h. If a fault occurs, indicated by a logic 1 on line f, the motor is to stop automatically and light l is to turn on. In addition, the start button s is to be disabled, until the fault is cleared and the circuit reset by pressing push-button r.

Design a suitable circuit and implement it using relays.

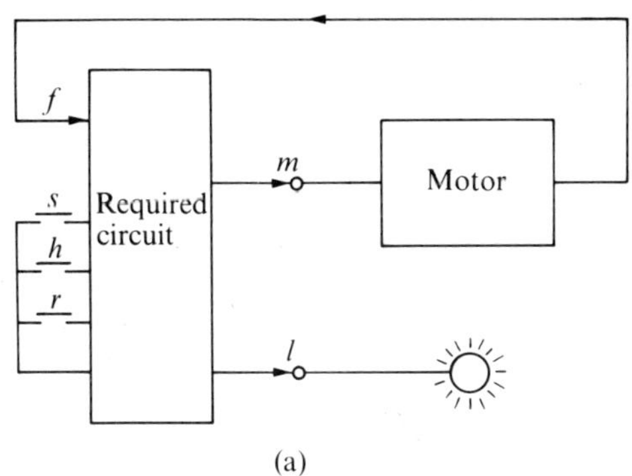

(a)

SOLUTION:

Step 1 *External (I/O) characteristics*

As specified.

Step 2 *Internal characteristics*

The state diagram of a suitable control circuit is shown in Figure (b). Its operation is as follows.

When in state $S0$ $m = 1 = 0$; that is the motor is stationary and the light is turned off. Activating switch s moves our circuit to state $S1$. In this state $m = 1$, causing the motor to run. The light remains turned off. Note that by ANDing start signal s with $\bar{h}$, we ensure that the half signal overrides

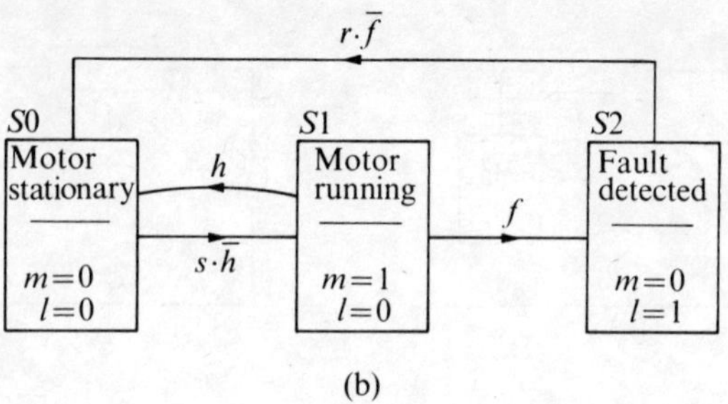

(b)

the start signal, since the transition to state $S1$ cannot take place when $h = 1$. To stop the motor we activate push-button h, which causes our circuit to move back to state $S0$.

If, while in state $S1$, a fault occurs, our circuit moves to state $S2$. This stops the motor and turns the light on. Exit from state $S2$ can only take place by activating reset switch r, after the fault has been cleared.

Step 3 *State reduction*

Reference to the partially-drawn state table in Figure (c), shows that because the three entries in the first column are different, merging of rows is not possible.

shrf	0000	0100	1100	1000	1010	1110	0110	0010	0011	0111	1111	1011	1001	1101	0101	0001
S0 m,l=	(S0) 0,0	(S0) 0,0		S1 ϕ,0												
S1	(S1) 1,0			(S1) 1,0												S2 ϕ,ϕ
S2	(S2) 0,1															(S2) 0,1

(c)

Step 4 *Primitive circuit*

To meet the constraint of 2^n states, specified in Section 8 of Chapter 1, we must add a dummy state to our three-state diagram in Figure (b). In our case we shall insert the dummy state between $S2$ and $S3$, as shown in Figure (d). For additional security, we equate signal m in state $S1$ to $\overline{h}$. This allows for the motor to turn off, even if our circuit fails to move back to state $S0$ from state $S1$ when push-button h is activated. By direct reference to the state diagram, we obtain

$$\text{turn-on set of } A = B\,.\,f$$
$$\text{turn-off set of } A = \overline{B} \xrightarrow{\text{Invert}} B$$
$$\text{turn-on set of } B = \overline{A}\,.\,s\,.\,\overline{b}$$
$$\text{turn-off set of } B = \overline{A}\,.\,h + A\,.\,r\,.\,\overline{f} \xrightarrow{\text{Invert}} (A+\overline{h})\,.\,(\overline{A}+\overline{r}+f).$$

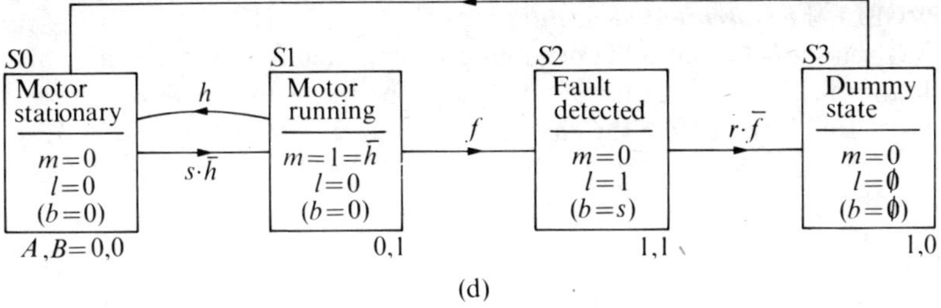

(d)

Therefore, the circuit equations are

$$
\begin{aligned}
A &= [B \,.\, f + A] \,.\, B \\
  &= [f + A] \,.\, B \\
B &= [\overline{A} \,.\, s \,.\, \overline{h} + B]\,(A + \overline{h})(\overline{A} + \overline{r} + f) \\
m &= S1 \,.\, \overline{h} \\
  &= \overline{A} \,.\, B \,.\, \overline{h} \\
l &= S2 + (S3) \\
  &= A \,.\, B + A \,.\, \overline{B} \\
  &= A.
\end{aligned}
$$

The corresponding relay circuit is shown in Figure (e). Ignore the presence of the buzzer.

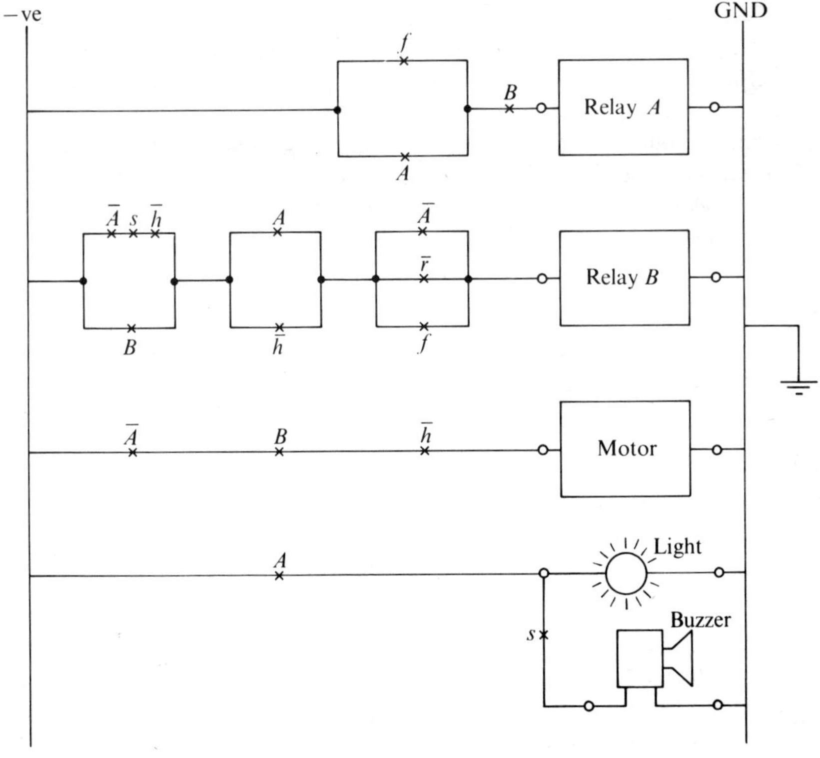

(e)

PROBLEM 8: *Circuit Modification*

Given the solution to the previous problem, modify the motor control circuit to allow a buzzer to turn on, each time the operator presses the start push-button before the circuit has been reset after a fault.

SOLUTION

The solution consists of introducing a buzzer and generating an appropriate signal to drive it. We denote this signal by variable b. Its logic levels are as shown in Figure (d) of the previous problem. By direct reference to this Figure, we obtain

$$\begin{aligned} b &= S2 \cdot s + (S3) \\ &= A \cdot B \cdot s + (A \cdot \overline{B}) \\ &= A \cdot s \end{aligned}$$

The modification, therefore, in our case consists of adding a normally-open contact on push-button s and a buzzer to the given circuit, as shown in Figure (e) of the previous problem.

PROBLEM 9: *An Incremental Shaft Encoder**

A shaft encoder generates two pulse trains X and Y. The X pulses occur before the Y pulses when the shaft is rotated in a clockwise direction, and the Y pulses occur before X pulses when the shaft is rotated in an anti-clockwise direction (see diagram (a)). Design a circuit that generates step-up pulses on terminal $Z1$ when the shaft moves in a clockwise direction, and step-down pulses on terminal $Z2$ when the shaft rotates in an anti-clockwise direction.

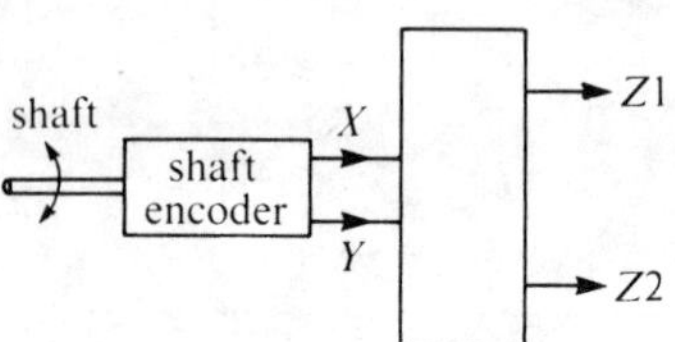

*An incremental shaft encoder is an optical device (known also as DeMoire's fringe device) attached to a shaft and used to digitize the angular displacement of the shaft. It is used extensively where fine control of rotations is required.

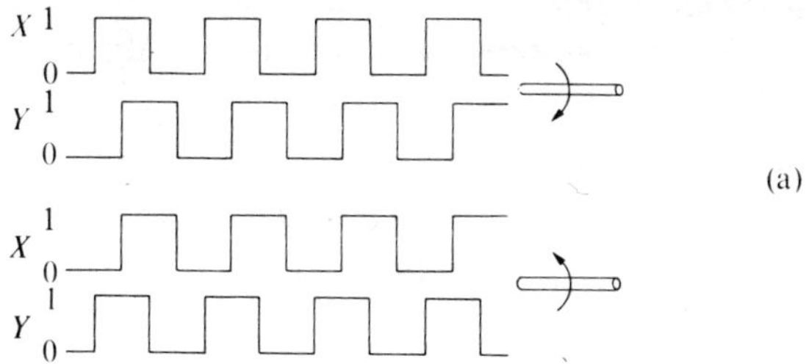

(a)

SOLUTION

Step 1 *I/O characteristics*

As stated.

Step 2 *Internal characteristics*

A suitable state diagram is shown in Figure (b).

Step 3 *State reduction*

The equivalent state table in Figure (c) does not reduce.

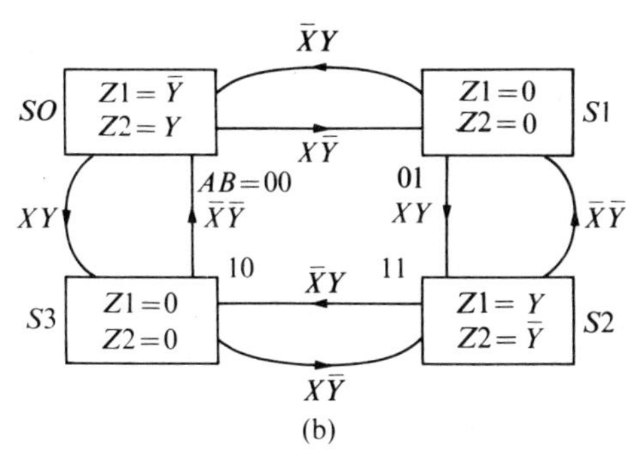

(b)

S \ XY	00	01	11	10
S0	(S0) Z1Z2 =10	(S0) 01	S3 0ϕ	S1 ϕ1
S1	(S1) 00	S0 0ϕ	S2 0	(S1) 00
S2	S1 ϕ0	S3 0ϕ	(S2) 10	(S2) 01
S3	S0 00	(S3) 00	(S3) 00	S2 0ϕ

(c)

Step 4 *Primitive circuit*

Suitable state codes are shown in Figure (b). By direct reference to this figure, we obtain

$$
\begin{aligned}
\text{Turn-on set of } A &= BXY + \bar{B}XY = XY \\
\text{Turn-off set of } A &= \bar{B}\bar{X}\bar{Y} + B\bar{X}\bar{Y} = \bar{X}\bar{Y}
\end{aligned}
$$

$$
\begin{aligned}
\text{Turn-on set of } B &= \bar{A}X\bar{Y} + AX\bar{Y} = X\bar{Y} \\
\text{Turn-off set of } B &= A\bar{X}Y + \bar{A}\bar{X}Y = \bar{X}Y.
\end{aligned}
$$

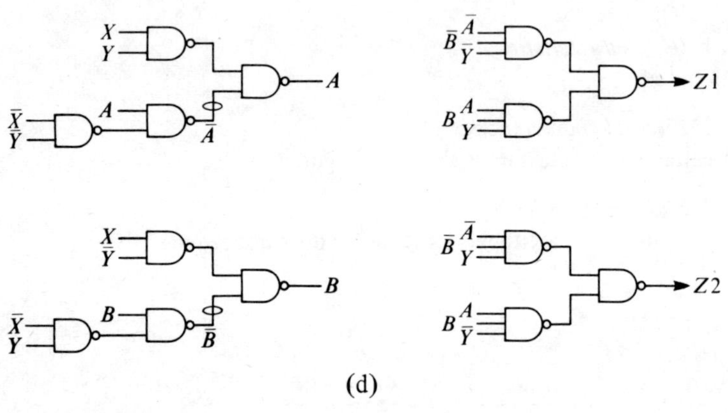

(d)

Therefore, the NAND circuit equations are:

$$
\begin{aligned}
A &= XY + A(X + Y) \\
B &= X\bar{Y} + B(X + \bar{Y}) \\
Z1 &= \bar{A}\bar{B}\bar{Y} + ABY \\
Z2 &= \bar{A}\bar{B}Y + AB\bar{Y}.
\end{aligned}
$$

The corresponding NAND circuit is shown in Figure (d).

PROBLEM 10: *The Two-wire Interface**

Show that the interface between a pair of action/status devices working in a hand-shake mode, shown in Figures (a) and (b), consists of two wires.

Action/status devices have two terminals, an *action terminal a* and a *status terminal r*, as shown in Figure (a). Signals *a* and *r* have the following meaning.

* The two-wire interface is used extensively in the design and implementation of microprocessor systems. The interested reader is referred to *System Design with Microprocessors*, by D. Zissos, Academic Press, 1978.

Signal a A 0-to-1 transition of this signal activates the device.
Signal r When the device is available ('ready'), $r = 1$; otherwise $r = 0$. No activation is possible when $r = 0$.

(All digital equipment can be converted into action/status devices, as we show in the next problem.)

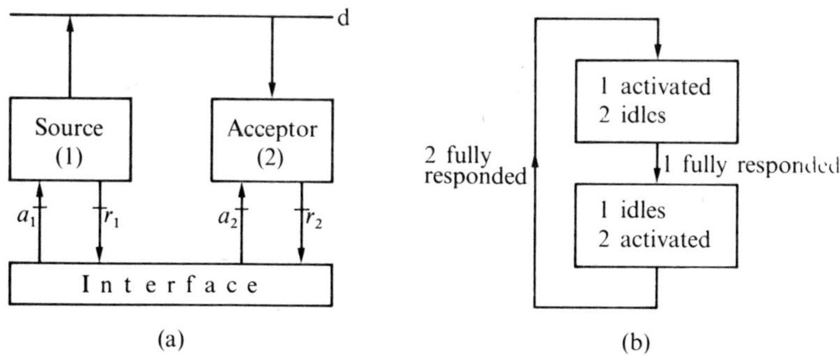

(a) (b)

SOLUTION:

Step 1 *External characteristics*

These are as defined. From our point of view, the required interface is a logic circuit with the two ready signals as inputs and the two action signals as outputs – see Figure (c).

Step 2 *Internal characteristics*

A suitable internal state diagram is shown in Figure (d). Its operation is as follows.

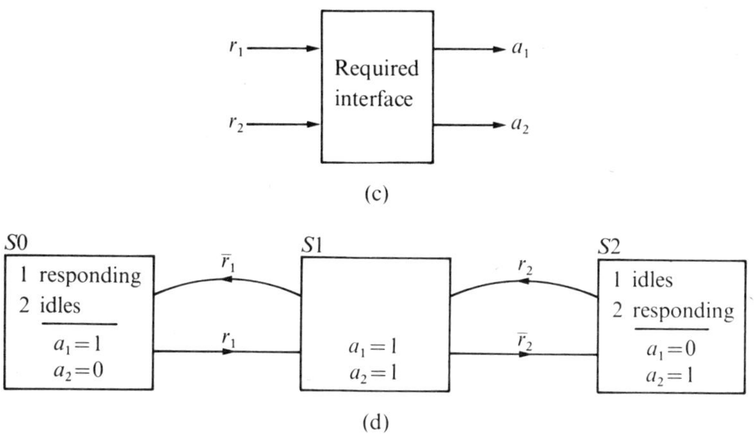

(c)

(d)

Let us assume that device 1 is active and device 2 inactive. The corresponding state in our diagram is $S0$. This state is maintained while device 1 remains active. When it has fully responded, indicated by r_1 changing to 1, our circuit moves to state $S1$. Reference to Figure (d) shows that a_2 equals

0 in state $S0$ and 1 in state $S1$, that is the $S0$ to $S1$ circuit transition causes action signal a_2 to change from 0 to 1. This signal change activates device 2. When r_2 changes to 0, indicating that device 2 has begun to respond, our circuit moves to state $S2$. It remains in this state until device 2 has fully responded, indicated by r_2 changing to 1. When r_2 equals 1 our circuit moves to state $S1$. As a_1 equals 0 in state $S2$ and 1 in state $S1$, the $S2$ to $S1$ circuit transition activates device 1. When it responds, indicated by signal r_1 changing to 0, our circuit moves to state $S0$, where it remains until device 1 has fully responded. The cycle repeats itself.

Step 3 *State reduction*

The state table corresponding to our state diagram in Figure (d) is shown in Figure (e). Applying the reduction steps described in Section 10 of Chapter 1, the three rows of the table merge into a single row, as shown in Figure (f). In the first square we enter circled entry $S012$, since there is no other state that our circuit can assume. The outputs in this square at this stage are Ø, Ø, indicating optional values.

$r_1 r_2$	00	01	11	10
$S0$		($S0$) a_1,a_2=1,0	$S1$ 1,Ø	
$S1$		$S0$ 1,Ø	($S1$) 1,1	$S2$ Ø,1
$S2$			$S1$ Ø,1	($S2$) 0,1

(e)

$r_1 r_2$	00	01	11	10
$S012$	($S012$) a_1,a_2=Ø,Ø =0,0	($S012$) 1,0	($S012$) 1,1	($S012$) 0,1

(f)

Step 4 *Circuit implementation*

By direct reference to the reduced state table in Figure (f), we obtain

$$a_1 = \overline{r}_1 . r_2 + r_1 . r_2 + (\overline{r}_1 . \overline{r}_2) = r_2$$
$$a_2 = r_1 . r_2 + r_1 . \overline{r}_2 + (\overline{r}_1 . \overline{r}_2) = r_1$$

Since the optional product $\overline{r}_1 . \overline{r}_2$ has not been used in the derivation of our final expressions for signals a_1 and a_2, $a_1 = a_2 = 0$ in the first square in Figure (f).

We refer to the above equations as *primitive interface equations.* Their implementation consists of two wires, as shown in Figure (g).

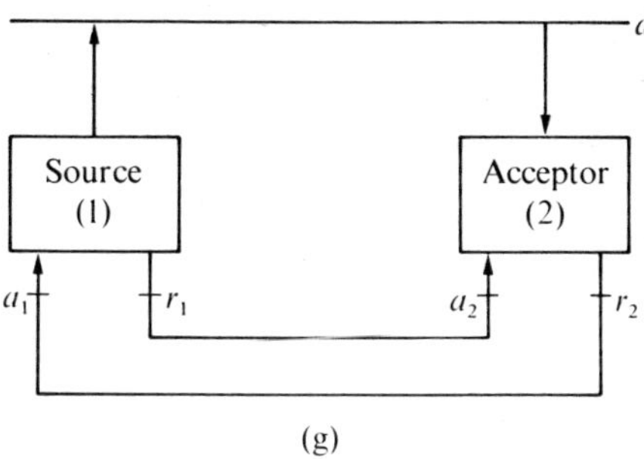

(g)

PROBLEM 11: *Front-end logic*

Design and implement the front-end logic for a digital printer, whose block diagram is shown in Figure (a), and whose terminal characteristics are:

Terminal w A ground on this terminal ($w = 0$) positions the print wheels according to the input data.

Terminal x While the print wheels are being positioned $x = 0$. This signal changes to 1 when the wheels are correctly positioned.

Terminal y Grounding terminal y causes the print hammers to strike and the paper to advance to its next line position.

Terminal z Signal $z = 0$ when the print hammers are being activated and the paper is advancing, otherwise $z = 1$.

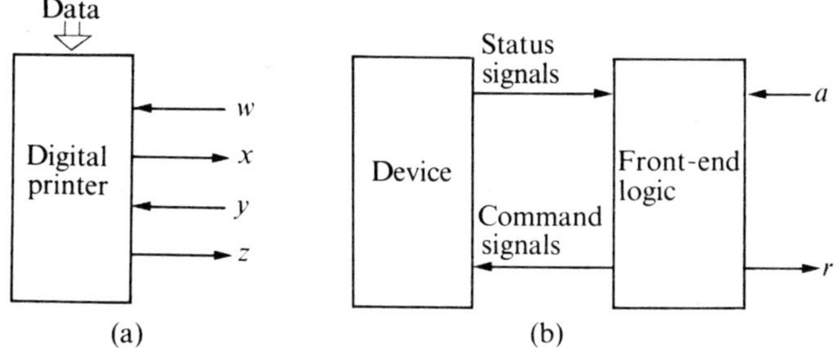

(a) (b)

SOLUTION:

The block diagram of a front-end logic is shown in Figure (a). Its function is to monitor the status signals of the device and to generate the correct sequence of command signals to drive the device when the action signal changes from 0 to 1. In addition it generates the status signal *r.*

Step 1 *External characteristics*

The block diagram of our solution is shown in Figure (c). Its function is to allow the characters specified by the input data lines to be printed each time the signal on its action terminal changes from 0 to 1.

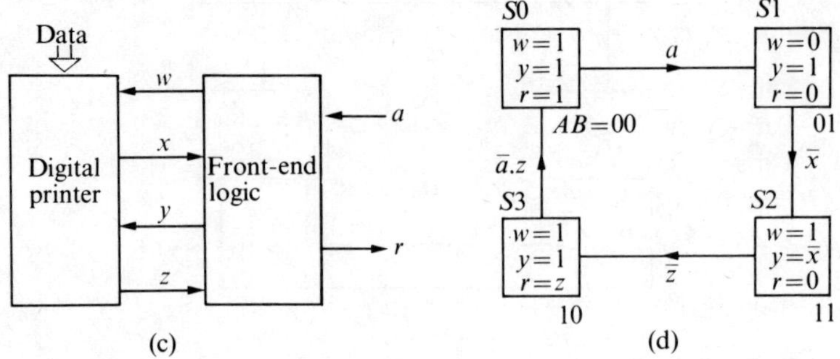

(c) (d)

Step 2 *Internal characteristics*

The internal state diagram of a suitable circuit is shown in Figure (d). Its operation is as follows.

Its 'normal' state is $S0$. This state is maintained while the printer is inactive. In this state we make $w = y = 1$, to maintain the print wheels and the print hammers stationary; ready signal r is made equal to 1 to indicate to the 'outside world' that the printer is ready to print.

When action signal a changes to 1, our circuit moves to state $S1$. In this state we pull the printer's w line low, that is we ground it. This causes the print wheels to start positioning themselves according to the input data. When the print wheels start moving, status signal x changes to 0 and our circuit moves to state $S2$.

In state $S2$ we remove the ground from the w terminal and equate y to $\overline{x}$. This allows the y line to be maintained at logic 1 during the period that the print wheels are being positioned. When the print wheels have positioned themselves correctly, status signal x changes to 1, and therefore $\overline{x}$ to 0. Since in state $S2$ $y = \overline{x}$, the y line is grounded immediately the print wheels stop moving, activating the print hammers.

When the print hammers begin to move, status signal z changes to 0, causing our circuit to move to state $S3$.

When the print hammers return to their quiescent position, status signal z changes to 1. In this state we equate ready signal r to z, causing it (r) to change to 1 at the end of each printing cycle, indicating that the printer is now ready to print again. Note, however, that the printer cannot be activated until it returns to state $S0$.

Now, the circuit transition to state $S0$ is initiated with signal $\overline{a}.\,z$. That is in addition to the printer being ready, the action signal must be zero. This ensures that the printer specifically, and all action/status devices generally, are triggered into action on the leading edge of a positive-going pulse.

Step 3 *State reduction*

To maintain clarity of design, state reduction will not be attempted.

Step 4 *Primitive circuit*

By direct reference to our state diagram in Figure (d), we obtain

$$\begin{aligned}
\text{Turn-on set of } A &= B\,.\,\overline{x} \\
\text{Turn-off set of } A &= \overline{B}\,.\,\overline{a}\,.\,z \xrightarrow{\text{Invert}} B + a + \overline{z} \\
\text{Turn-on set of } B &= \overline{A}\,.\,a \\
\text{Turn-off set of } B &= A\,.\,\overline{z} \xrightarrow{\text{Invert}} \overline{A} + z.
\end{aligned}$$

Therefore, the circuit equations are

$$A = B\,.\,\overline{x} + A\,.(B + a + \overline{z})$$

$$B = \overline{A}\,.\,a + B\,.\,(\overline{A} + z)$$

$$w = \overline{S1} = \overline{\overline{A}\,.\,B} = A + \overline{B}$$

$$\begin{aligned}
y &= S0 + S1 + S2\,.\,\overline{x} + S3 \\
&= \overline{S2} + S2\,.\,\overline{x} \\
&= \overline{S2} + \overline{x} \\
&= \overline{A} + \overline{B} + \overline{x}
\end{aligned}$$

$$\begin{aligned}
r &= S0 + S3\,.\,z \\
&= AB + ABz \\
&= AB + Bz.
\end{aligned}$$

The corresponding NAND circuit, which constitutes the front-end logic (f.e.l.) of our printer, is shown in Figure (e).

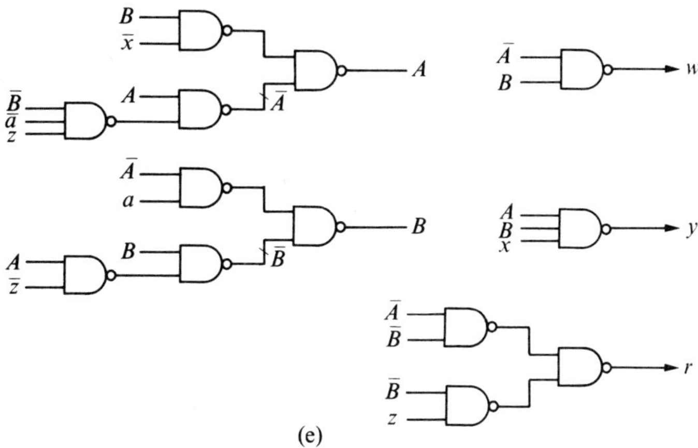

(e)

PROBLEM 12: *A Pulse-train Generator*

Clock pulses appear on terminal c in Figure (a). Design and implement a circuit that allows a pulse-train of predetermined length (n pulses) to be output on terminal k each time switch m is activated. Complete pulses only to be output.

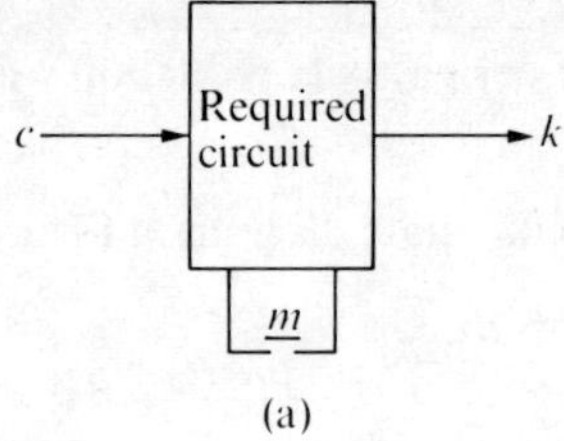

(a)

SOLUTION:

Step 1 *External (I/O) characteristics*

The block diagram of our solution is shown in Figure (b). It consists of an electronic switch, a pulse counter, and a NOR gate. Its operation is as follows.

Activation of manual switch m 'closes' our electronic switch, allowing the clock pulses on terminal c to appear on the output terminal, k. Each time a pulse is output our counter, which initially is empty, is stepped up. After the last (nth) pulse is output, the count becomes zero, causing signal e to change to 1. We use the 0 to 1 transition in signal e to 'open' our electronic switch, thus isolating the output from the input.

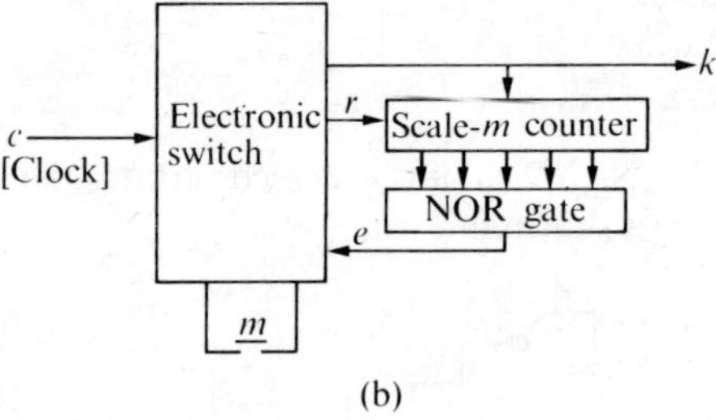

(b)

Step 2 *Internal characteristics*

The internal state diagram of a suitable circuit is shown in Figure (c). $S0$ is the quiescent state of our circuit. In this state we maintain our electronic switch 'open'. We do this by equating signal k to 0. In this state we also generate signal r, which resets our counter to 0.

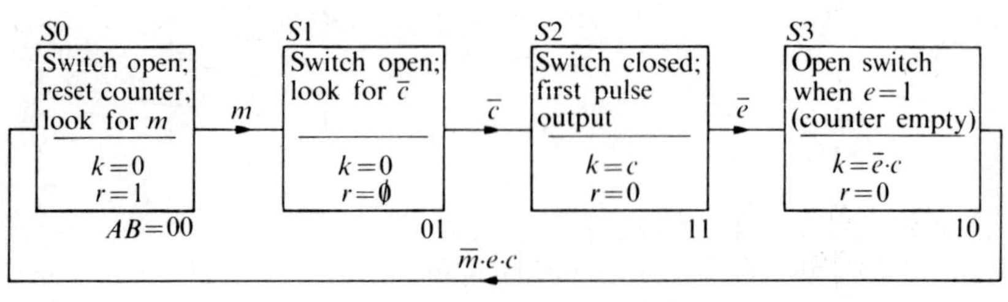

(c)

When switch m is activated, indicated by the appearance of signal m, our circuit moves to state $S1$. In this state our electronic switch is maintained 'open' by equating, as before, k to 0. As no pulses are being output in this state, we have the option of defining the counter reset signal as 0 or 1. In order to ensure that complete pulses only are output, we initiate the transition to state $S2$ with $\overline{c}$, that is when no pulse is present at the input terminal.

In state $S2$ we 'close' our electronic switch by equating signal k to clock signal c. We also remove the reset signal r, allowing our counter to keep count of the pulses that appear on terminal k.

After the first pulse is output, the count becomes 1 and $e = 0$. This causes our circuit to move to state $S3$. In state $S3$ our switch is initially 'closed', allowing the input pulses to be output. After the nth pulse is output, signal e changes to one and we 'open' the switch. This is achieved simply by ANDing the output signal with $\overline{e}$. Our circuit resets, that is it assumes its initial state, when switch m is released and $e = 1$.

Clearly, a signal spike generated on line e in Figure (b) when the count is being incremented (and $m = 0$) will reset our circuit prematurely. This can be avoided either by using Gray code counters, or by ANDing signal $\overline{m}\,.\,e$ in Figure (c) with signal c if the counter is incremented on the trailing edge of a pulse. If the counter is incremented on the leading edge of a pulse, signal $\overline{m}\,.\,e$ must be ANDed with $\overline{c}$.

Step 3 *State reduction*

For the sake of clarity we shall omit this step.

Step 4 *Primitive circuit*

By direct reference to our state diagram in Figure (c), we obtain

$$\begin{aligned}
\text{Turn-on set of } A &= B\,.\,\overline{c},\\
\text{Turn-off set of } A &= \overline{B}\,.\,\overline{m}\,.\,e\,.\,c,\\
\text{Turn-on set of } B &= \overline{A}\,.\,m, \text{ and}\\
\text{Turn-off set of } B &= A\,.\,\overline{e}.
\end{aligned}$$

Therefore, the NAND circuit equations are,

$$A = B\,.\,\overline{c} + A(B + m + \overline{e} + \overline{c})$$

$$B = \overline{A}\,.\,m + B(\overline{A} + e)$$

$$\begin{aligned}
K &= S2\,.\,c + S3\,.\,\overline{e}\,.\,c\\
&= ABc + A\overline{B}\overline{e}c\\
&= ABc + A\overline{e}c
\end{aligned}$$

$$\begin{aligned}
r &= S0 + (S1)\\
&= \overline{A}\overline{B} + (\overline{A}B)\\
&= \overline{A}.
\end{aligned}$$

The equivalent circuit with a scale-4 counter is shown in Figure (d).

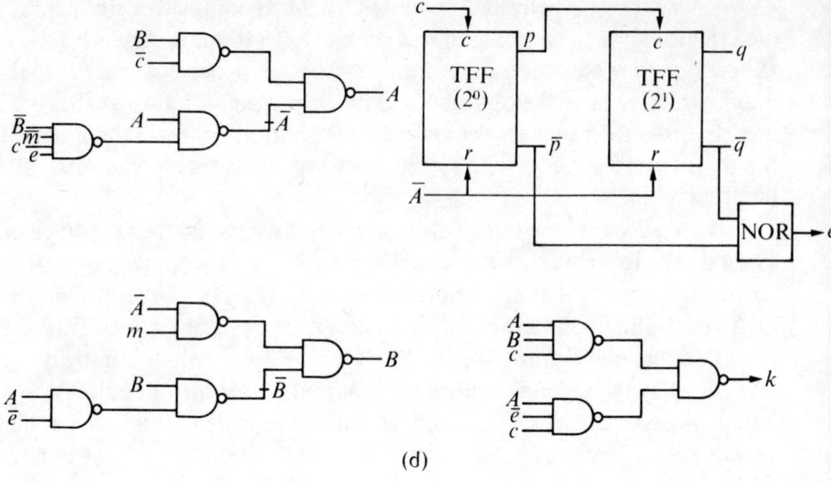

(d)

PROBLEM 13: *A Flag Circuit*

Design and implement a flag circuit with *set*, *clear*, *enable*, and *disable* facilities.

A flag is defined as a signal generated and used by a device to inform some other device that it wishes to communicate with it.

SOLUTION:

Step 1 *External (I/O) characteristics*

The block diagram of a flag circuit with set, clear, enable, and disable facilities is shown in Figure (a). The function of each of the input signals is as follows. A signal on terminal e enables the circuit, whereas a signal on terminal d disables the circuit. Clearly, in practice these two signals are not applied simultaneously. When the circuit is enabled, a signal on terminal k sets (turns on) the flag. The flag is cleared (turned off) by a signal on terminal c. If enable and disable facilities are not needed, terminals e and d may be omitted.

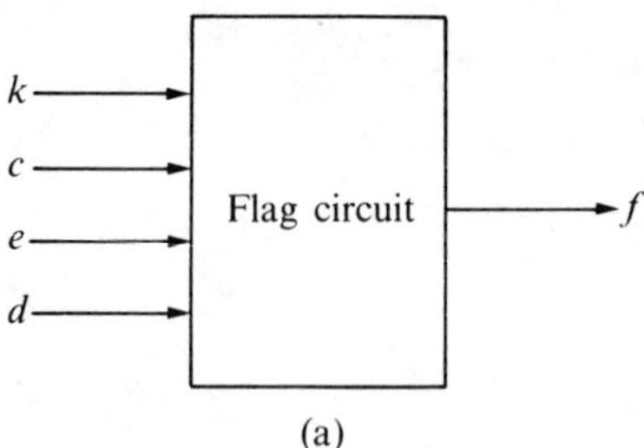

(a)

Step 2 *Internal characteristics*

The internal state diagram of a suitable circuit is shown in Figure (b). Its operation is self-explanatory.

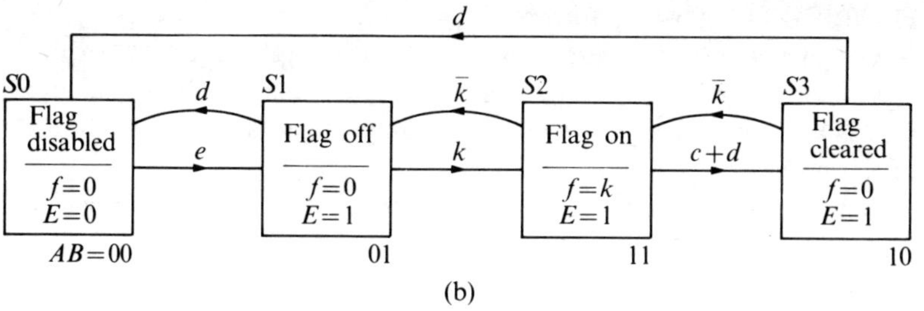

(b)

Step 3 *State reduction*

To maintain clarity of design, we omit this step.

Step 4 *Primitive circuit*

By direct reference to Figure (b), we obtain

$$\begin{aligned}
\text{Turn-on set of } A &= B \,.\, k \\
\text{Turn-off set of } A &= B \,.\, \overline{k} + B \,.\, \overline{d} \xrightarrow{\text{Invert}} (\overline{B} + k)(B + \overline{d}) \\
\text{Turn-on set of } B &= \overline{A} \,.\, e + A \,.\, \overline{k} \\
\text{Turn-off set of } B &= \overline{A} \,.\, d + A \,.\, c + A \,.\, d \\
&= d + Ac \xrightarrow{\text{Invert}} \overline{d} \,.\, (\overline{A} + \overline{c}).
\end{aligned}$$

Therefore, the circuit equations are

$$\begin{aligned}
A &= B \,.\, k + A(\overline{B} + k)(B + \overline{d}) \\
B &= \overline{A} \,.\, e + A \,.\, \overline{k} + B(\overline{A} + \overline{c})\overline{d} \\
f &= S2 \,.\, k = A \,.\, B \,.\, k.
\end{aligned}$$

The equivalent NAND circuit is shown in Figure (c).

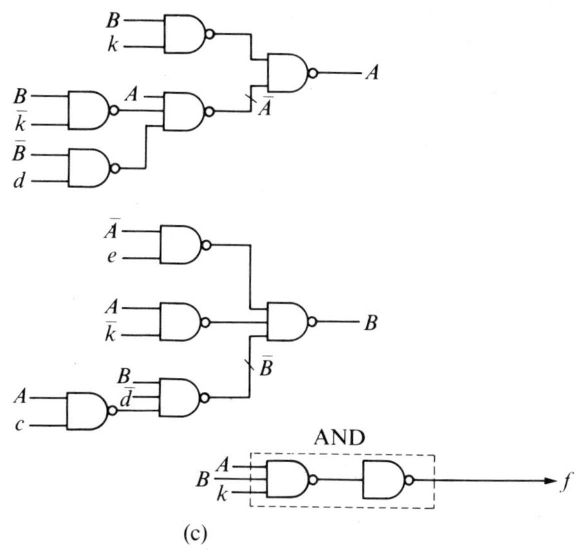

(c)

PROBLEM 14: *A 3-Flag Sorter*

Design a circuit to monitor the state of three flags* (such as three alarm signals). If a flag is set, the circuit is to generate a number identifying it, as well as an 'interrupt' signal, I. (Signal I will be the master alarm in the case of alarm signals.)

Implement your design using NAND gates.

SOLUTION

Step 1 *I/O characteristics*

Signals $f1, f2$, and $f3$ in Figure (a) are used to denote the three flags. Signals A and B are the address signals. A suitable external state diagram giving the signal a cyclic priority is shown in Figure (b).

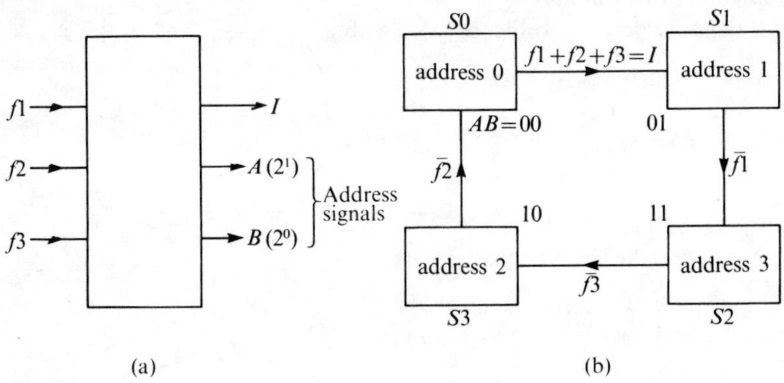

(a) (b)

Step 2 *Internal characteristics*

No additional states are required - therefore the internal characteristics are the same as the external.

Step 3 *State reduction*

To maintain clarity of design, we omit this step.

Step 4 *Primitive circuit*

Suitable codes that allow the state variables (A and B) to be used as address signals are shown in Figure (b). By direct reference to (b), we obtain:

Turn-on set of $A = B\overline{f1}$ Turn-on set of $B = \overline{A}I$

Turn-off set of $A = \overline{B}\overline{f2}$ Turn-off set of $B = A\overline{f3}$.

Therefore the circuit's primitive NAND equations are:

$$A = B\overline{f1} + A(B + f2)$$
$$B = \overline{A}I + B(\overline{A} + f3)$$
$$I = f1 + f2 + f3.$$

* For combinational circuit implementation and larger systems see Zissos, D. *System Design with Microprocessors*, Academic Press, 1978.

Its circuit implementation is shown in Figure (c).

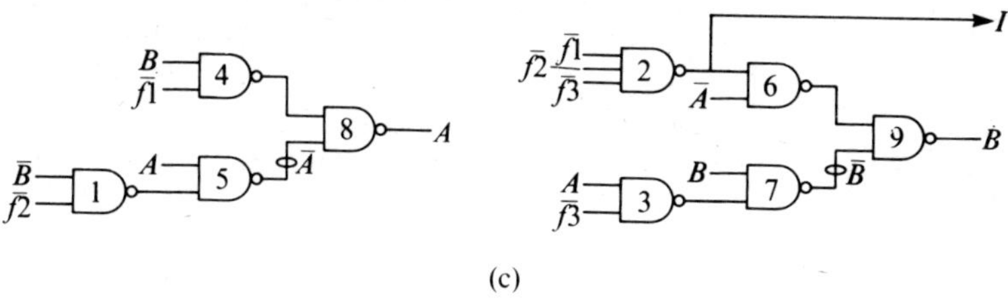

(c)

PROBLEM 15: *One Short Circuit**

High frequency clock pulses are presented at input terminal c in the figure shown below. Each activation of manual switch m is to allow one complete clock pulse to be output at K. It can be assumed that at least one clock pulse will be presented during the activation of switch m.

Design a suitable circuit.

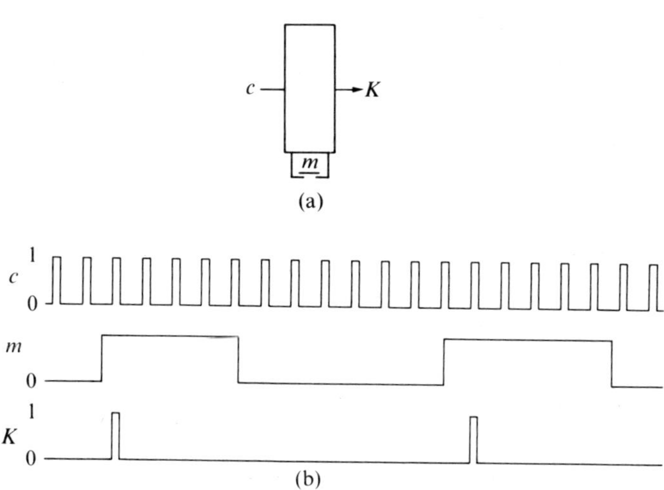

(a)

(b)

SOLUTION

Step 1 *I/O characteristics*

As stated.

Step 2 *Internal characteristics*

A suitable state diagram is shown on following page.

Step 3 *State reduction*

No rows in the state table shown can be merged.

* Circuits of this type are used extensively to slow down high speed operations, such as computer operations, to manual speeds.

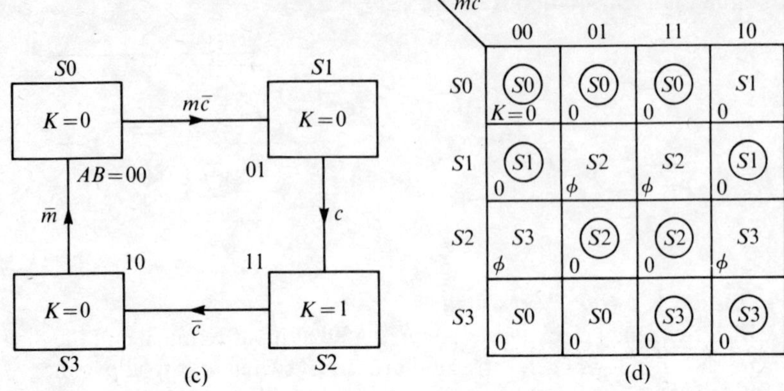

(c) (d)

Step 4 *Primitive circuit*

Suitable state codes are shown in the state diagram. By direct reference to this figure, we obtain:

Turn-on set of A = Bc Turn-on set of B = $\bar{A}m\bar{c}$
Turn-off set of A = $\bar{B}\bar{m}$ Turn-off set of B = $A\bar{c}$.

Therefore, the NAND circuit equations are:

$$A = Bc + A(B + m)$$
$$B = \bar{A}m\bar{c} + B(\bar{A} + c)$$
$$K = AB.$$

The corresponding circuit implementation is shown in Figure (e).

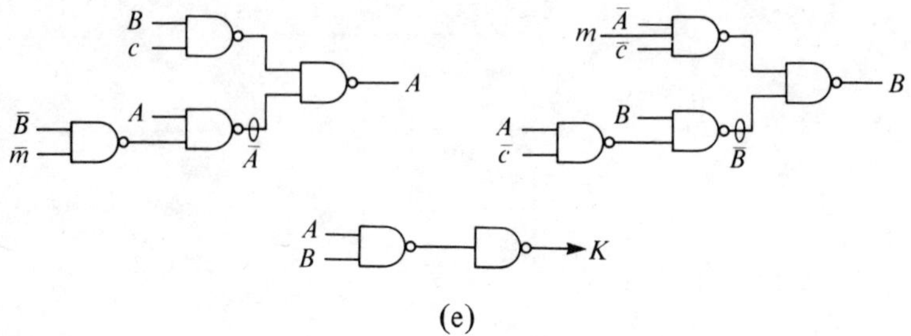

(e)

PROBLEM 16: *A Pulse Synchronizer*

Data pulses arrive randomly on terminal d and clock pulses arrive regularly on terminal c - see Figure (a).

Design a circuit that allows each data pulse to be output during the following clock pulse as shown above. A maximum of one data pulse can appear between two consecutive clock pulses.

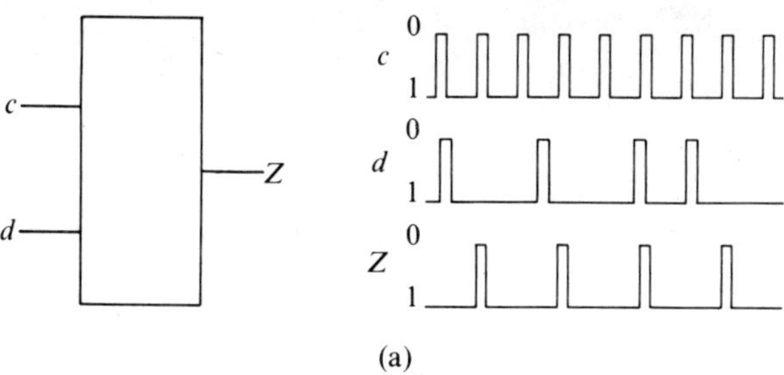

(a)

SOLUTION

Step 1 *External characteristics*

As stated.

Step 2 *Internal characteristics*

A suitable internal state diagram is shown in Figure (b).

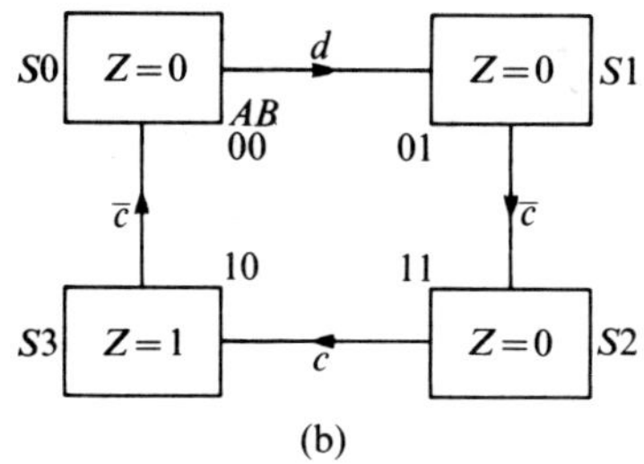

(b)

Step 3 *State reduction*

The corresponding state table in Figure (c) does not reduce.

dc	00	01	11	10
S0	(S0) Z=0	(S0) 0	S1 0	S1 0
S1	S2 0	(S1) 0	(S1) 0	S2 0
S2	(S2) 0	S3 ϕ	S3 ϕ	(S2) 0
S3	S0 ϕ	(S3) 1	(S3) 1	S0 0

(c)

Step 4 *Primitive circuit*

Suitable state codes are shown in the state diagram. By direct reference to this figure, we obtain

Turn-on set of $A = B\bar{c}$ Turn-on set of $B = \bar{A}d$

Turn-off set of $A = \bar{B}\bar{c}$ Turn-off set of $B = Ac$.

Therefore, the NAND circuit equations are

$$A = B\bar{c} + A(B + c)$$
$$B = \bar{A}d + B(\bar{A} + \bar{c})$$
$$Z = S3 = A\bar{B}.$$

Their corresponding circuit implementation using NAND gates is shown in Figure (d).

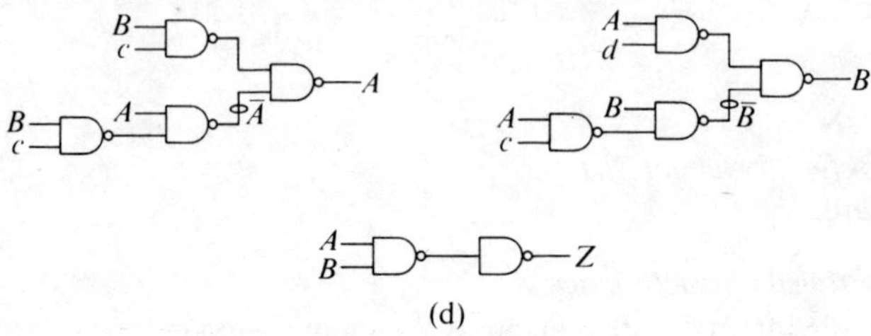

(d)

PROBLEM 17: *Traffic Lights*

A road intersection is controlled by a set of traffic lights. For each road the cycle of light sequence is as follows:

Road 1:	green	amber	red	red	red	red
Road 2:	red	red	red	green	amber	red
Duration:	2 min	10 sec	10 sec	2 min	10 sec	10 sec

The lights are driven by a timing signal X shown in Figure (a).

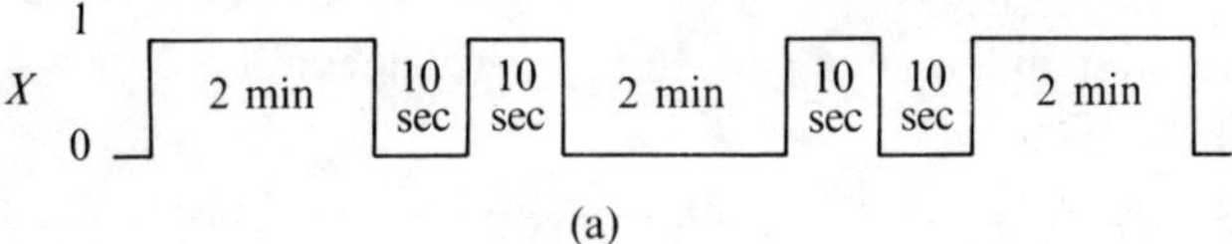

(a)

Design a suitable circuit.

SOLUTION

Step 1 *I/O characteristics*

As stated.

Step 2 *Internal characteristics*

The internal state diagram of a suitable control system is shown in Figure (b).

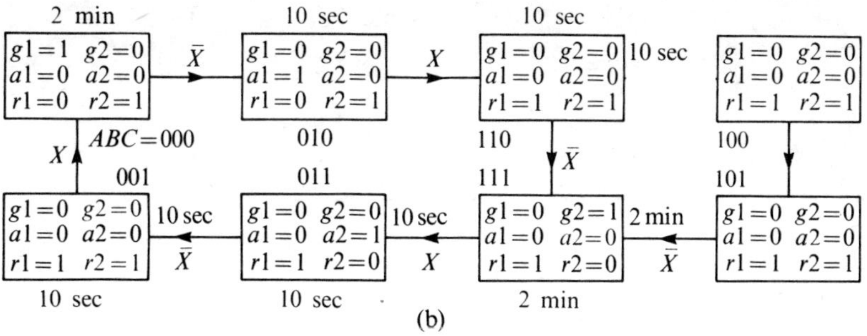

(b)

Step 3 *State reduction*

Omitted.

Step 4 *Primitive circuit*

Suitable state codes are shown in Figure (b). By direct reference to this diagram, we obtain:

Turn-on set of $A = B\bar{C}X$ Turn-on set of $B = \bar{A}\bar{C}\bar{X} + AC\bar{X}$

Turn-off set of $A = BCX$ Turn-off set of $B = \bar{A}C\bar{X}$

Turn-on set of $C = A\bar{X} + A\bar{B}$

Turn-off set of $C = \bar{A}\bar{B}X$.

Therefore, the NAND circuit equations are:

$$A = B\bar{C}X + A(\bar{B} + \bar{C} + \bar{X})$$
$$B = \bar{A}\bar{C}\bar{X} + AC\bar{X} + B(A + \bar{C} + X)$$
$$C = A\bar{X} + A\bar{B} + C(A + B + \bar{X})$$

$$g1 = \bar{A}\bar{B}\bar{C}$$
$$a1 = \bar{A}B\bar{C}$$
$$r1 = AB\bar{C} + ABC + \bar{A}BC + \bar{A}\bar{B}C + A\bar{B} = A + C$$

$$g2 = ABC$$
$$a2 = \bar{A}BC$$
$$r2 = \bar{A}\bar{B}\bar{C} + \bar{A}B\bar{C} + AB\bar{C} + \bar{A}\bar{B}C + A\bar{B} = \bar{B} + \bar{C}.$$

Their circuit implementation is shown in Figure (c) on the next page.

PROBLEM 18: *A Bounce Eliminator*

A common problem associated with mechanical switches is contact bounce. When contact is first made the armature bounces several times before settling to its new state – see I/O diagram below. It can be assumed that the armature does not bounce back far enough to make contact with the other terminal.

Design a NAND circuit to eliminate this problem.*

* A floating gate input is assumed to be at logic 1.

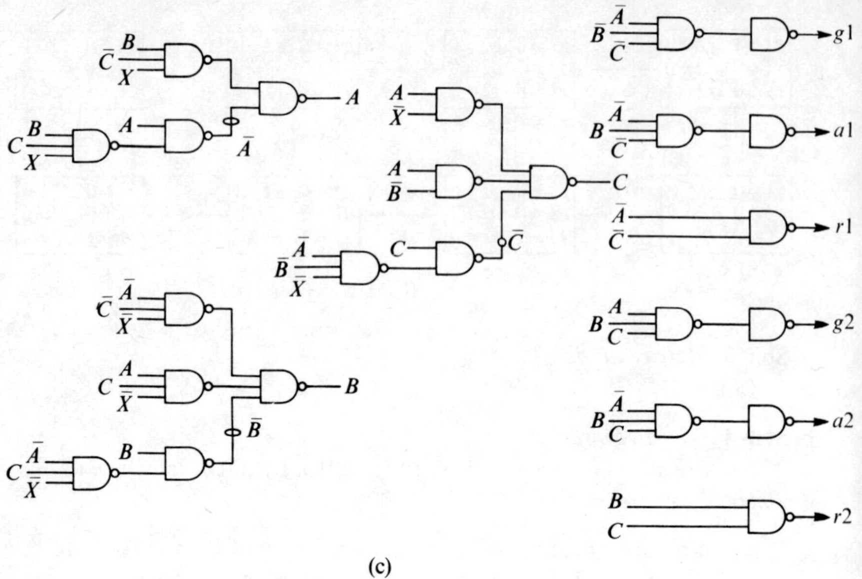

(c)

SOLUTION

Step 1 *I/O characteristics*

The I/O signals are shown in Figure (a).

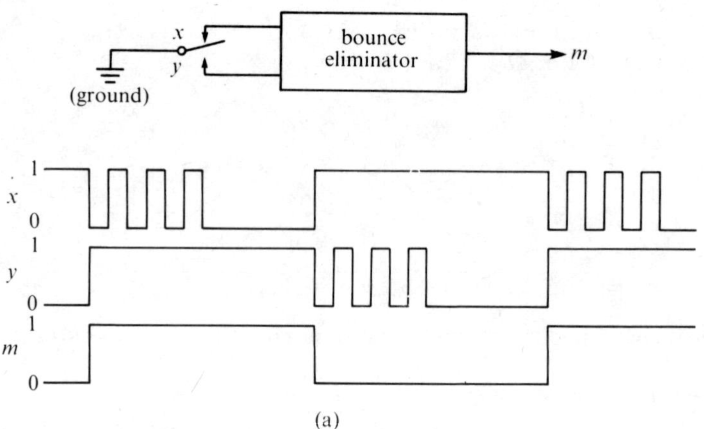

(a)

Step 2 *Internal characteristics*

A suitable internal state diagram is shown in Figure (b).

Step 3 *State reduction*

The corresponding state table in Figure (c) does not reduce.

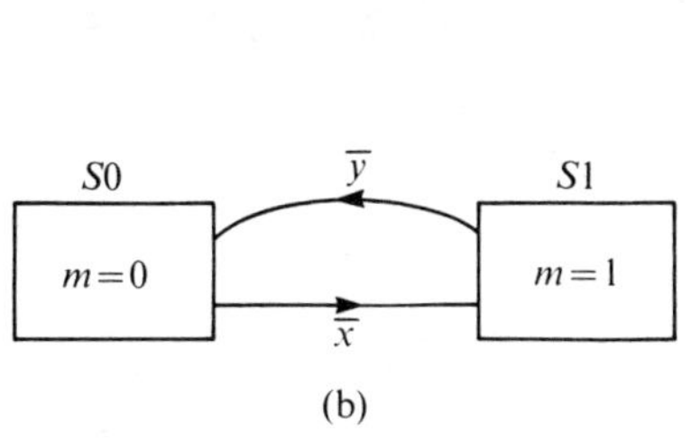

(b)

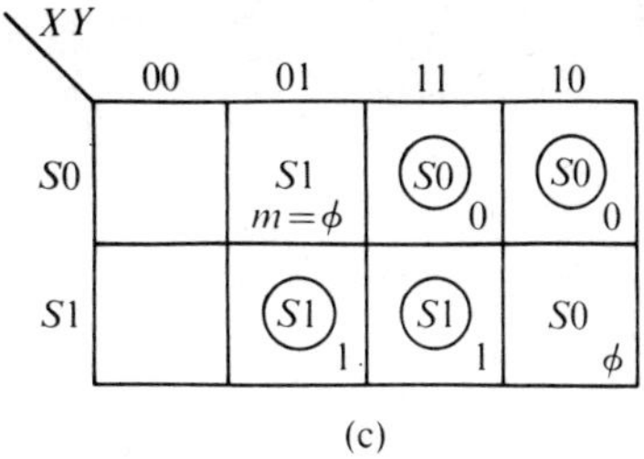

(c)

Step 4 *Primitive circuit*

Signal m is used to code the two-states as shown in Figure (b). By direct reference to (b), we obtain:

$$\text{Turn-on set of } m = \overline{x}$$
$$\text{Turn-off set of } m = \overline{y}.$$

Therefore the NAND circuit equation is $m = x + my$. Its circuit implementation is shown in Figure (d).

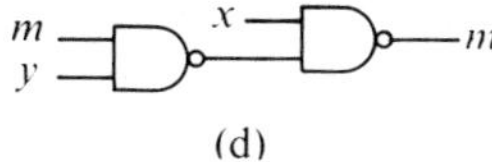

(d)

PROBLEM 19: *T Flip-Flop (TFF)*

Design a TFF, i.e. a bistable circuit whose output changes value (toggles) with every (clock) pulse at its input.

SOLUTION

Step 1 *I/O characteristics*

The circuit's I/O signals characteristics are as shown below in Figures (a) and (b).

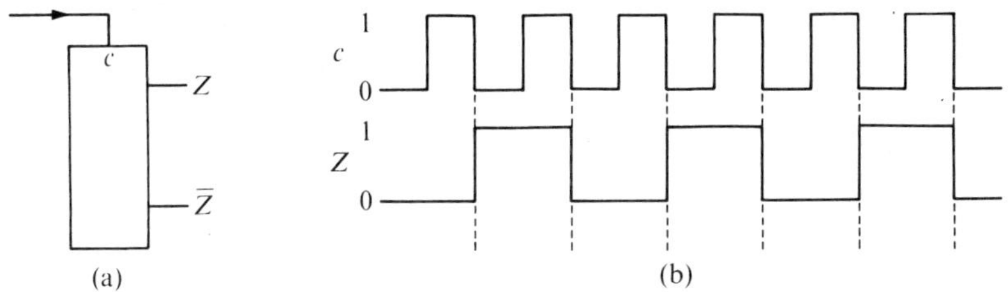

(a) (b)

Step 2 *Internal characteristics*

The circuit recycles after four changes in the input signal c. Therefore a circuit with four internal states is required to record each of the four changes in c, as shown on following page.*

* This circuit configuration is often referred to as the master-slave flip-flop.

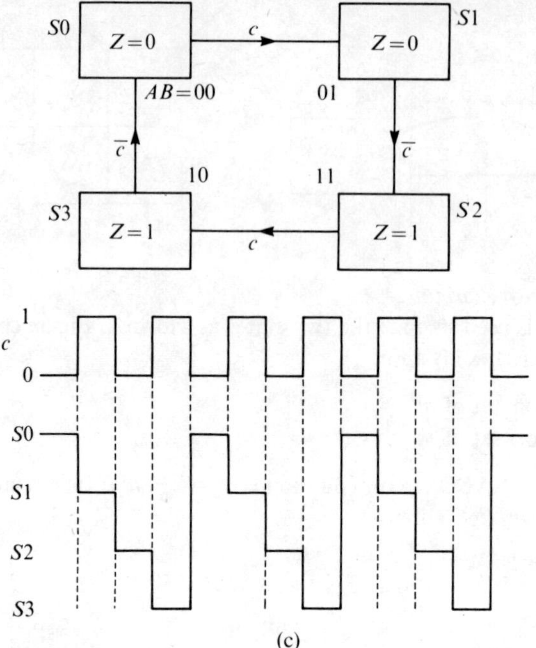

(c)

Step 3 *State reduction*

The corresponding state table is shown in Figure (d). No rows can be merged.

Step 4 *Primitive circuit*

Suitable state codes are shown on the circuit's internal-state diagram. By direct reference to this diagram, we obtain:

Turn-on set of $A = B\overline{c}$ Turn-on set of $B = \overline{A}c$
Turn-off set of $A = \overline{B}\overline{c}$ Turn-off set of $B = Ac$

Therefore, the NAND circuit equations are:

$$A = B\overline{c} + A(B + c)$$
$$B = \overline{A}c + B(\overline{A} + \overline{c})$$
$$Z = A.$$

Their circuit implementation is shown in Figure (e).*

* The minimal circuit implementation of the TFF is discussed in Chapter 6 of *Logic Design Algorithms* (1972).

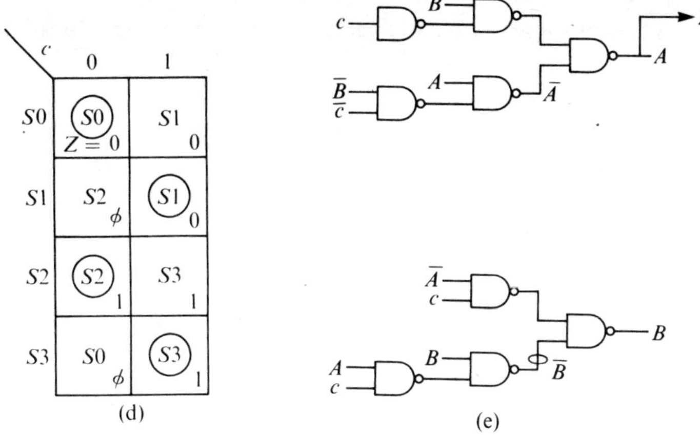

(d) (e)

PROBLEM 20: *D Flip-Flop* (*DFF*)

Design a DFF, i.e. a bistable circuit whose output assumes the value of the input at the time of a clock pulse.

SOLUTION

Step 1 *I/O characteristics*

The circuit's I/O characteristics are shown below in Figures (a) and (b).

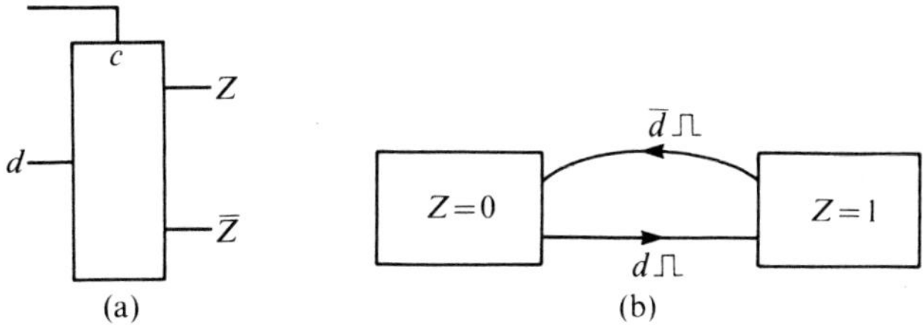

(a) (b)

Step 2 *Internal characteristics*

A suitable internal state diagram is shown in Figure (c).

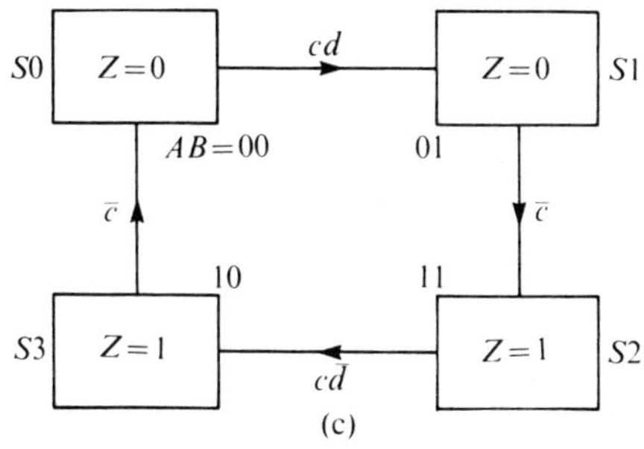

(c)

Step 3 *State reduction*

As can be seen from the state table (d), no state reduction is possible.

cd	00	01	11	10
$S0$	($S0$) $Z=0$	($S0$) 0	$S1$ 0	($S0$) 0
$S1$	$S2$ ϕ	$S2$ ϕ	($S1$) 0	($S1$) 0
$S2$	($S2$) 1	($S2$) 1	($S2$) 1	$S3$ ϕ
$S3$	$S0$ ϕ	$S0$ ϕ	($S3$) 1	($S3$) 1

(d)

Step 4 *Primitive circuit*

Suitable state codes are shown on the circuit's internal-state diagram. By direct reference to this diagram, we obtain:

Turn-on set of $A = B\overline{c}$ Turn-on set of $B = \overline{A}cd$

Turn-off set of $A = \overline{B}\overline{c}$ Turn-off set of $B = Ac\overline{d}$.

Therefore, the NAND circuit equations are:

$$A = B\overline{c} + A(B + c)$$
$$B = \overline{A}cd + B(\overline{A} + \overline{c} + d)$$
$$Z = A.$$

Their NAND circuit implementation is shown in Figure (e).

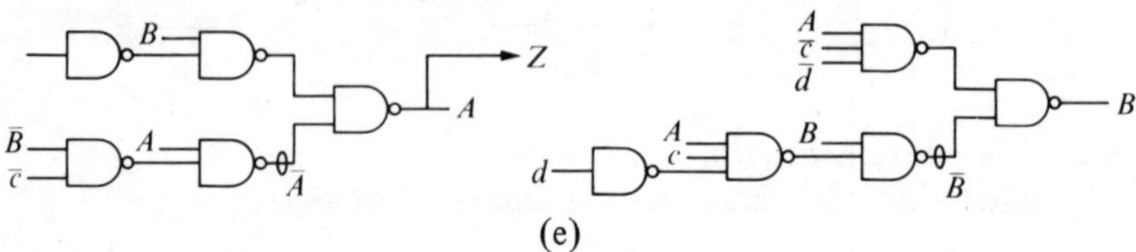

(e)

PROBLEM 21: *JK Flip-Flop (JKFF)*

Design a JKFF, i.e. a bistable element with the following terminal characteristics. The output assumes the value of 1 if $J = 1$ at the time a clock pulse on terminal c, and the value of 0 if $K = 1$ at the time of a clock pulse on terminal c.

SOLUTION

Step 1 *I/O characteristics*

The circuit's I/O characteristics are shown below in Figures (a) and (b).

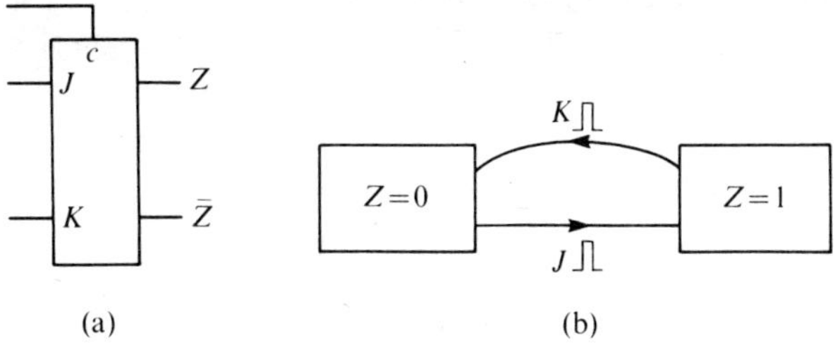

(a) (b)

Step 2 *Internal characteristics*

A suitable internal-state diagram is shown in (c).

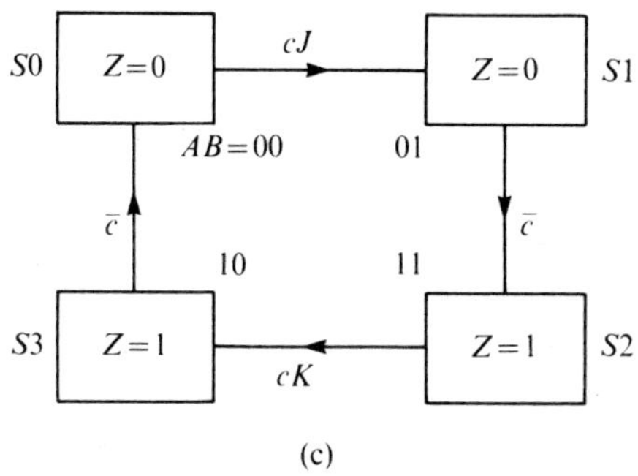

(c)

Step 3 *State reduction*

As can be seen from the state table (d) no state reduction is possible.

cJK	000	010	110	100	101	111	011	001
S0	(S0) Z = 0	(S0) 0	S1 0	(S0) 0	(S0) 0	S1 0	(S0) 0	(S0) 0
S1	S2 ϕ	S2 ϕ	(S1) 0	(S1) 0	(S1) 0	(S1) 0	S2 ϕ	S2 ϕ
S2	(S2) 1	(S2) 1	(S2) 1	(S2) 1	S3 1	S3 1	(S2) 1	(S2) 1
S3	S0 ϕ	S0 ϕ	(S3) 1	(S3) 1	(S3) 1	(S3) 1	S0 ϕ	S0 ϕ

(d)

Step 4 *Primitive circuit*

Suitable state codes are shown on the circuit's internal state diagram. By direct reference to this diagram, we obtain:

Turn-on set of $A = B\overline{c}$ Turn-on set of $B = \overline{A}cJ$

Turn-off set of $A = \overline{B}\,\overline{c}$ Turn-off set of $B = AcK$

Therefore, the NAND circuit equations are:

$$A = B\bar{c} + A(B + c)$$
$$B = \bar{A}cJ + B(\bar{A} + \bar{c} + \bar{K})$$
$$Z = A.$$

Their circuit implementation is shown in Figure (e).

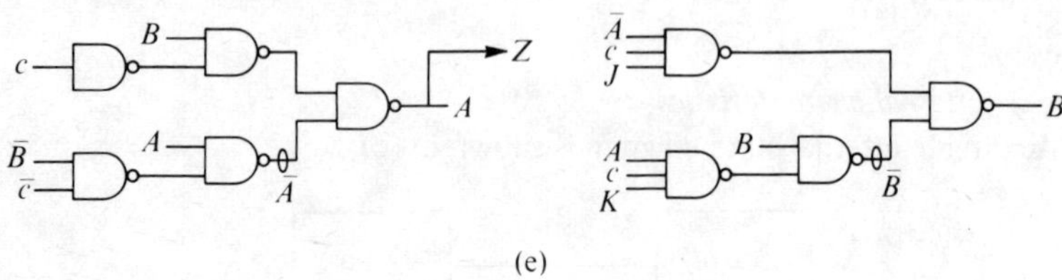

(e)

PROBLEM 22: *A Panel Game*

Three players in a panel game are all asked the same question. Each player is provided with a push button, which he presses when he has decided the answer.

The player who pressed his key first is to be indicated on a question master's panel on a display of three lamps. In addition a buzzer is to come on when the first player responds.

Pressing a switch, m, on the question master's panel turns the buzzer off, if it is on, otherwise clears the light panel. Note that the second and third players' responses are not recorded.

Design a suitable circuit.

PARTIAL SOLUTION

The internal state diagram of a suitable circuit is shown below.

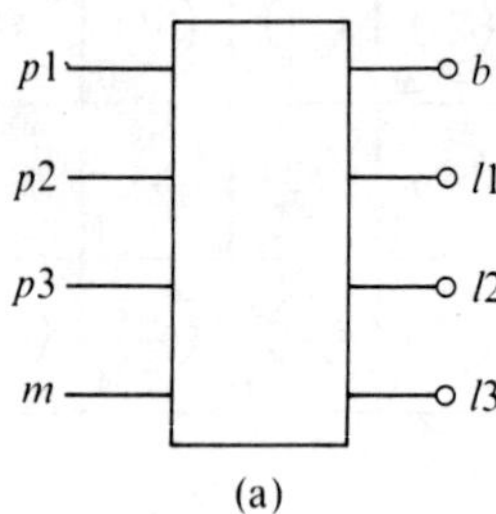

(a)

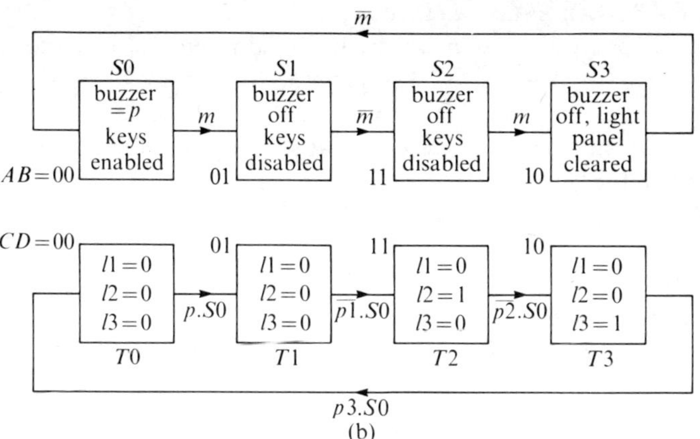

(b)

By direct reference to Figure (b), we obtain the circuit's equations:

$$A = B\overline{m} + A(B + m) \qquad l1 = T1 = \overline{C}D$$
$$B = \overline{A}m + B(\overline{A} + \overline{m}) \qquad l2 = T2 = CD$$
$$C = \overline{A}\overline{B}D\overline{p1} + C(A + B + D + p3) \qquad l3 = T3 = C\overline{D}$$
$$D = \overline{A}\overline{B}\overline{C}p + D(A + B + \overline{C} + p2) \qquad \text{buzzer} = pS0 = \overline{A}\overline{B}(p1 + p2 + p3).$$

Their circuit implementation is shown in Figure (c).

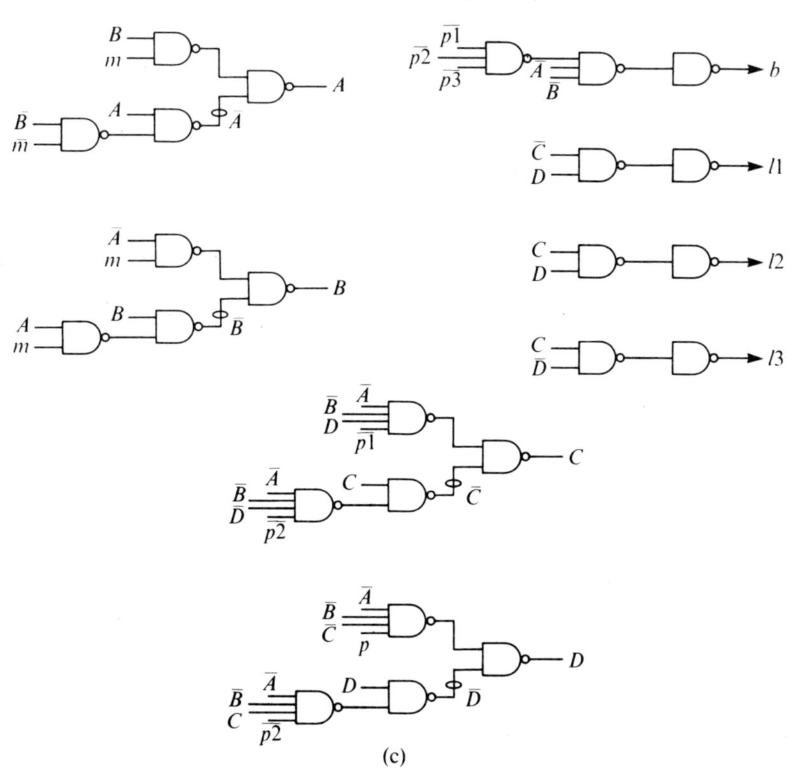

(c)

PROBLEM 23: *An Electronic Dice*

Seven lamps are arranged in a pattern that corresponds to the spot positions of a dice. When a key, k, is pressed, the circuit is to go through a cycle of the six states repeatedly. When the key is released, the digit corresponding to the state of the circuit at the moment of release is to be displayed on the lamps.

Design a suitable NAND circuit.

SOLUTION

Step 1 *I/O characteristics*

The required I/O characteristics are shown below (states $S6$ and $S7$ excluded).

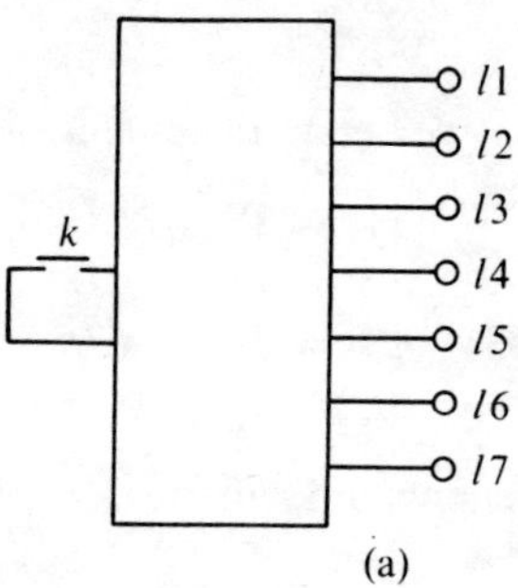

(a)

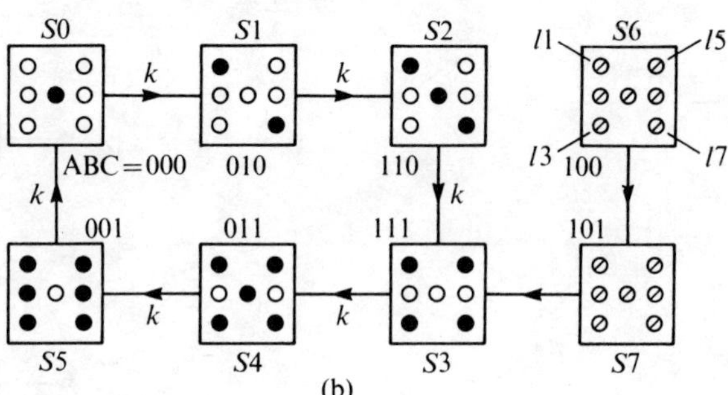

(b)

Step 2 *Internal characteristics*

Same as I/O characteristics with states $S6$ and $S7$ included.

Step 3 *State reduction*

Not attempted for clarity of design.

Step 4 Primitive circuit

Suitable state codes are shown in the figure above. By direct reference to this figure, we obtain:

Turn-on set of $A = B\bar{C}k$ Turn-on set of $B = \bar{A}\bar{C}k + AC$

Turn-off set of $A = BCk$ Turn-off set of $B = \bar{A}Ck$

$$\text{Turn-on set of } C = ABk + A\overline{B} = Ak + A\overline{B}$$
$$\text{Turn-off set of } C = \overline{A}\overline{B}k.$$

Therefore, the NAND circuit equations are:

$$\begin{aligned} A &= B\overline{C}k + A(\overline{B} + \overline{C} + \overline{k}) \\ B &= \overline{A}\overline{C}k + AC + B(A + \overline{C} + \overline{k}) \\ C &= Ak + A\overline{B} + C(A + B + \overline{k}) \end{aligned}$$

$$\begin{aligned} I1 &= I7 = \overline{S0} + (A\overline{B}) = B + C \\ I2 &= S5 + (A\overline{B}) = \overline{A}C \\ I3 &= I5 = S3 + S4 + S5 + (A\overline{B}) = C \\ I4 &= S0 + S2 + S4 + (A\overline{B}) = \overline{B}\overline{C} + A\overline{C} + \overline{A}BC \\ I6 &= S5 + (A\overline{B}) = \overline{A}\overline{B}C + (A\overline{B}) = \overline{B}C. \end{aligned}$$

The NAND circuit corresponding to the above equations is shown in Figure (c).

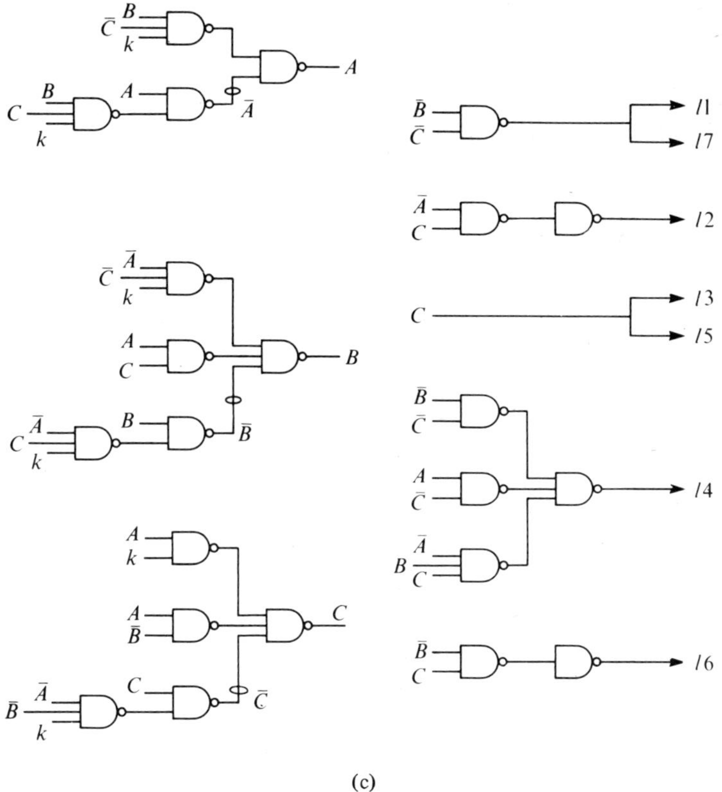

(c)

PROBLEM 24: *State reduction*

Implement using NAND gates the circuit whose internal-state diagram is shown in Figure (a).

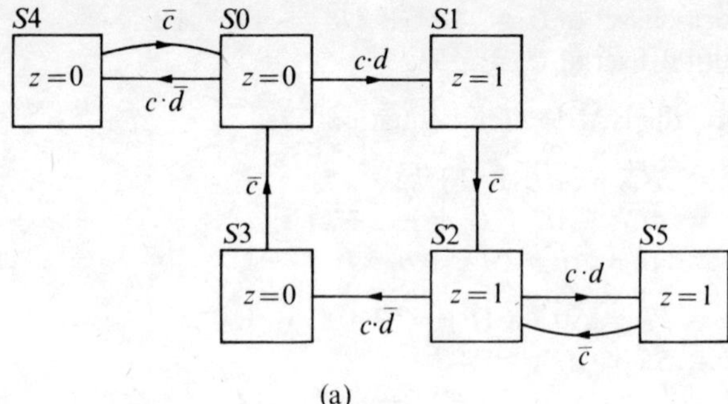

(a)

SOLUTION

Because the internal state diagrams is given to us, we can proceed directly to step 3.

Step 3 *State reduction*

As the number of states in the given state diagram is six (not a power of 2), it cannot be implemented directly. This necessitates that we execute this step with a view to reducing the number of states to 4, 2, or 1.

Applying the state reduction steps outlined in Section 10 of Chapter 1, we note that states $S1$ and $S3$ merge with states $S5$ and $S4$ respectively. The reduced state table is shown in Figure (c). No further merging of rows is possible.

As the reduced state table contains four states, we can proceed directly to step 4.

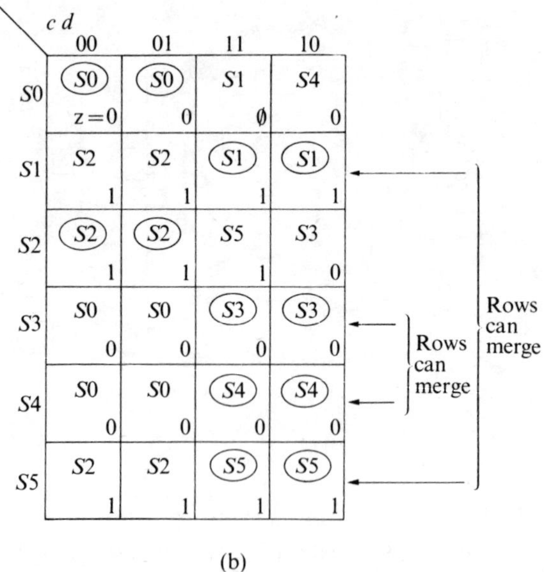

	cd = 00	01	11	10
S0	(S0) z=0	(S0) 0	S1 ∅	S4 0
S1	S2 1	S2 1	(S1) 1	(S1) 1
S2	(S2) 1	(S2) 1	S5 1	S3 0
S3	S0 0	S0 0	(S3) 0	(S3) 0
S4	S0 0	S0 0	(S4) 0	(S4) 0
S5	S2 1	S2 1	(S5) 1	(S5) 1

(b)

	cd = 00	01	11	10
S0	S0, 0	S0, 0	S15, 1	S34, 0
S15	S2, 1	S2, 1	S15, 1	S15, 1
S2	S2, 1	S2, 1	S15, 1	S34, 0
S34	S0, 0	S0, 0	S34, 0	S34, 0

(c)

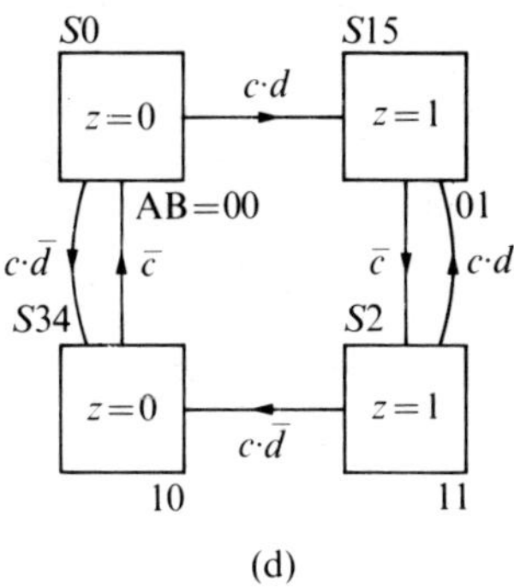

(d)

Step 4 *Circuit implementation*

The state diagram which corresponds to our reduced state table in Figure (c), with the four states suitably coded, is shown in Figure (d). By direct reference to it, we obtain

$$\text{Turn-on sets of } A = B\,.\,\bar{c} + \bar{B}\,.\,c\,.\,\bar{d}$$
$$\text{Turn-off sets of } A = \bar{B}\,.\,\bar{c} + B\,.\,c\,.\,d$$

$$\text{Turn-on sets of } B = \bar{A}\,.\,c\,.\,d$$
$$\text{Turn-off sets of } B = A\,.\,c\,.\,\bar{d}$$

Therefore, the circuit equations are

$$\begin{aligned} A &= B\,.\,\bar{c} + B\,.\,c\,.\,\bar{d} + A\,.\,(B + c)(\bar{B} + \bar{c} + \bar{d}) \\ B &= \bar{A}\,.\,c\,.\,d + B\,.\,(\bar{A} + \bar{c} + d) \\ Z &= S15 + S2 \\ &= \bar{A}B + AB \\ &= B. \end{aligned}$$

The corresponding NAND circuit is shown in Figure (e).

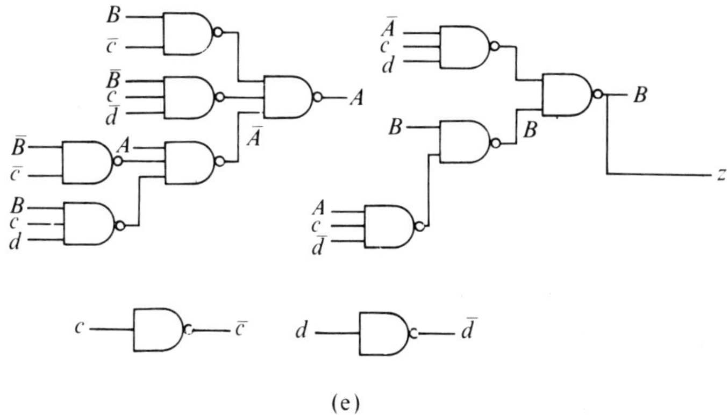

(e)

3 *Clocked Sequential Circuits*

A four-step algorithm for the design of clocked (synchronous) sequential circuits is described. Realistic circuit constraints are taken automatically into account by our design process. Shift register arrangements are discussed and twelve problems and solutions are used to demonstrate the design steps.

3.1 INTRODUCTION

Functionally the essential characteristic of synchronous sequential circuits is that their operation is synchronized with the application of clock pulses, between which no changes of state can occur. In hardware terms, these circuits depend on clocked flip-flops, the principal types of which are described in the next section. Design factors met are:

1. *Circuit reliability.* All circuits function correctly and reliably.
2. *Gate minimality.* Generally speaking not all our circuits will be minimal.
3. *Circuit maintainability.* Our circuits are easy to maintain.
4. *Design effort.* This is minimal.
5. *Documentation.* No additional documentation is needed.
6. *The design steps.* These are easy to apply. No specialist knowledge is necessary.
7. *Gate fan-in and fan-out restrictions.* These are met reliably though not elegantly.

3.2 CLOCKED FLIP-FLOPS

These are bistable elements in which the change of the output signal, A, is coincident with either the leading or the trailing edge of a pulse signal, commonly referred to as the *clock pulse.* Unless we specify otherwise, it will be assumed that a change in the output signal, A, takes place at the trailing edge of the clock pulse.

There are four basic types of flip-flops, viz.

(i) D flip-flops (DFF)
(ii) T flip-flops (TFF)
(iii) SR flip-flops (SRFF), and
(iv) JK flip-flops (JKFF).

Their terminal characteristics are shown in Figure 3.1.

D flip-flop

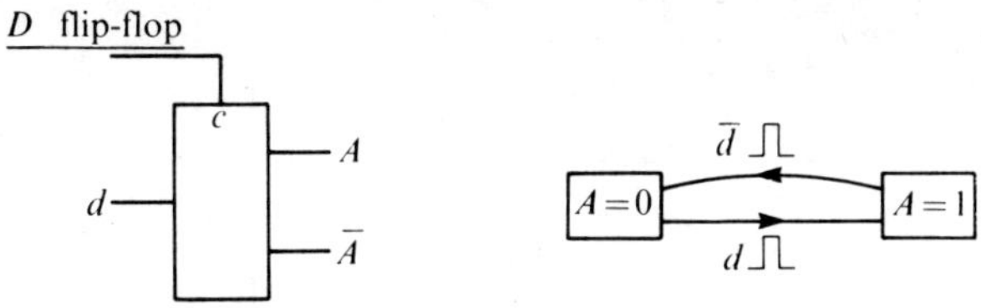

Output assumes the value of input at the time of the clock pulse.

T flip-flop

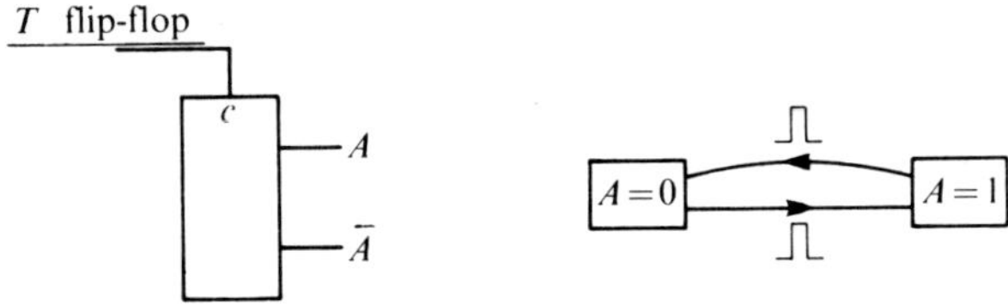

Output 'toggles', i.e. it changes state with every clock pulse.

S–R flip-flop

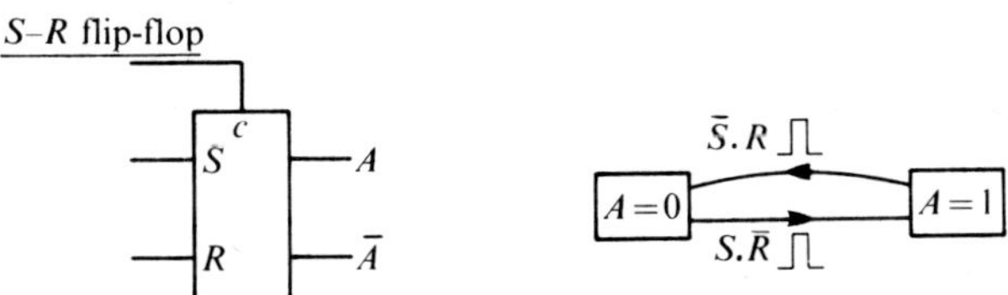

Output assumes the value of 1 when $S=1$ and $R=0$ and the value of 0 when $S=0$ and $R=1$. Flip-flop locks when $S=R=0$ and when $S=R=1$ the response is indeterminate.

J–K flip-flop

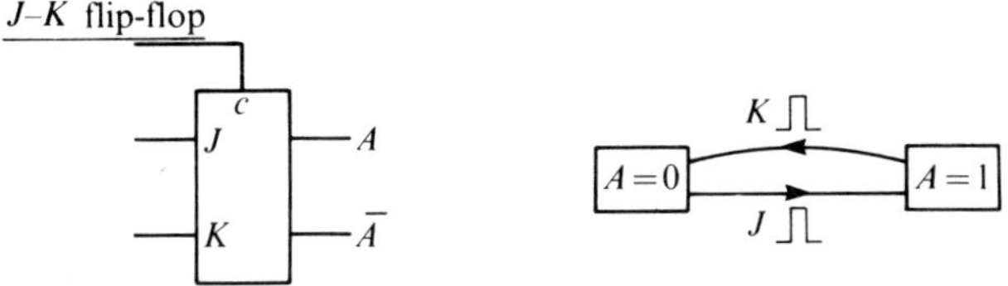

Output assumes the value of 1 when $J=1$ and the value of 0 when $K=1$; i.e. (*i*) when $J=\bar{K}=d$ the flip-flop behaves like a DFF, (*ii*) when $J=K=1$ the flip-flop toggles, and (*iii*) when $J=K=0$ the flip-flop locks.

FIG 3.1.

3.3 THE DESIGN STEPS

The sequence in which the four design steps are executed is shown in Figure 3.2.

Step 1 *I/O characteristics*

In this step we draw a block diagram to show the available input signals and the required output signals. We next use either a state diagram or waveforms to define the relationship between the two sets of signals which must be established by our circuit.

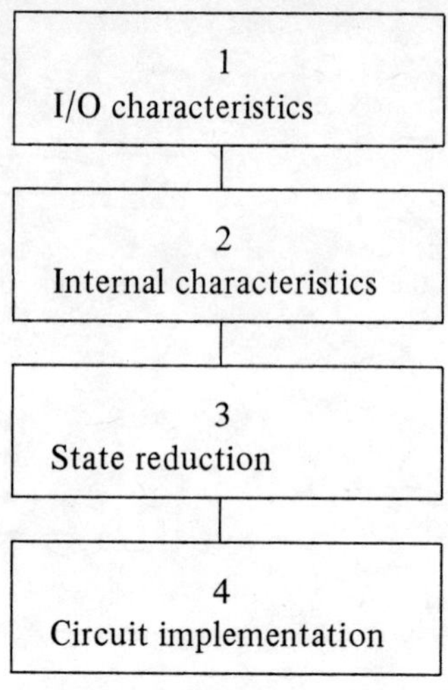

FIG. 3.2

Step 2 *Internal characteristics*

In the second step the designer specifies the internal performance of the circuit. Although experience, intuition and foresight play an important part at this stage, the inexperienced designer should be primarily concerned that his specification of the internal circuit operation is complete and free of ambiguities. To this end he should avoid short cuts and use as many states as he finds necessary to give a complete and unambiguous specification of the circuit performance. The next step can be used to eliminate unwanted states.

Step 3 *State reduction*

This step is optional and can be omitted. Its main purpose is to provide the designer with the means for reducing the number of internal states he used in step 2, if such a reduction is possible.

The circuit's state table (1.9) is drawn and the state reduction steps (1.10) are used to merge its rows.

Clearly to avoid redundant states we would only use this step to reduce the number of states to some power of 2. For example, whereas we would use it to reduce five states to four, we would not use it to reduce four states to three.

Step 4 *Primitive circuits*

In contrast to the situation with asynchronous circuits, the design of clocked circuits does not require that only one secondary signal may change during a transition between two states. This is based on the assumption that all changes of secondary signals take place on the trailing (or leading) edge of the clock pulse that initiates them and, of course, before the next clock pulse. Having allocated the secondary signals we are now in a position to write down the turn-on and turn-off conditions of each secondary signal. The turn-on condition of a secondary signal A, denoted by S_A, is the disjunction (0Ring) of the total states which are necessary for the next clock pulse to cause A to change value from 0 to 1. Similarly the turn-off condition of a secondary signal A, denoted by R_A, is the disjunction of the total states which are necessary to cause A to change values from 1 to 0.

The expressions for the turn-on and turn-off conditions of the flip-flops can be reduced using an optional products, products defining 'don't care' circuit conditions and products which define total states involved in transitions in which the signal concerned does not change its value. For example when we move from state $S2$ to state $S3$ in Figure 3.6, signal A remains static at 1 and therefore we can allow its turn-on conditions to arise during this transition.

The turn-on and turn-off conditions as derived by the foregoing process define directly the set and reset signals respectively for SR flip-flops. The most readily available and versatile flip-flop is the JKFF. As this is used extensively it is worthwhile to express the state diagram in terms of expressions for J and K (the inputs to the JK flip-flops) in preference to expressions for S and R (the inputs to the SR flip-flops). The most convenient way of deriving the values of J and K is by realizing the JK flip-flop characteristics in Figure 3.1 (d) using SR flip-flops.

By direct reference to Figure 3.1 (d), we obtain:

$$S_A = \bar{A} \cdot J_A, \text{ and}$$
$$R_A = A \cdot K_A.$$

A block schematic realization is shown in Figure 3.3. *Clearly the expressions of J and K can be obtained from the expressions of S and R by dropping $\bar{A}$ and A respectively.* This is a very useful result and the reader is urged to make a note of it.

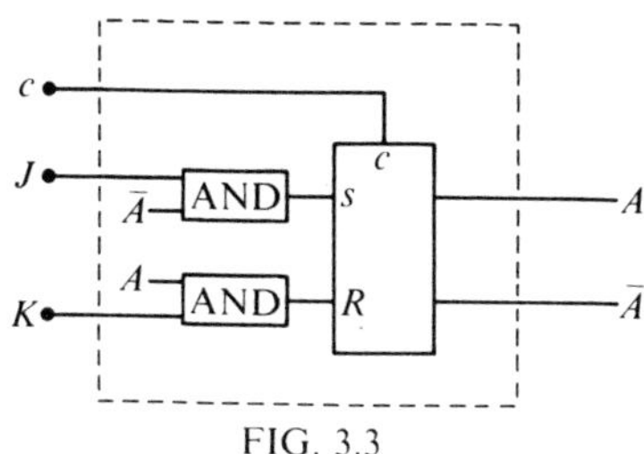

FIG. 3.3

Reference to Figure 3.1 reveals that the DFF and TFF characteristics can be implemented using a JKFF by making $J = d$ and $K = \bar{d}$ in the first case and $J = K = 1$ in the second case. See Figure 3.4.

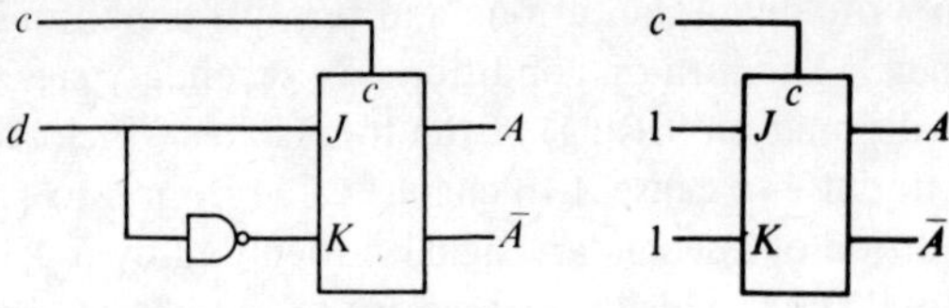

FIG. 3.4.

3.4 SHIFT REGISTER ARRANGEMENT

This flip-flop arrangement is used to overcome a major problem in IC (integrated circuit) design, which is that whereas the capacity of the IC 'chip' for logic components is very large, the number of pins available for input and output is limited by the physical sizes of the chips (14, 16 and 24 pins on a chip being standard).

Physically a shift register configuration consists of a group of flip-flops connected in cascade, as shown in Figure 3.5. Flip-flop output signals are normally available in parallel. This arrangement causes each flip-flop to assume the state of the flip-flop to its left on receipt of a clock pulse, except for the first flip-flop whose value is determined by the external signals. It is therefore only necessary to determine the turn-on and turn-off conditions of the first flip-flop.

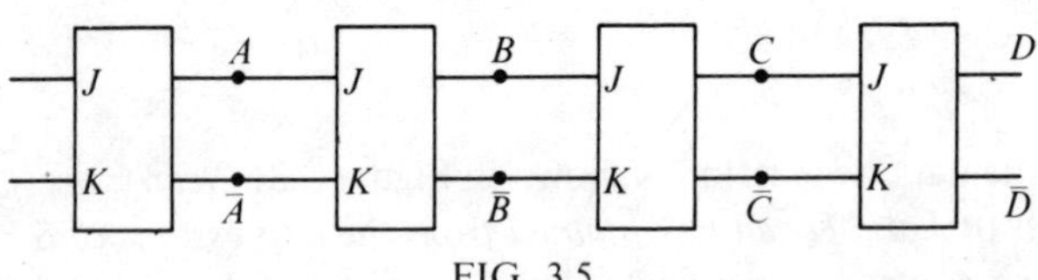

FIG. 3.5

The shift register arrangement is particularly suited to the design of cyclic circuits described in the next section, where its application is demonstrated.

Maximum length shift register sequences for 3, 4 and 5 variables are:

(i) 000, 100, 010, 101, 110, 111, 011, 001, 000 . . . .

(ii) 0000, 1000, 1100, 1110, 1111, 0111, 1011, 0101, 1010, 1101, 0110, 0011, 1001, 0100, 0010, 0001, 0000 . . . .

(iii) 00000, 10000, 01000, 00100, 10010, 01001, 10100, 11010, 01101, 00110, 10011, 11001, 11100, 11110, 11111, 01111, 00111, 00011, 10001, 11000, 01100, 10110, 11011, 11101, 01110, 10111, 01011, 10101, 01010, 00101, 00010, 00001, 00000 . . . .

Other sequences are possible.

3.5 CYCLIC CIRCUITS

These are circuits that return to their initial state after a fixed number of input pulses. They are used primarily for frequency reduction. For example to reduce the frequency of a pulse train, c, by four we would use c to drive a circuit that returns to its initial state after four pulses, as shown in Figure 3.6. $Z = S0 . c, S1 . c, S2 . c$ or $S3 . c$ if the output pulse is to be coincident with the first, second, third or fourth pulse of each 4-pulse cycle respectively.

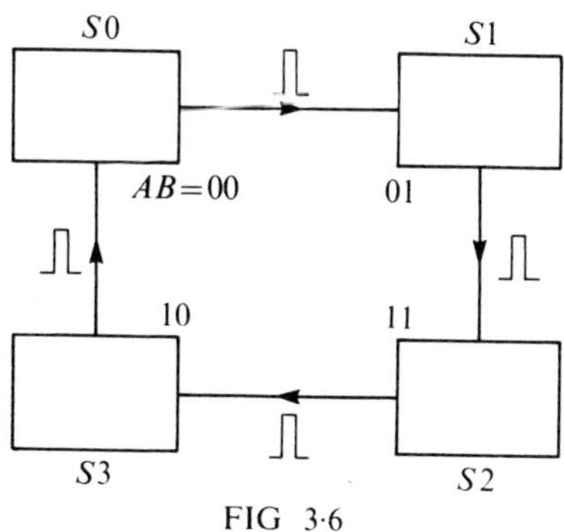

FIG 3·6

A special case of cyclic circuits are pulse counters which, as we shall see in the next chapter, give the number of pulses received since the circuit left its initial state – i.e. at the end of the first pulse a counter would output 1, at the end of the second pulse 2, and so on.

Two special features of cyclic circuits that are particularly useful to the designer of digital circuits and systems are listed below.

The first applies to *reversible cyclic circuits* that are implemented using JK flip-flops. If each circuit transition involves the change of a single state variable only, the values of the J and K signals in the forward mode are the same as the values of the K and J signals respectively for the reverse mode.

For example, in Figure 3.6, $J_A = B, K_A = \overline{B}, J_B = \overline{A}$, and $K_B = A$. To move in the reverse direction i.e. $S0$ - $S3$ - $S2$ - $S1$, the flip-flop inputs are $J_A = \overline{B}, J_A = B, J_B = A$, and $K_B = \overline{A}$. This property is particularly useful when designing reversible Gray counters, as we shall see in the next chapter. Only optional products defining unused states can be used to reduce the JKFF equations. Although in special cases it is possible to use these products to reduce the SRFF equations, the reader is advised to avoid doing so.

The second feature is that they can be implemented using the *shift register* arrangement described in the previous section. An eight-state diagram in which all shift-register transitions are marked is shown in Figure 3.7. We shall use this diagram to design cyclic circuits for 8, 7, 6, and 5 states. If an unused state is inadvertently assumed during normal operation, we shall lock the clock out and trip an alarm. This of course is

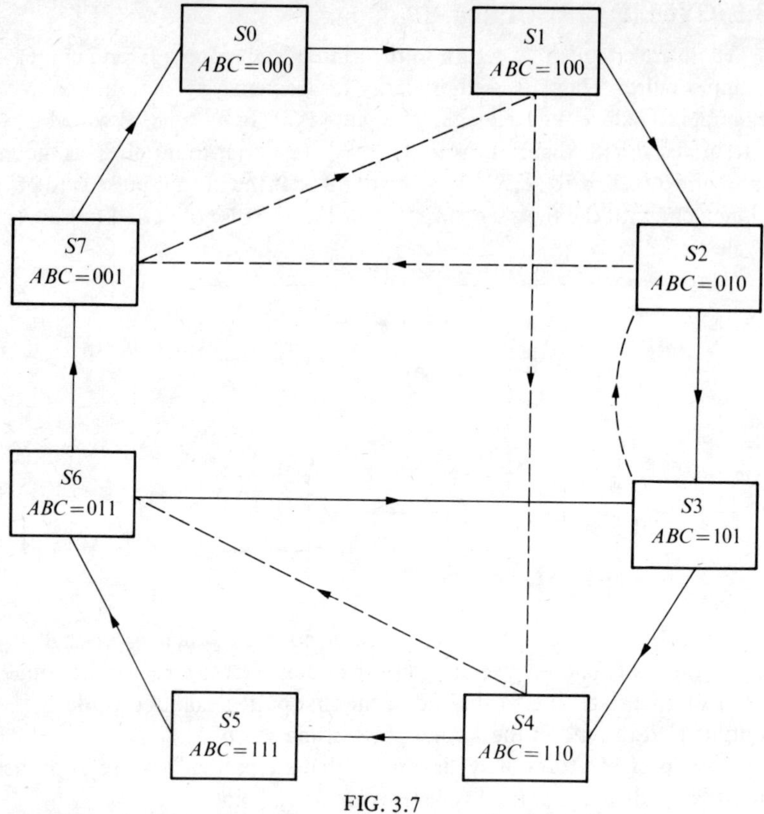

FIG. 3.7

an arbitrary course of action and a different course of action may well be more suitable in a given situation. Our chosen course of action allows us to use the codes of unused states as algebraically optional products, since the circuit is automatically locked if an unused state is assumed.

Eight states

By direct reference to Figure 3.7 we obtain:

$S_A = S0 + S2 + (S3) + (S4) = \overline{A}\overline{C}$ Therefore, $J_A = \overline{C}$

$R_A = S1 + S5 + (S6) + (S7) = A\overline{B}\overline{C} + BC$ Therefore, $K_A = \overline{B}\overline{C} + BC.$

Seven states

Either state $S0$ or state $S5$ in Fig. 3.7 can be skipped to obtain a seven-state cycle. This is because in both cases the values of A and B of the previous states $S7$ and $S4$, are the same as the values of B and C of the next states, $S1$ and $S6$, respectively. We choose to skip state $S5$, in which case we obtain:

$S_A = S0 + S2 + (S3) + (S5) = \overline{A}\overline{C}$ Therefore, $J_A = \overline{C}$

$R_A = S1 + S4 + (S5) + (S6) + (S7) = A\overline{C}$ Therefore, $K_A = \overline{C}.$

Trip alarm signal, $a = S5 = ABC$
Clock signal $= c \cdot \overline{a}$.

Six states

In the case of a six-state cycle we skip states $S2$ and $S3$, since as before the values of A and B in state $S1$ are the same as the values of B and C in state $S4$ - see the figure below. In such a case, we obtain

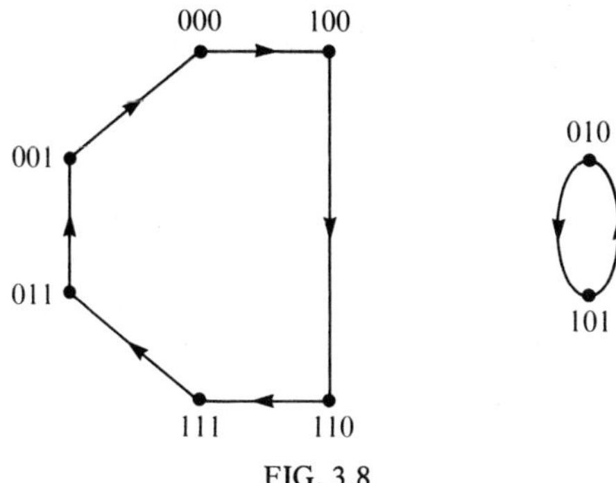

FIG. 3.8

$$\begin{aligned} S_A &= S0 + (S1) + (S2) + (S3) + (S4) \\ &= \overline{A}\overline{B}\overline{C} + (A\overline{B}\overline{C}) + (\overline{A}B\overline{C}) + (A\overline{B}C) + (AB\overline{C}) \\ &= \overline{C}. \qquad \text{Therefore, } J_A = \overline{C} \end{aligned}$$

$$\begin{aligned} R_A &= S5 + (S2) + (S3) + (S6) + (S7) \\ &= ABC + (\overline{A}B\overline{C}) + (A\overline{B}C) + (\overline{A}BC) + (\overline{A}\overline{B}C) \\ &= C. \qquad \text{Therefore, } K_A = C. \end{aligned}$$

Trip alarm signal, $a = S2 + S3 = \overline{A}B\overline{C} + A\overline{B}C$.
Clock signal $= c \cdot \overline{a}$.

This configuration is known as the Johnson counter.

Five states

We realize a five-star cycle by skipping states $S2$, $S3$, and $S5$, in which case we obtain:

$$\begin{aligned} S_A &= S0 + (S1) + (S2) + (S3) + (S5) \\ &= \overline{A}\overline{B}\overline{C} + (A\overline{B}\overline{C}) + (\overline{A}B\overline{C}) + (A\overline{B}C) + (ABC) \\ &= \overline{A}\overline{C}. \qquad \text{Therefore, } J_A = C \end{aligned}$$

$$\begin{aligned} R_A &= S4 + (S2) + (S3) + (S5) + (S6) + (S7) \\ &= AB\overline{C} + (\overline{A}B\overline{C}) + (A\overline{B}C) + (ABC) + (\overline{A}BC) + (\overline{A}\overline{B}C) \\ &= B. \qquad \text{Therefore, } K_A = B. \end{aligned}$$

Trim alarm signal, $a = S2 + S3 + S5 = \overline{A}B\overline{C} + A\overline{B}C + ABC = AC + \overline{A}B\overline{C}$.

Clock signal $= c \cdot \overline{a}$.

3.6 PROBLEMS AND SOLUTIONS

Twelve problems and solutions are used to illustrate the four design steps.

PROBLEM 1: *A Pulse Distributor*

Signal c in Figure (a) below is a pulse train. The input pulses are to appear at the output terminals in the order shown in (b).

Design a suitable circuit.

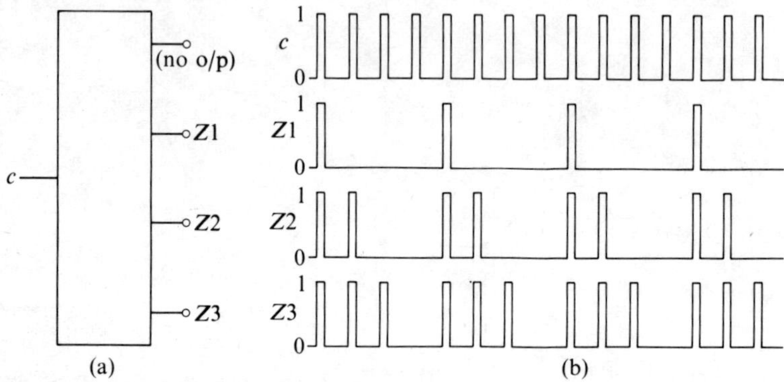

SOLUTION

Step 1 *I/O characteristics*

As stated.

Step 2 *Internal characteristics*

The internal state diagram of the required circuit is shown below in Figure (c).

Step 3 *State reduction*

No state reduction is possible – see state table in Figure (d).

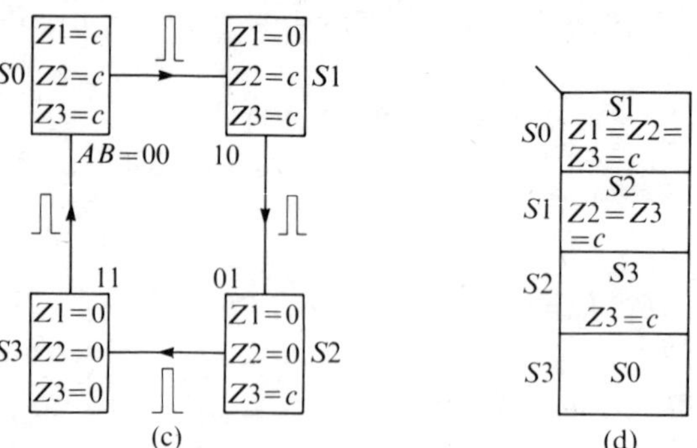

(c) (d)

Step 4 *Primitive circuit*

Suitable binary codes are shown on the state diagram in Figure (c). By direct reference to this diagram, we obtain:

$$
\begin{aligned}
S_A &= S0 + S2 = \bar{A}\bar{B} + \bar{A}B = \bar{A} & \text{Therefore, } J_A &= 1 \\
R_A &= S1 + S3 = A\bar{B} + AB = A & \text{Therefore, } K_A &= 1 \\
S_B &= S1 + (S) = A\bar{B} + (\bar{A}B) = A\bar{B} & \text{Therefore, } J_B &= A \\
R_B &= S3 + (S) = AB = (\bar{A}\bar{B}) = AB & \text{Therefore, } K_B &= A \\
Z1 &= S0c = \bar{A}\bar{B}c \\
Z2 &= S0c + S1c = \bar{B}c \\
Z3 &= S0c + S1c + S2c = \overline{S3}c = (\bar{A} + \bar{B})c.
\end{aligned}
$$

The corresponding circuit is shown in Figure (e).

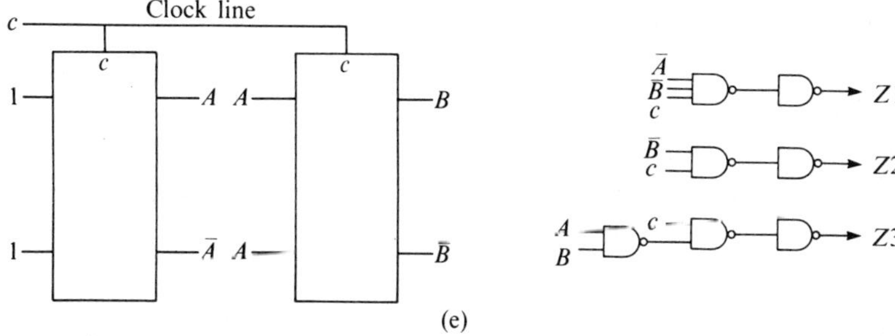

(e)

PROBLEM 2: *Pulse Frequency Reduction*

Signal c in Figure (a) below is a pulse train. It is required to output on terminal Z every fourth input pulse when signal m is absent and every third input pulse when signal m is present - see Figure (b).

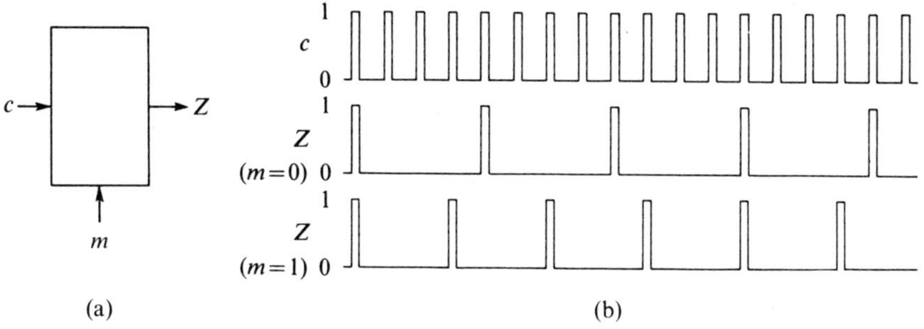

(a) (b)

SOLUTION

Step 1 *I/O characteristics*

As stated.

Step 2 *Internal characteristics*

A suitable internal state diagram of the circuit is shown in Figure (c) below.

Step 3 *State reduction*

No state reduction is possible – see state table (d) below.

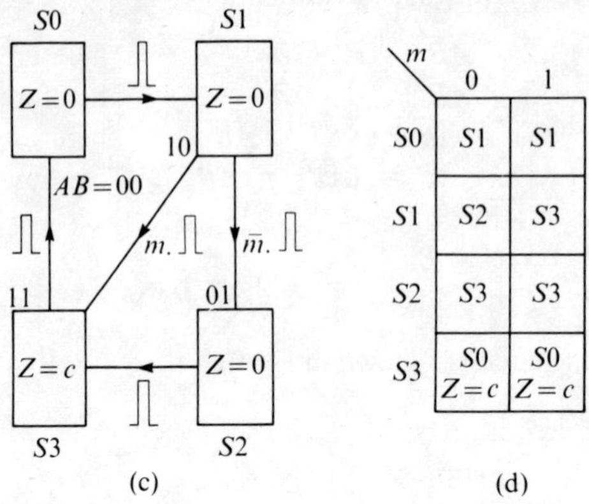

Step 4 *Primitive circuit*

Suitable binary codes are shown on the state diagram. By direct reference to this diagram, we obtain:

$S_A = S0 + S2 + (S1m) = \overline{A}\overline{B} + \overline{A}B + (A\overline{B}m) = \overline{A}$ Therefore, $J_A = 1$
$R_A = S1\overline{m} + S3 = \overline{A}\overline{B}\overline{m} + AB = A\overline{m} + AB$ Therefore, $K_A = B + \overline{m}$
$S_B = S1 + (S2) = A\overline{B} + (\overline{A}B) = A\overline{B}$
$R_B = S3 + (S0) = AB + (\overline{A}\overline{B}) = AB$ Therefore, $J_B = A$
$Z = S3 \cdot c = ABc.$ Therefore, $K_B = A$

The corresponding circuit implementation is shown in Figure (e).

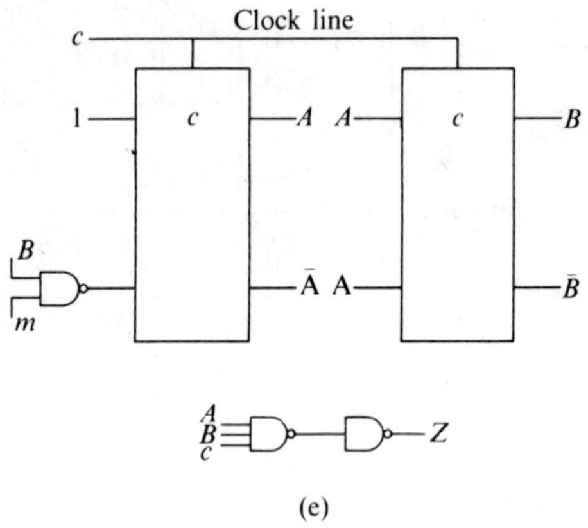

(e)

PROBLEM 3: *A Pulse Train Switch*

Signal X in the diagrams (a) and (b) below is a pulse train being output either at terminal $Z1$ or at terminal $Z2$. The input pulse train is switched

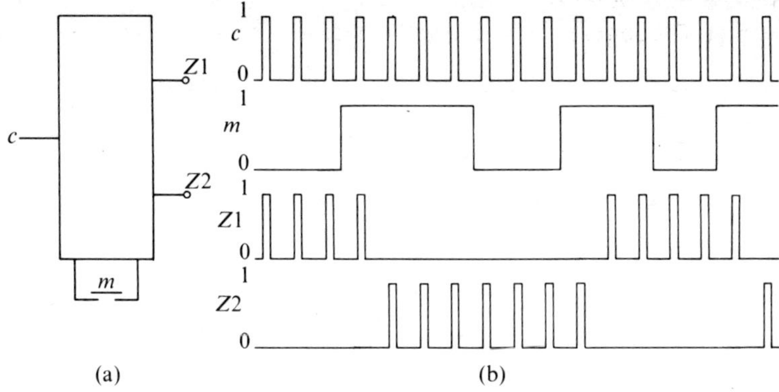

(a) (b)

from one output terminal to the other each time switch m is activated. Complete pulses only to be output.

Design a suitable circuit.

Step 1 *I/O characteristics*

As stated.

Step 2 *Internal characteristics*

A suitable internal state diagram of the required circuit is shown in Figure (c).

Step 3 *State reduction*

No state reduction is possible - see Figure (d).

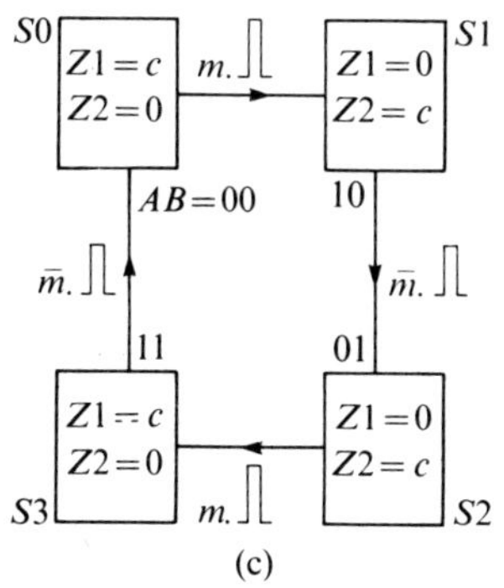

(c)

	m = 0	1
$S0$	$S0$ $Z1 = c$	$S1$ $Z1 = c$
$S1$	$S2$ $Z2 = c$	$S1$ $Z2 = c$
$S2$	$S2$ $Z2 = c$	$S3$ $Z2 = c$
$S3$	$S0$ $Z1 = c$	$S3$ $Z1 = c$

(d)

Step 4 *Primitive circuit*

Suitable binary codes are shown on the state diagram (c). By direct reference to this diagram, we obtain:

$$S_A = S0m + S2m = \bar{A}\bar{B}m + \bar{A}Bm = \bar{A}m \qquad \text{Therefore, } J_A = \bar{m}$$
$$R_A = S1\bar{m} + S3\bar{m} = A\bar{B}\bar{m} + AB\bar{m} = A\bar{m} \qquad \text{Therefore, } K_A = \bar{m}$$
$$S_B = S1\bar{m} + (S2) = A\bar{B}\bar{m} + (\bar{A}B) = A\bar{B}\bar{m} \qquad \text{Therefore, } J_B = A\bar{m}$$
$$R_B = S3\bar{m} + (S0) = AB\bar{m} + (\bar{A}\bar{B}) = AB\bar{m} \qquad \text{Therefore, } K_B = A\bar{m}$$

$$Z1 = (S0 + S3)c = \overline{A}\overline{B}c + ABc$$
$$Z2 = (S1 + S2)c = \overline{Z1}c = g1g2c.$$

The corresponding circuit implementation is shown in Figure (e).

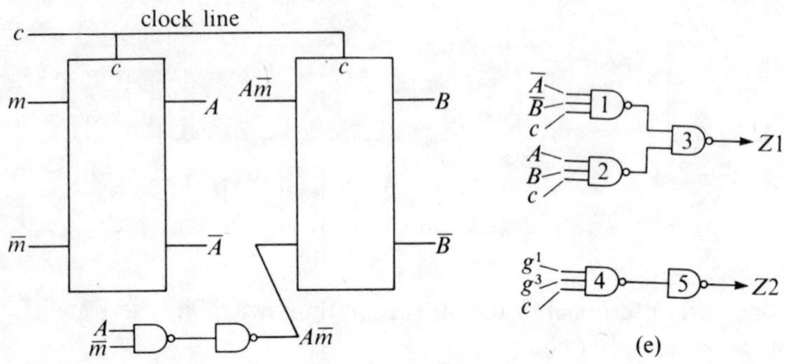

(e)

PROBLEM 4: *One Shot Circuit**

High frequency clock pulses are presented at input terminal *c* in diagrams (a) and (b) below. Each activation of manual switch, *m*, is to allow one complete clock pulse to be output at *Z*. The duration of signal *m* can be assumed in this case to be greater than the pulse width.

Design a suitable circuit.

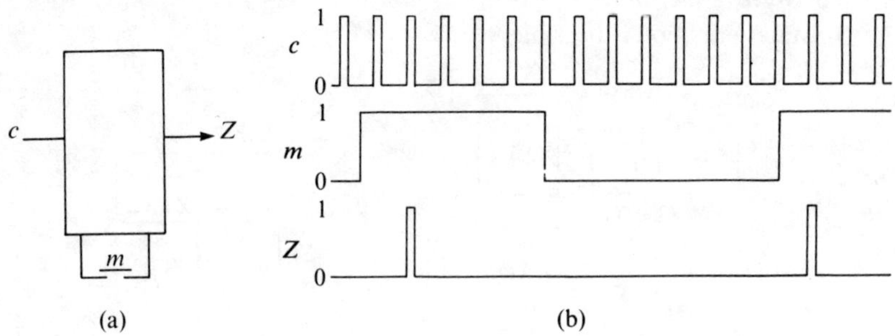

(a) (b)

SOLUTION

Step 1 *I/O characteristics*

As stated.

Step 2 *Internal characteristics*

A suitable state diagram is shown in Figure (c).

Step 3 *State reduction*

No state reduction is possible – see state table (d) below.

* Circuits of this type are used extensively to slow down high speed operations such as computer operations, to manual speeds.

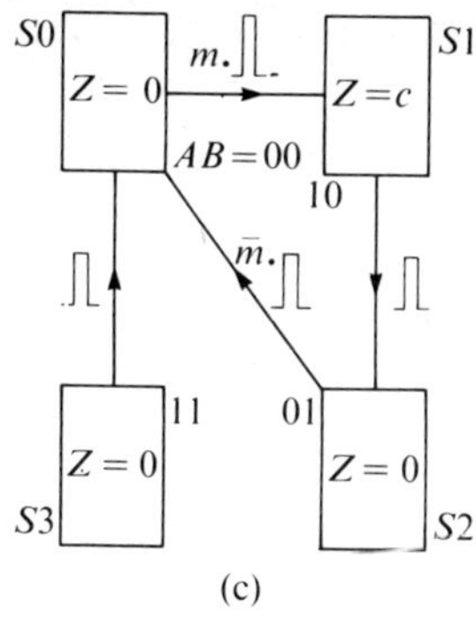

(c)

m	0	1
S0	S0 Z=0	S1 Z=0
S1	S2 Z=c	S2 Z=c
S2	S0 Z=0	S2 Z=0
S3	S0 Z=0	S0 Z=0

(d)

Step 4 *Primitive circuit*

By direct reference to the state diagram, we obtain:

$S_A = S0m = \bar{A}\bar{B}m$ — Therefore, $J_A = \bar{B}m$

$R_A = S1 + S3 + (S2) = A\bar{B} + AB + (\bar{A}B) = A$ — Therefore, $K_A = 1$

$S_A = S1 + (S2m) = A\bar{B} + (\bar{A}Bm) = A\bar{B}$ — Therefore, $J_B = A$

$R_B = S2m + S3 = \bar{A}B\bar{m} + AB = B\bar{m} + AB$ — Therefore, $K_B = A + \bar{m}$

$Z = S1c = ABc.$

The corresponding circuit implementation is shown in Figure (e).

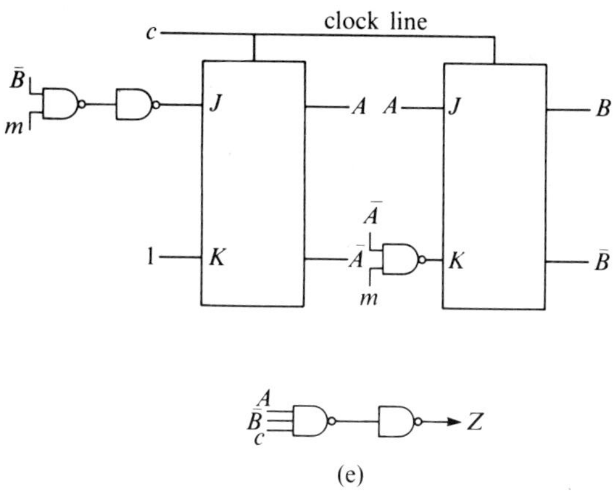

(e)

PROBLEM 5: *A Word Scanner*

Binary data arrive on line d serially, each data bit being synchronized with a clock pulse on line c - see Figure (a).

Design a circuit that examines three-bit segments consecutively. An output pulse is to be generated on Z whenever the last two bits in a segment are 11.

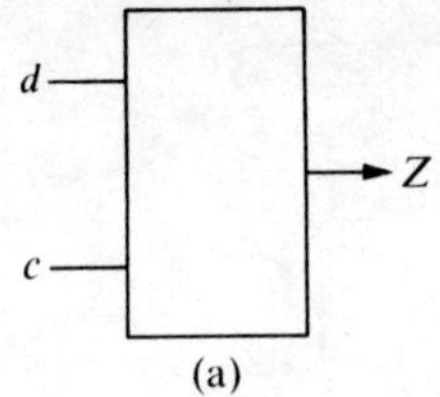

(a)

SOLUTION

Step 1 *I/O characteristics*

d	0111011111111010011
Z	1 1 1

Step 2 *Internal characteristics*

A suitable internal state diagram is shown in Figure (b).

Step 3 *State reduction*

Rows in the corresponding state table (c) cannot be merged, therefore no state reduction is possible.

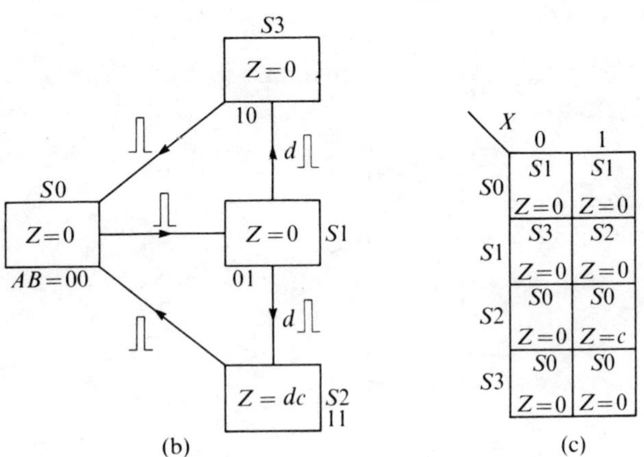

	0	1
S0	S1 Z=0	S1 Z=0
S1	S3 Z=0	S2 Z=0
S2	S0 Z=0	S0 Z=c
S3	S0 Z=0	S0 Z=0

(b) (c)

Step 4 *Primitive circuit*

Suitable binary codes are shown on the state diagram. By direct reference to the diagram, we obtain:

$S_A = S1 = \overline{A}B$ Therefore, $J_A = B$

$R_A = S2 + S3 = A$ Therefore, $K_A = 1$

$S_B = S0 = \overline{A}\overline{B}$ Therefore, $J_B = A$

$R_B = S1\overline{d} + S2 + (S3) = \overline{A}B\overline{d} + AB + (A\overline{B}) = B\overline{d} + A$ Therefore, $K_B = A + \overline{d}$

$Z1 = S2dc = ABdc.$

The corresponding circuit is shown in Figure (d).

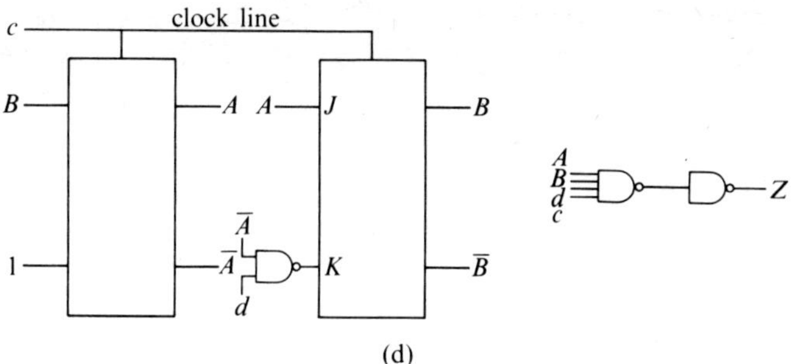

(d)

PROBLEM 6: *A Binary String Scanner*

Binary data arrive on line *c* in Figure (a), bit by bit, each bit being synchronized with a clock pulse on line *c*. An output signal is to be generated on *Z* each time the bit sequence '1001' is detected.

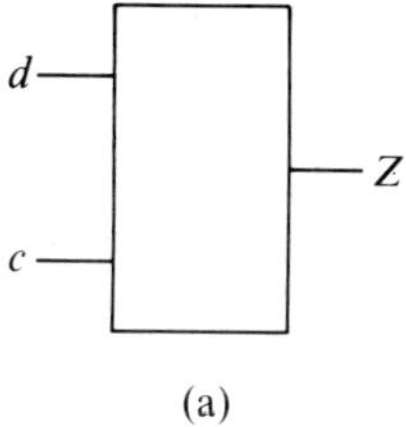

(a)

Design a suitable circuit.

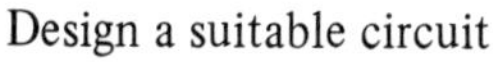

SOLUTION

Step 1 *I/O characteristics*

d 000 111 010 010 011 100 1
Z 1 1 1

Step 2 *Internal characteristics*

A suitable internal state diagram is shown in Figure (b).

Step 3 *State reduction*

Rows in the state table (c) cannot be merged – therefore no state reduction is possible.

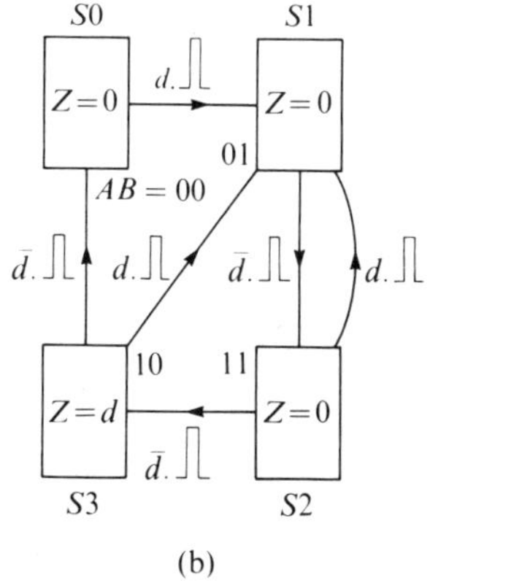

(b)

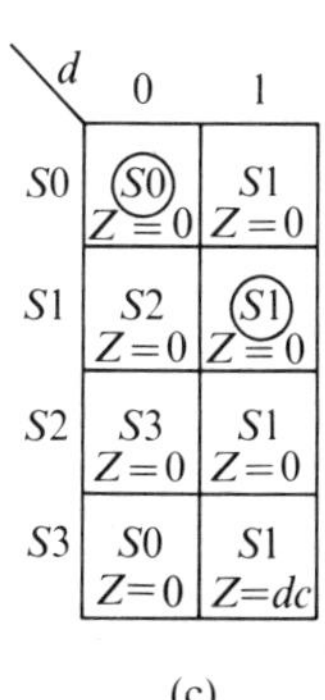

d	0	1
S0	(S0) Z=0	S1 Z=0
S1	S2 Z=0	(S1) Z=0
S2	S3 Z=0	S1 Z=0
S3	S0 Z=0	S1 Z=dc

(c)

Step 4 *Primitive circuit*

Suitable binary codes are shown on the state diagram. By direct reference to this diagram, we obtain:

$$S_A = S1\bar d + (S2\bar X) = \bar A B\bar d + (AB\bar d) = B\bar d \qquad \text{Therefore, } J_A = B\bar d$$
$$R_A = S2d + S3 + (S0) = ABd + A\bar B + (\bar A\bar B) = Ad + \bar B \qquad \text{Therefore, } K_A = \bar B + d = \bar J_A$$
$$S_B = S0d + S3d + (S1) + (S2d) = d \qquad \text{Therefore, } J_B = d$$
$$R_B = S2\bar d + (S3\bar d) + (S0\bar d) = A\bar d \qquad \text{Therefore, } K_B = A\bar d$$
$$Z = S3dc = A\bar B dc.$$

The corresponding circuit is shown in Figure (d).

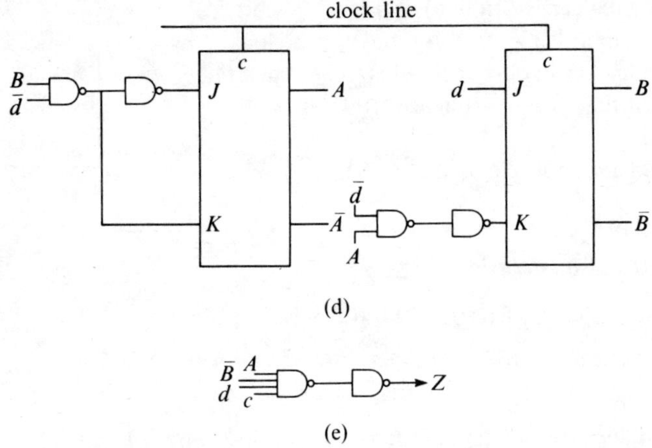

(d)

(e)

PROBLEM 7: *4–5–6 detector*

Design a circuit that will stop the paper tape reader shown in Figure (a) (by turning signal *m* off) and generate a buzzer signal, when the character sequence 4-5-6 is detected. A synchronizing pulse is generated by the reader each time a new character is output. Implement your design with JK flip-flops and NAND gates.

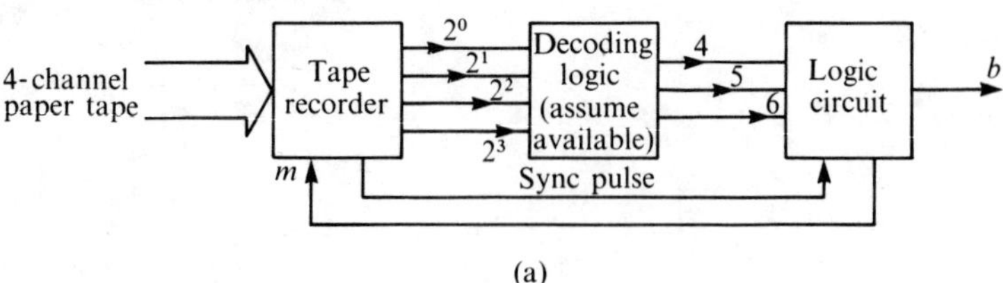

(a)

SOLUTION

Step 1 *I/O characteristics*

As stated.

Step 2 *Internal characteristics*

A suitable internal state diagram is shown in Figure (b).

Step 3 *State reduction*

No merging of rows in Figure (c) is possible.

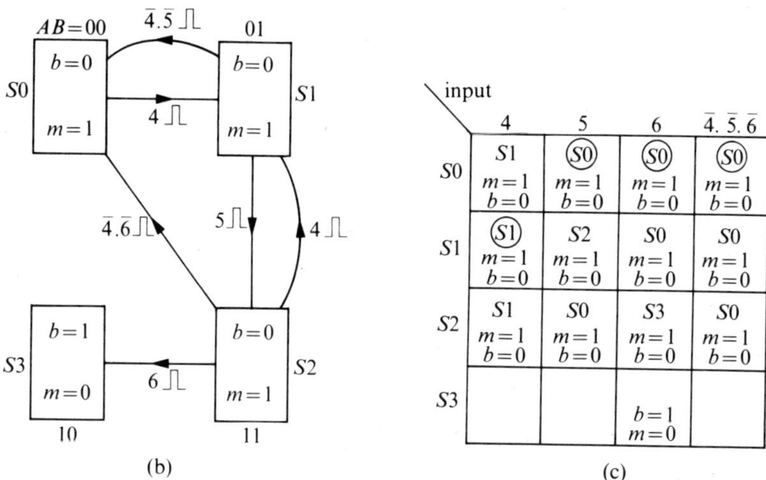

	4	5	6	$\bar{4}.\bar{5}.\bar{6}$
S0	S1 m=1 b=0	(S0) m=1 b=0	(S0) m=1 b=0	(S0) m=1 b=0
S1	(S1) m=1 b=0	S2 m=1 b=0	S0 m=1 b=0	S0 m=1 b=0
S2	S1 m=1 b=0	S0 m=1 b=0	S3 m=1 b=0	S0 m=1 b=0
S3			b=1 m=0	

(b) (c)

Step 4 *Primitive circuit*

Suitable binary codes are shown on the state diagram. By direct reference to this diagram, we obtain:

$$S_A = S1.5 + (S2.6) + (S3),$$
$$= \bar{A}B5 + (AB6) + (A\bar{B}),$$
$$= \bar{A}B5, \qquad \text{Therefore } J_A = B5.$$

$$R_A = S2.4 + S2.\bar{4}.\bar{6} + (S0) + (S1.\bar{5}) + (S3),$$
$$= S2.4 + S2.\bar{6} + (S0) + (S1.\bar{5}) + (S3),$$
$$= S2.[4 + \bar{6}] + (S0) + (S1.\bar{5}) + (S3),$$
$$= S2.\bar{6} + (S0) + (S1.\bar{5}) + (S3),$$
$$= AB\bar{6} + (\bar{A}\bar{B}) + (\bar{A}B\bar{5}) + (A\bar{B}),$$
$$= A\bar{6}, \qquad \text{Therefore } K_A = \bar{6}.$$

$$S_B = S0.4 + (S\ 1.4) + (S1.5) + (S2.4) + (S3),$$
$$= (S0 + S1 + S2).4 + (S3) + (S1.5),$$
$$= \overline{S3}.4 + (S3) + (S1.5),$$
$$= 4 + (S3) + (S1.5),$$
$$= 4, \qquad \text{Therefore, } J_B = 4.$$

$$R_B = S1.\bar{4}.\bar{5} + S2.\bar{4}.\bar{6} + S2.6 + (S3),$$
$$= S1.\bar{4}.\bar{5} + S2(\bar{4}.\bar{6} + 6) + (S3),$$
$$= S1.\bar{4}.\bar{5} + S2(\bar{4} + 6) + (S3),$$
$$= S1.\bar{4}.\bar{5} + S2.\bar{4} + (S3),$$

$$= AB\overline{4}\overline{5} + AB\overline{4} + (A\overline{B}),$$
$$= B\overline{4}\overline{5} + A\overline{4}, \qquad \text{Therefore } K_B = \overline{4}\overline{5} + A\overline{4}.$$

$$m = \overline{S3}$$
$$= \overline{A\overline{B}},$$
$$= \overline{A} + B, \text{ and}$$

$$b = S3$$
$$= A\overline{B}.$$

The corresponding circuit is shown below in Figure (d).

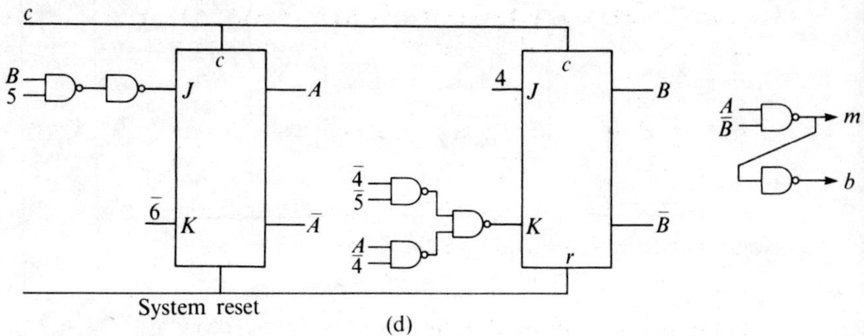

(d)

PROBLEM 8: *Blank Entries*

Determine the circuit responses if the tape reader motor in the previous problem fails to stop; that is, fill in the blank squares in the state table, Figure (c) of the previous problem.

SOLUTION:

For ease of reference we reproduce the state below and we number its squares - see Figure (a).

Input	4	5	6	$\overline{4}.\overline{5}.\overline{6}$
S0	1 S1 m=1 b=0	2 (S0) m=1 b=0	3 (S0) m=1 b=0	4 (S0) m=1 b=0
S1	5 (S1) m=1 b=0	6 S2 m=1 b=0	7 S0 m=1 b=0	8 S0 m=1 b=0
S2	9 S1 m=1 b=0	10 S0 m=1 b=0	11 S3 m=1 b=0	12 S0 m=1 b=0
S3	13 S1 m=1 b=0	14 S0 m=1 b=0	15 (S3) m=0 b=1	16 S0 m=1 b=0

(a)

Considering each square in turn, we obtain

Square 13

In this square $A = 1, B = 0$, and '4' = 1. Substituting these values in the JKFF equations, we obtain

$$\begin{array}{llll} J_A = B.5 & K_A = \overline{6} & J_B = \text{`4'} & K_B = \overline{4}\,\overline{5} + A\overline{4} \\ \quad = 0 & \quad 1 & \quad 1 & \quad 0; \end{array}$$

that is, JKFFA resets and JKFFB sets, causing the circuit to move to state $S1$. We indicate this by inserting $S1$ in this blank square.

Square 14

In square 14 $A = 1, B = 0$, and '5' = 1. Substituting these values in the JKFF equations, we obtain

$$\begin{array}{llll} J_A = B.5 & K_A = \overline{6} & J_B = \text{`4'} & K_B = \overline{4}.\overline{5} + A.\overline{4} \\ \quad 0 & \quad 1 & \quad 0 & \quad 1; \end{array}$$

therefore JKFFA resets and JKFFB remains reset, causing the circuit to move to state $S0$ – therefore we insert $S0$ in square 14.

Square 15

In this square $A = 1, B = 0$, and '6' = 1. Substituting these values in the circuit's JKFF equations as before, we obtain

$$\begin{array}{llll} J_A = B.5 & K_A = \overline{6} & J_B = 4 & K_B = \overline{4}.\overline{5} + A.4 \\ \quad = 0 & \quad 0 & \quad 0 & \quad = 1; \end{array}$$

The above values indicate that JKFFA locks in its set state and JKFFB remains reset; that is the circuit does not move out of this square. Therefore, we insert $S3$ in this blank square.

Square 16

In this square $A = 1, B = 0$, and '4' = '5' = '6' = 0. Substituting these values in the JKFF equations of the previous problem, we obtain

$$\begin{array}{llll} J_A = B.5 & K_A = \text{`}\overline{6}\text{'} & J_B = \text{`4'} & K_B = \overline{4}\,\overline{5} + A\overline{4} \\ \quad = 0 & \quad = 1 & \quad = 0 & \quad = 1; \end{array}$$

that is JKFFA resets and JKFFB remains reset, causing the circuit to move to state $S0$. We indicate this by inserting $S0$ in square 16 – see Figure (a).

PROBLEM 9: *Radar Control*

A radar system operates in four modes: wide angle scan, narrow angle scan, penetration mode, and 'lock-to-target' mode. In the last two modes the position of the beam is specified by the navigation computer, shown in Figure (a).

Design and implement a logic circuit to allow switching from one mode to another in a fixed cycle of the above sequence each time a push-button is activated and released.

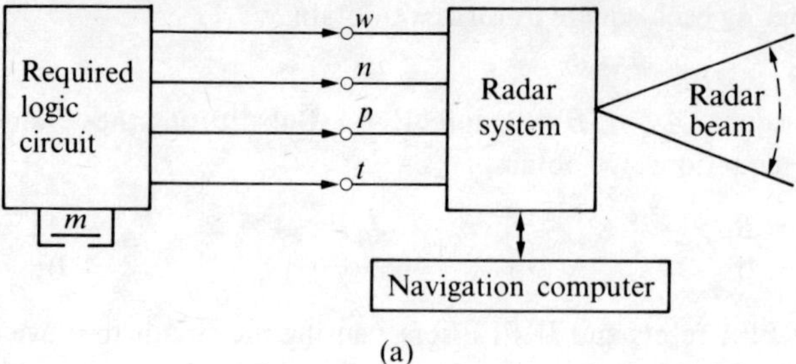

(a)

The signals defining the four modes of operation are

w = 1 for wide angle scan,
n = 1 for narrow angle scan,
p = 1 for penetration mode, and
t = 1 for 'lock-to-target' mode.

SOLUTION:
Step 1 *External (I/O) characteristics*
As specified.

Step 2 *Internal characteristics*
A suitable internal state diagram is shown in Figure (b). We use the activation release of push-button m to generate our clock pulse.

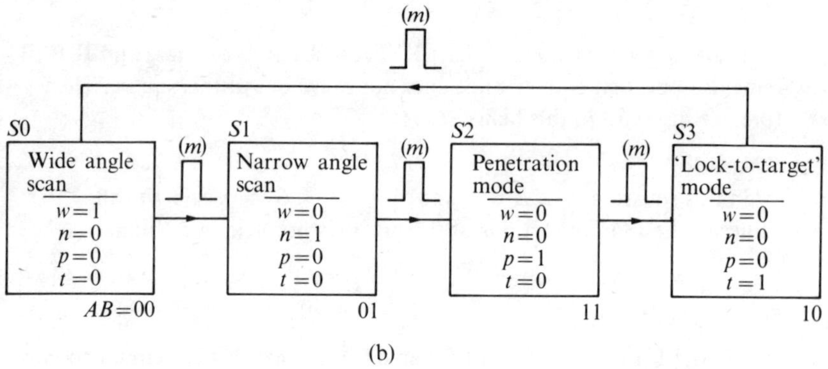

(b)

Step 3 *State reduction*
The state table of our solution, derived directly from the state diagram in Figure (b), is shown in Figure (c). No state reduction is possible in this case – see Section 10 in Chapter 1.

Step 4 *Primitive circuit*
In order to avoid signal spikes (race-hazards) at the input terminals of the radar system when we change states, we shall use a race-free code for our four states. The code used is derived by direct reference to our race-free diagram – see Section 6 of Chapter 1.

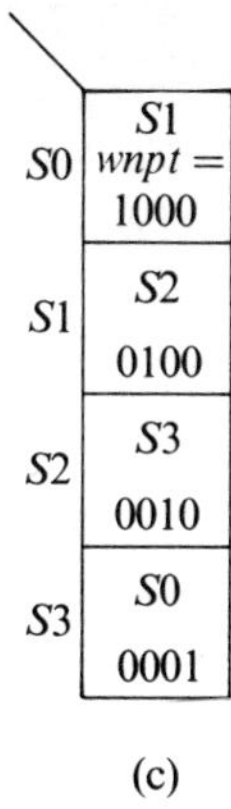

(c)

To derive the circuit equations we refer to our state diagram in Figure (b). They are

$$\begin{aligned} S_A &= S1 + (S2) \\ &= AB + (AB) \\ &= B, \end{aligned} \qquad \text{Therefore } J_A = B.$$

$$\begin{aligned} R_A &= S3 + (S0) \\ &= AB + (\bar{A}\bar{B}) \\ &= \bar{B}, \end{aligned} \qquad \text{Therefore } K_A = \bar{B}.$$

$$\begin{aligned} S_B &= S0 + (S1) \\ &= \bar{A}\bar{B} + (\bar{A}B) \\ &= \bar{A}, \end{aligned} \qquad \text{Therefore } J_B = \bar{A}.$$

$$\begin{aligned} R_B &= S2 + (S3) \\ &= AB + (AB) \\ &= A, \end{aligned} \qquad \text{Therefore } K_B = A.$$

$$\begin{aligned} w &= S0 \\ &= \bar{A}\bar{B}, \end{aligned}$$

$$\begin{aligned} n &= S1 \\ &= \bar{A}B, \end{aligned}$$

$$\begin{aligned} p &= S2 \\ &= AB, \text{ and} \end{aligned}$$

$$\begin{aligned} t &= S3 \\ &= A\,.\,\bar{B}. \end{aligned}$$

The corresponding circuit is shown in Figure (d).

Note that because of its cyclic nature the state diagrams in Figure (b) can be implemented directly using a scale-4 pulse counter.

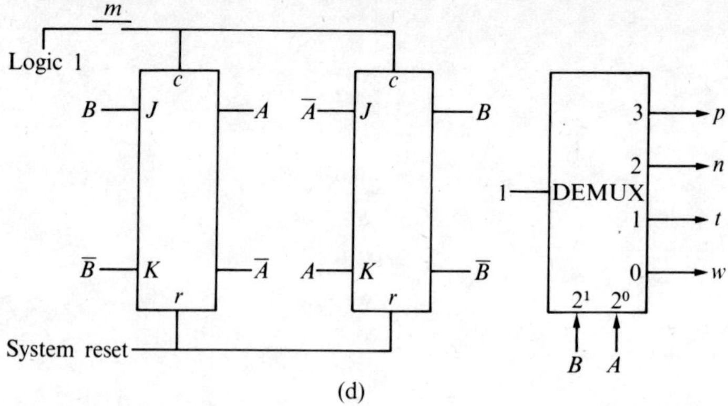

(d)

PROBLEM 10: *A Digital Scanner*

Given a clock, design a logic circuit to sample sequentially the four pins of a thumbwheel switch in the following manner.

Each time switch *m* in Figure (a) is activated four pulses are to be output on line *c*. A pulse is to be output on line *d*, if the pin being sampled is at a logic 1, otherwise no pulse is to be output.

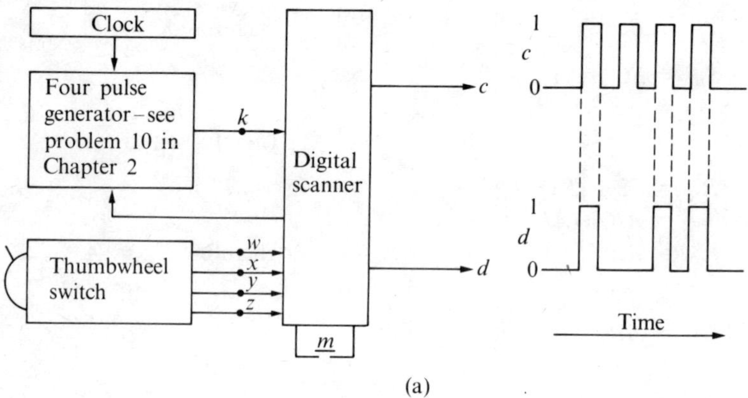

(a)

SOLUTION:

A four-pulse generator has been designed and implemented in the previous chapter – see problem 12. We shall, therefore, assume that each time switch *m* is activated four pulses are automatically generated on line *k* in Figure (a).

Step 1 *External (I/O) characteristics*

In Figure (a) we show the signal to be generated on line *d* when $w = y = z = 1$ and $x = 0$.

Step 2 *Internal characteristics*

A suitable internal state diagram is shown in Figure (b).

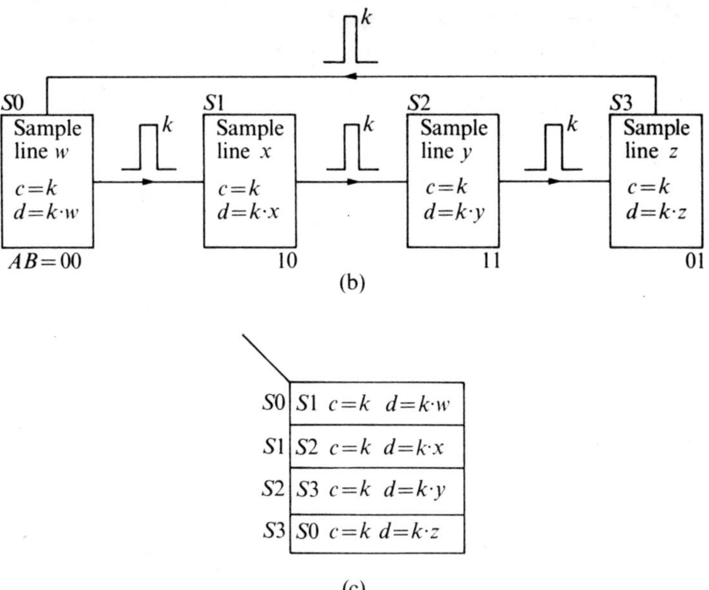

(b)

(c)

Step 3 *State reduction*

Reference to the state table of our solution shows that rows cannot be combined – see Section 10 of Chapter 1.

Step 4 *Primitive circuit*

To avoid race hazards (unwanted signal spikes) on line d, we shall use a race-free code (see Section 6 in Chapter 1) for the four states in Figure (b). By direct reference to this Figure, we obtain

$$S_A = S0 + (S1) = \bar{A}\bar{B} + (A\bar{B}) = \bar{B}, \quad \text{Therefore } J_A = \bar{B}$$
$$R_A = S2 + (S3) = AB + (\bar{A}B) = B, \quad \text{Therefore } K_A = B$$
$$S_B = S1 + (S2) = A\bar{B} + (AB) = A, \quad \text{Therefore } J_B = A$$
$$R_B = S3 + (S0) = \bar{A}B + (\bar{A}\bar{B}) = \bar{A}, \quad \text{Therefore } K_B = \bar{A}, \text{ and}$$

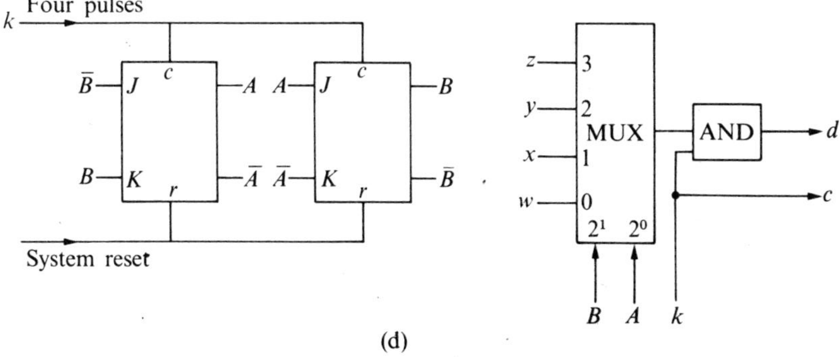

(d)

$$\begin{aligned} d &= S0.K.w + S7.K.x + S2.K.y + S3.K.z \\ &= \bar{A}\bar{B}Kw + A\bar{B}Kx + ABKy + \bar{A}BKz. \end{aligned}$$

The equivalent circuit is shown in Figure (d). Note that as in the case of the previous problem, a scale-4 counter can be used.

PROBLEM 11: *A Three-pump Controller*

A reservoir is connected to a lake by a pipe line. Water is taken from the lake to the reservoir by a system of three pumps.

Three level sensors are installed on the reservoir. Their outputs are denoted by variables a_1, a_2, and a_3. Signal $a_1 = 1$ when the water is above level 1 in Figure (a). Similarly, $a_2 = 1$ and $a_3 = 1$, when the water is above levels 2 and 3 respectively, as shown in our block schematic. The number of pumps that are on at any one time depends on the water level in the reservoir and is shown in Figure (a).

In order to equalize wear on the pumps, they should come in a cyclic manner.

Design and implement a suitable logic circuit.

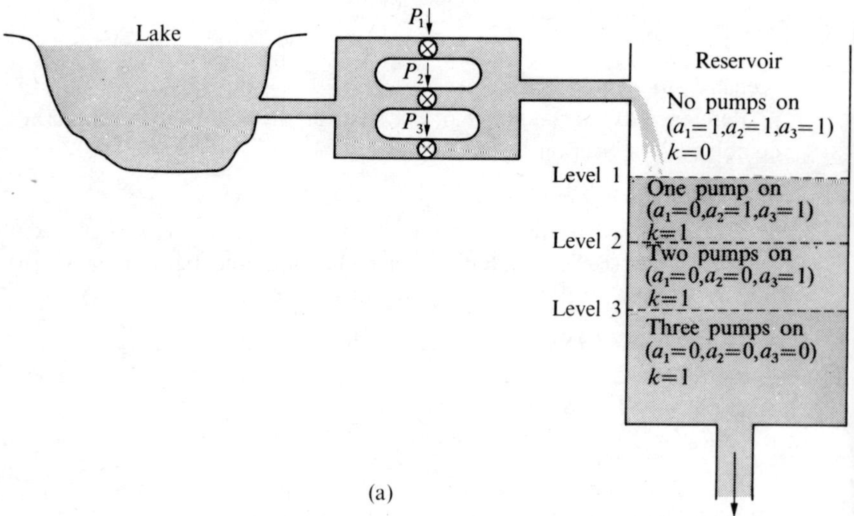

(a)

SOLUTION

Step 1 *External (I/O) characteristics*

In our solution we shall change the pump sequence each time the water goes above level 1 in Figure (a). We shall use the three sequences shown below.

	Below level 1	Below level 2	Below level 3
Pumps on	1	1 and 2	1, 2, and 3
Pumps on	2	2 and 3	2, 3, and 1
Pumps on	3	3 and 2	3, 2, and 1

Step 2 *Internal characteristics*

It is clearly desirable to change the pump sequence when the pumps are turned off, that is when the water level is above level 1, indicated by $a_1 = 1$. Since our flip-flops are assumed to change state on the trailing edge of a clock pulse, c, we can derive c by inverting level signal a_1. A suitable state diagram in such a case is shown in Figure (b).

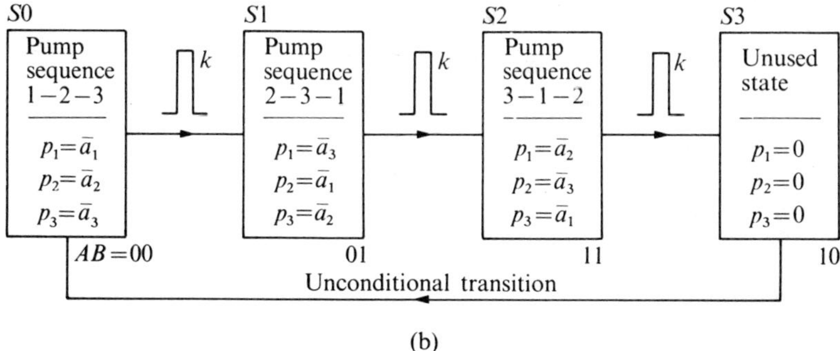

(b)

Step 3 *State reduction*

The state table of our solution, derived directly from the state diagram in Figure (b), is shown in Figure (c). No state reduction is possible in this case - see Section 10 in Chapter 1.

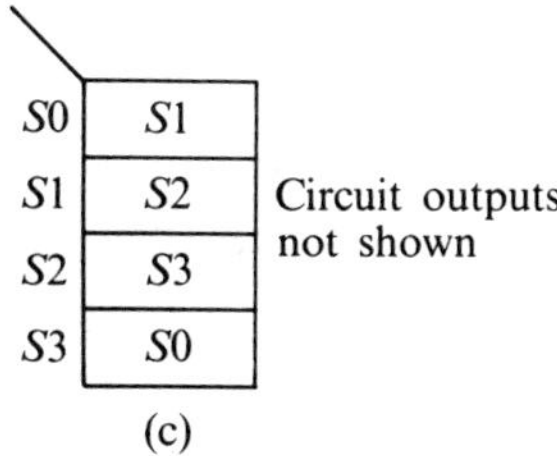

(c)

Step 4 *Primitive circuit*

A suitable code for our four states is shown in Figure (b). In this case any code can be used, as signal spikes are not likely to affect pumps.

By direct reference to our state diagram in Figure (b), we obtain the circuit's equations shown below:

$$S_A = S1 + (S2) = \bar{A}B + (AB) = B, \qquad \text{Therefore, } J_A = B$$

$$R_A = 0, \qquad \text{Therefore, } K_A = 0$$

$$r_A = S3 + (S0) = A\bar{B} + (\bar{A}\bar{B}) = \bar{B},$$

$$\begin{aligned} S_B &= S0 + (S1) \\ &= \overline{A}\overline{B} + (\overline{A}B) \\ &= \overline{A}, \qquad \text{Therefore, } J_B = \overline{A} \end{aligned}$$

$$\begin{aligned} R_B &= S2 \\ &= AB, \qquad \text{Therefore, } K_B = A \end{aligned}$$

$$\begin{aligned} P_1 &= S0 . \overline{a}_1 + S1 . \overline{a}_3 + S2 . \overline{a}_2 \\ &= \overline{A}\overline{B}\overline{a}_1 + \overline{A}B\overline{a}_3 + AB\overline{a}_2, \end{aligned}$$

$$\begin{aligned} P_2 &= S0 . \overline{a}_2 + S1 . \overline{a}_1 + S2 . \overline{a}_3 \\ &= \overline{A}\overline{B}\overline{a}_2 + \overline{A}B\overline{a}_1 + AB\overline{a}_3, \text{ and} \end{aligned}$$

$$\begin{aligned} P_3 &= S0 . \overline{a}_3 + S1 . \overline{a}_2 + S2 . \overline{a}_1 \\ &= \overline{A}\overline{B}\overline{a}_3 + \overline{A}B\overline{a}_2 + AB\overline{a}_1 \end{aligned}$$

The corresponding circuit is shown in Figure (d).

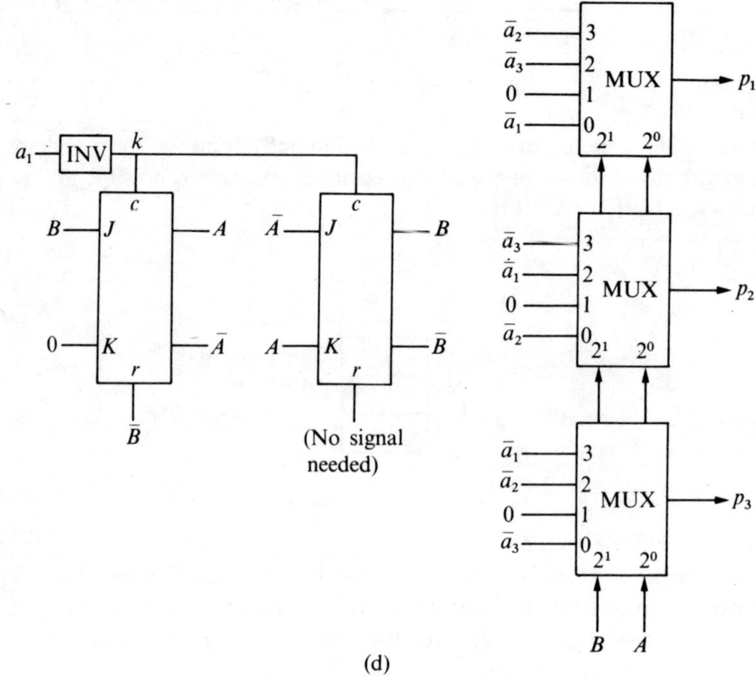

(d)

PROBLEM 12: *Invalid Code Detection*

Serial b-c-d messages whose magnitude is denoted by n, arrive on line X, most significant digit first. Each data bit is synchronized with a clock pulse on line c.

Design a circuit that generates a fault signal on terminal f each time an invalid code is received, as shown in the diagram.

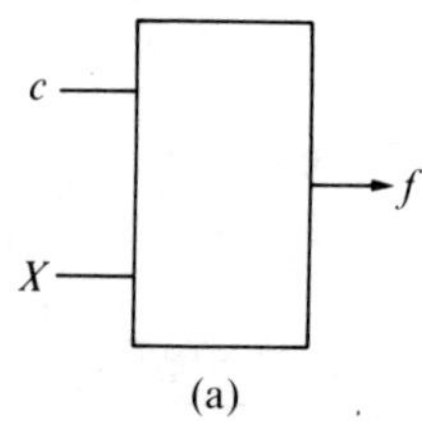

(a)

SOLUTION

Step 1 *I/O characteristics*

As stated.

Step 2 *Internal characteristics*

A suitable state diagram is shown below in (b).

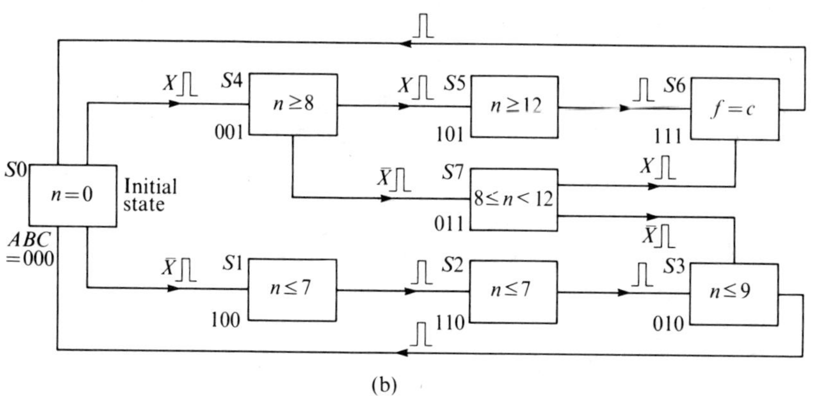

(b)

Step 3 *State reduction*

Not attempted to maintain clarity of design.

Step 4 *Primitive circuit*

Suitable state codes are shown in the diagram. By direct reference to this diagram, we obtain:

$$S_A = S0\bar{X} + S4X + S7X + (S1) + (S5) = \bar{B}\bar{C}\bar{X} + \bar{A}CX$$

Therefore, $J_A = \bar{B}\bar{C}\bar{X} + CX$

$$R_A = S2 + S6 = AB\bar{C} + ABC = AB$$

Therefore, $K_A = B$

$$S_B = S1 + S4\bar{X} + S5 + (S2) + (S7) = A\bar{C} + \bar{B}C\bar{X} + A\bar{B}$$

Therefore, $J_B = A + \bar{C}\bar{X}$

$$R_B = S3 + S6 + (S0) = \bar{A}\bar{C} + ABC$$

Therefore, $K_B = \bar{A}\bar{C} + AC$

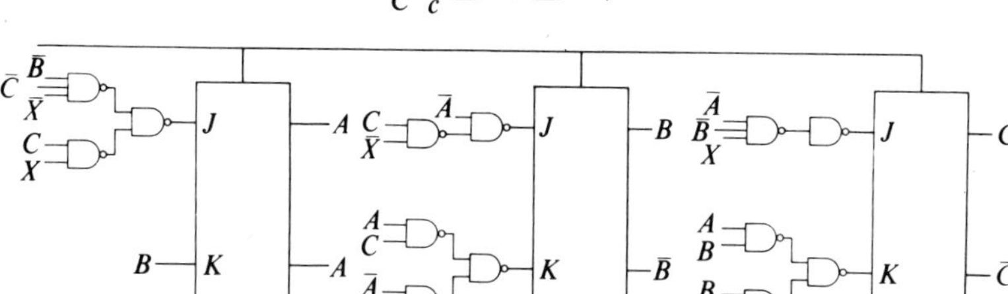

(c)

$$S_C = S0X + (S4) + (S5) + (S7X) = \overline{A}\overline{B}X$$

Therefore, $J_C = \overline{A}\overline{B}X$

$$R_C = S6 + S7\overline{X} + (S0\overline{X}) + (S1) + (S2) = AB + BC\overline{X}$$

Therefore, $K_C = AB + B\overline{X}$

$$f = S6\,.\,c = ABCc.$$

The corresponding circuit is shown in (c).

PROBLEM 13: *A Parity Circuit*

Binary-coded-decimal (b-c-d) messages arrive on line X serially, each binary bit being synchronized with a clock pulse on line c – see Figure (a). Design a circuit to establish odd parity by generating the appropriate parity bit. A clock pulse between consecutive messages is available.

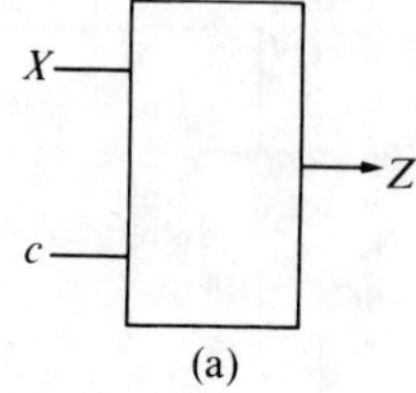

(a)

SOLUTION

Step 1 *I/O characteristics*

The fifth clock pulse will be output to establish odd parity whenever necessary.

Step 2 *Internal characteristics*

A suitable state diagram is shown below in Figure (b). Signal M is generated by modulo-5 counter in (c).

Step 3 *State reduction*

State table in Figure (d) cannot be reduced.

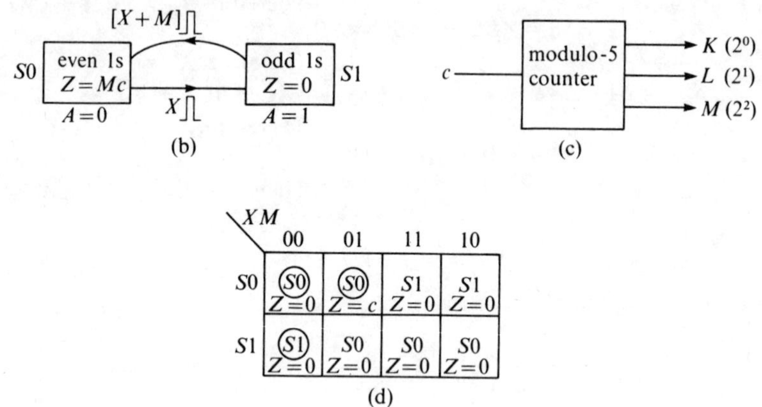

(b) (c)

	XM = 00	01	11	10
S0	(S0) Z=0	(S0) Z=c	S1 Z=0	S1 Z=0
S1	(S1) Z=0	S0 Z=0	S0 Z=0	S0 Z=0

(d)

Step 4 *Primitive circuit*

By direct reference to the state diagram, we obtain:

$S_A = S0 . X = \bar{A}X$ Therefore, $J_A = X$
$R_A = S1(X + M) = A(X + M)$ Therefore, $K_A = X + M$
$Z = S0Mc = \bar{A}Mc.$

The corresponding circuit is shown in Figure (e).

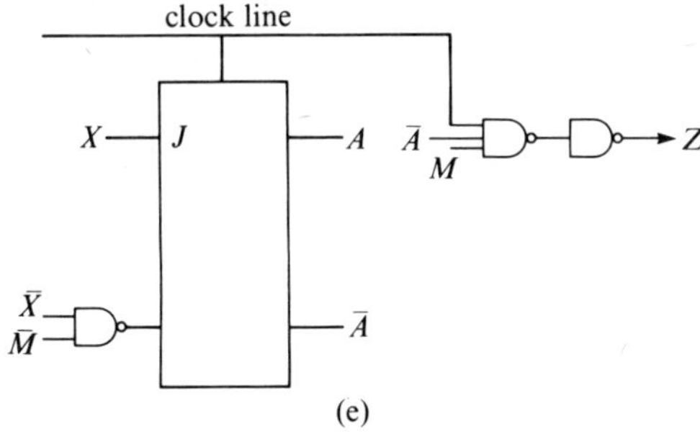

(e)

PROBLEM 14: *A Word Comparator*

Four-bit serial b-c-d messages arrive, most significant digit first, on terminals X and Y in Figure (a), bit by bit. Variables x and y are used to denote their magnitude. Each data bit is synchronized with a clock pulse on terminal c.

Design a circuit that generates a pulse on terminal $Z1$ if $x > y$, on terminal $Z2$ if $x < y$, and on terminal $Z3$ if $x = y$.

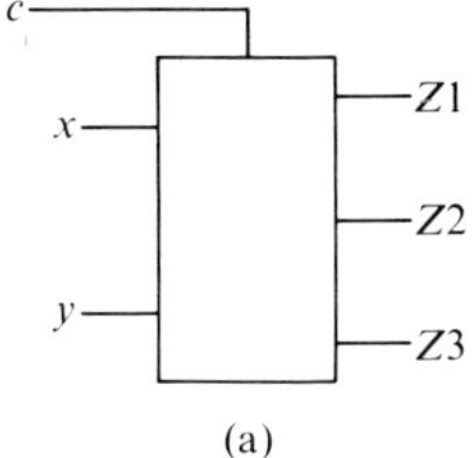

(a)

SOLUTION

Step 1 *I/O characteristics*

The fourth clock pulse will be output on the appropriate Z terminal - a modulo-4 counter shown in (b) is assumed available.

Step 2 *Internal characteristics*

A suitable state diagram is shown in Figure (c).

Step 3 *State reduction*

This step is not attempted to maintain clarity of design.

Step 4 *Primitive circuit*

Suitable state codes are shown in the diagram. By direct reference to it, we obtain:

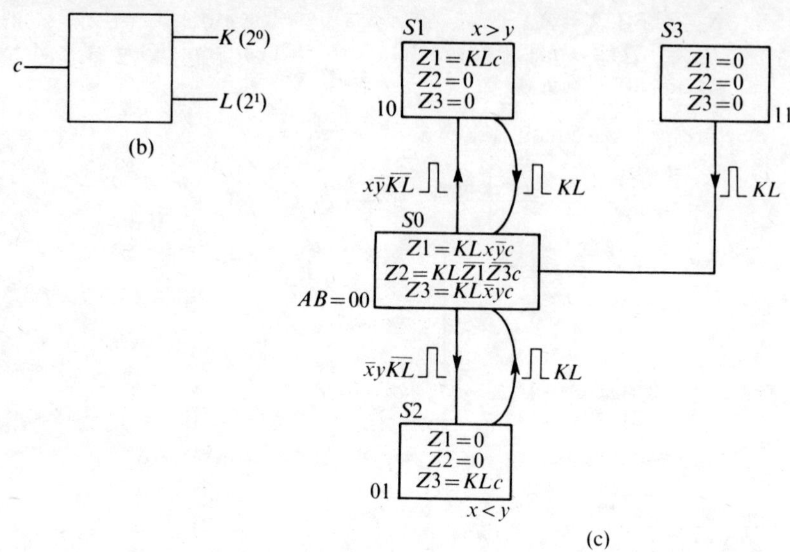

(b)

(c)

$$
\begin{aligned}
S_A &= S0x\bar{y}\bar{K}\bar{L} = \bar{A}\bar{B}x\bar{y}(\bar{K}+\bar{L}) && \text{Therefore, } J_A = \bar{B}x\bar{y}(\bar{K}+\bar{L}) \\
R_A &= S1KL + S3KL = AKL && \text{Therefore, } K_A = KL \\
S_B &= S0\bar{x}y\bar{K}\bar{L} = \bar{A}\bar{B}\bar{x}y(\bar{K}+\bar{L}) && \text{Therefore, } J_B = \bar{A}\bar{x}y(\bar{K}+\bar{L}) \\
R_B &= S2KL + S3KL = BKL && \text{Therefore, } K_B = KL \\
Z1 &= (S0x\bar{y} + X1)KLc = (\bar{A}\bar{B}x\bar{y} + A\bar{B})KLc = A\bar{B}(KL)c \\
&\quad + \bar{B}x\bar{y}(KL)c \\
Z2 &= S0\overline{Z1}\,\overline{Z3}KLc \\
Z3 &= (S0\bar{x}y + S2)KLc = (\bar{A}\bar{B}\bar{x}y + \bar{A}B)KLc = \bar{A}B(KL)c \\
&\quad + \bar{A}\bar{x}y(KL)c
\end{aligned}
$$

The corresponding circuit is shown in Figure (d).

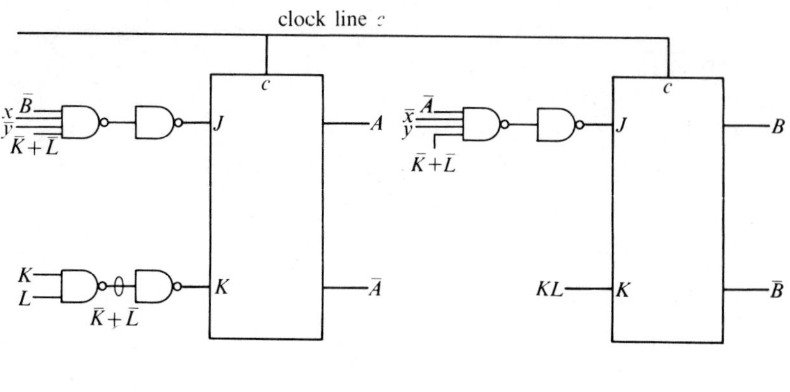

(d)

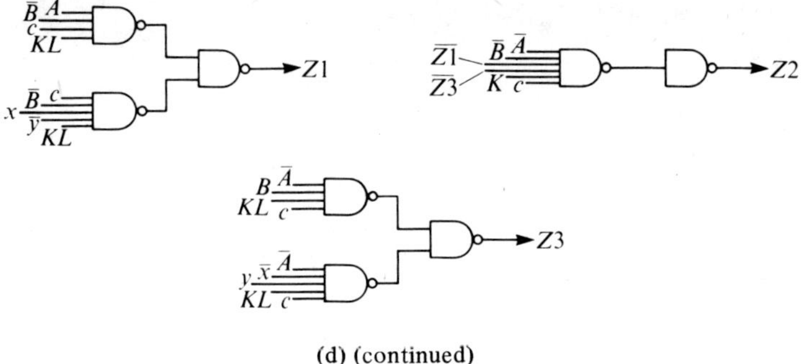

(d) (continued)

PROBLEM 15: *A Self-Locking Data Buffer*

Data bits arrive serially on terminal X, each data bit being synchronized with a clock pulse on terminal c - see Figure (a).

Design a buffer which will store the N bits that arrive after an initializing pulse has been applied on terminal r. The buffer must not accept any further bits after the N bits have been stored until another initializing pulse has been received on terminal r.

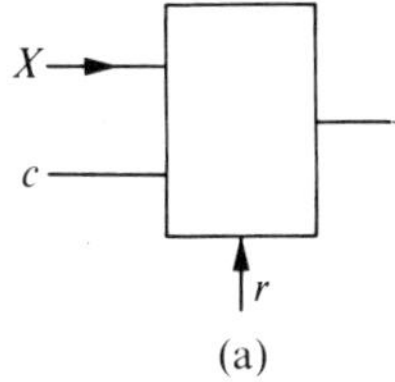

(a)

SOLUTION

A pulse on the reset line sets the register into state 1000. After three clock pulses the '1' in the first flip-flop is shifted into the marker flip-flop changing $\overline{m}$ from 1 to 0. This automatically cuts off further clock pulses from appearing on the register's clock line, thus allowing the three data bits $b0$, $b1$, and $b2$ to be staticized.

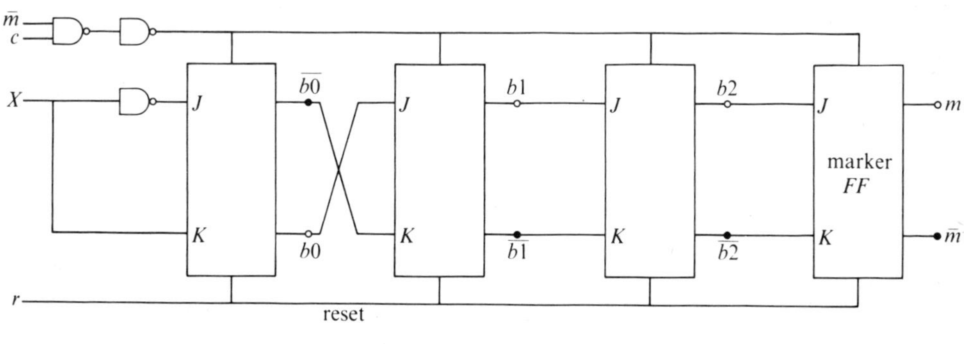

(b)

PROBLEM 16: *A Double Data Buffer*

Data bits arrive serially on terminal X, each data bit being synchronized with a clock pulse on terminal c - see Figure (a).

It is required to design a double buffer with the following characteristics. The double buffer is constructed with two buffers, $R1$ and $R2$. The first word arriving at X is staticized in $R1$ and the second in $R2$. During the time in which $R2$ is being filled, the word in $R1$ is to be output. The third word received at X is steered into $R1$, during which time the word in $R2$ (second word) is output. The double buffer proceeds in this manner indefinitely, odd-numbered words going to $R1$ and even-numbered words to $R2$, and each single buffer being available for output while the other is being filled.

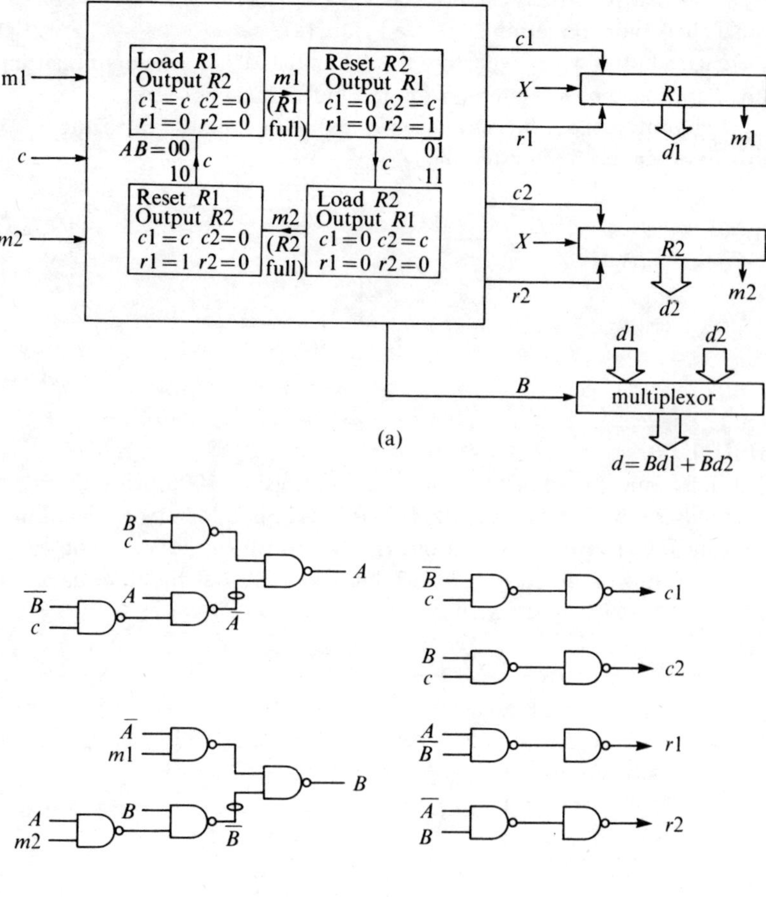

(a)

(b)

4 *Pulse-driven Circuits*

A new category of sequential circuits, *the pulse-driven circuits*, which incorporates the fast response of event-driven (asynchronous) circuits and the simplicity of clock-driven (synchronous) circuits is described. Formalized methods for their design and implementation are outlined. The design steps are demonstrated by means of problems and solutions.

4.1 INTRODUCTION

The design and implementation of digital sequential operations using (i) event-driven (unclocked) circuits and (ii) clock-driven (clocked) circuits have been described in Chapters 2 and 3 respectively. In the first case the circuits respond directly to changes in their input signals, whereas in the second case the circuit operation is synchronized with clock pulses, between which no circuit changes can occur. Event-driven circuits can therefore operate at speeds which are limited only by the response time of their components, in contrast to the clock-driven circuits whose speed of operation is limited by the clock frequency, which must be low enough to accommodate the slowest circuit response. On the other hand, clock-driven circuits are easier to design and implement than event-driven circuits, particularly when the number of input and output signals involved is high, and/or their relationship is complex, as in the case of microprocessor systems.

As the capacity of i.c. chips for logic components is progressively increasing, time constraints are becoming proportionately more difficult to meet in practice. For example, a microprocessor system cannot respond directly to signal changes occurring within, say, 30 to 50 ns, whereas a simple logic circuit can.

When the input signals are non-overlapping pulses, simplicity of design and fast circuit response can be readily accommodated using TFFs and logic gates, as it is shown in the next section. We shall refer to these circuits as *pulse-driven circuits.* Clearly, in such cases event-driven circuits can be used, but the circuit must respond to each of the double change of the pulse signals, necessitating approximately twice as many internal states, as would be needed by a pulse-driven circuit.

4.2 PULSE-DRIVEN CIRCUITS

In pulse-driven circuits the TFFs generate the state variables (secondary

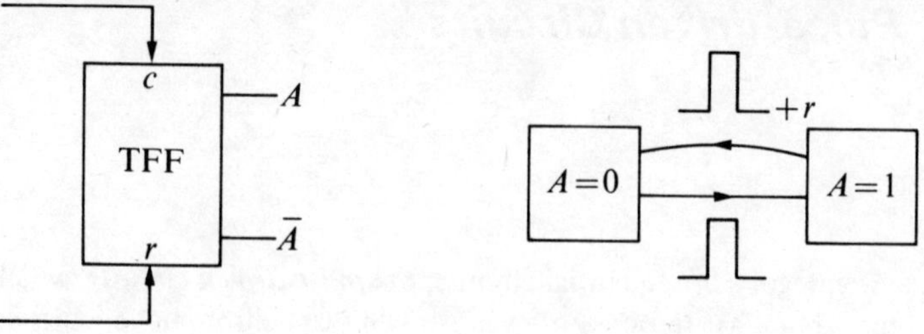

FIG. 4.1

signals), and the logic gates the clock and output signals. A TFF is a bistable element which changes state with every clock pulse, as shown in Figure 4.1. Note the TFF's have no data terminals.

The 1 to 0 transition of a TFF can also be implemented by a signal on its unconditional reset terminal, independently of clock pulses, if such a terminal is provided. In such cases, the designer has clearly the option of resetting a TFF by generating either a pulse on its clock terminal or a signal on its reset terminal. If the designer decides to exercise this option, he must observe the restrictions listed below.

1. If the TFFs switch on the leading edge of a clock pulse, the circuit may not enter a state by changing a set of state variables in which a *T* flip-flop, *A*, turns on, and exit the state by changing another set of signals in which TFFA is turned off unconditionally. Such a situation is shown in Figure 4.2 (a). The reason for this restriction is that when the circuit enters state *S*1, signal *w* equals 1 causing TFFA to reset. In our example the circuit will move to state *S*1, causing misoperation.
2. If the TFFs switch on the trailing edge, the opposite is true. That is, the circuit may not enter a state by changing a set of state variables in which a *T* flip-flop *A* turns off and exits the state by changing another set of signals in which TFFA is turned on, as shown in Figure 4.1 (b). The reason for this is that when the circuit enters state *S*1 signal $w = 1$, generating a clock signal. When *w* changes to 0, therefore, flip-flops *A* and *B* turn on causing the circuit to move to state *S*2. This clearly constitutes misoperation, since the circuit moved from state *S*0 to *S*1, and then to *S*2 with a single *w* pulse.

   These restrictions are automatically met either by using a race-free assignment of state variables (see Figure 1.6), or by not using the options mentioned above. Clearly in such a case the implementation may not be minimal. Otherwise, the design of pulse-driven circuits is accomplished conventionally in four steps, demonstrated by means of the example in the next section.

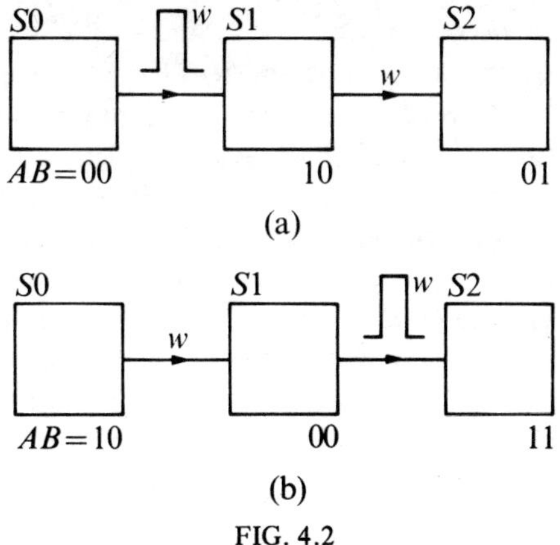

FIG. 4.2

4.3 THE DESIGN STEPS

Our design process is accomplished in four steps, and meets the design factors listed below:

1. *Circuit reliability.* All circuits function correctly and reliably.
2. *Gate minimality.* Generally speaking not all our circuits will be minimal.
3. *Circuit maintainability.* Our circuits are easy to maintain.
4. *Design effort.* This is minimal.
5. *Documentation.* No additional documentation is needed.
6. *The design steps.* These are easy to apply. No specialist knowledge is necessary.
7. *Gate fan-in and fan-out restrictions.* These are met reliably though not *elegantly.*

The sequence in which our design steps are executed is shown below:

Step 1 *I/O characteristics*

In this step we draw a block diagram to show the available input signals and the required output signals. We next use either a state diagram or waveforms to define the relationship between the two sets of signals which must be established by our circuit.

Step 2 *Internal characteristics*

In the second step the designer specifies the internal performance of the circuit. Although experience, intuition and foresight play an important part at this stage, the inexperienced designer should be primarily concerned that his specification of the internal circuit operation is complete and free of ambiguities. To this end he should avoid short cuts and use as many states as he finds necessary to give a complete and unambiguous specification of the circuit performance. The next step can be used to eliminate unwanted states.

Step 3 *State reduction*

This step is optional and can be omitted. Its main purpose is to provide the designer with the means for reducing the number of internal states he used in step 2, if such a reduction is possible.

The circuit's state table is drawn and the state reduction steps are used to merge its rows, as explained in Section 10 of Chapter 1.

Clearly to avoid redundant states we would only use this step to reduce the number of states to some power of 2. For example, whereas we would use it to reduce five states to four, we would not use it to reduce four states to three.

Step 4 *Primitive circuits*

As in the case of clocked sequential circuits, the design of pulse-driven circuits does not require that only one state variable (secondary signal) may change during a circuit transition between two states.

The Boolean expressions defining the clock and reset signals of the flip-flops are read directly from the state diagram. These expressions can be reduced using an optional terms, products that define

(i) unused states,
(ii) total states not arising during normal operation of the circuit, and
(iii) reset signals during a transition between two states in which the flip-flop concerned remains reset.

Note that pulses may be applied at the clock terminal of a flip-flop when the reset signal is present.

We shall demonstrate our design steps by means of the following problem.

DESIGN PROBLEM: *A Sequence Identifier*

Non-overlapping pulses appear on lines *w*, *x*, and *y* in Figure 4.3 (a). Each pulse occurs once only. Design and implement a circuit to determine the order in which the three pulses have appeared.

The circuit is to reset by activating a manual switch *m*.

SOLUTION

Step 1 *I/O characteristics*

In our solution the third pulse will be output on one of the six terminals *Z*0 to *Z*5 according to the sequences shown in brackets in Figure 4.3 (b). For example, if the pulse sequence is *w*/*y*/*x*, the *x* pulse will be output on line *Z*1.

Step 2 *Internal characteristics*

A suitable internal state diagram is shown in Figure 4.3 – ignore the presence of the three unused states. For the sake of clarity 'zero' outputs are not shown.

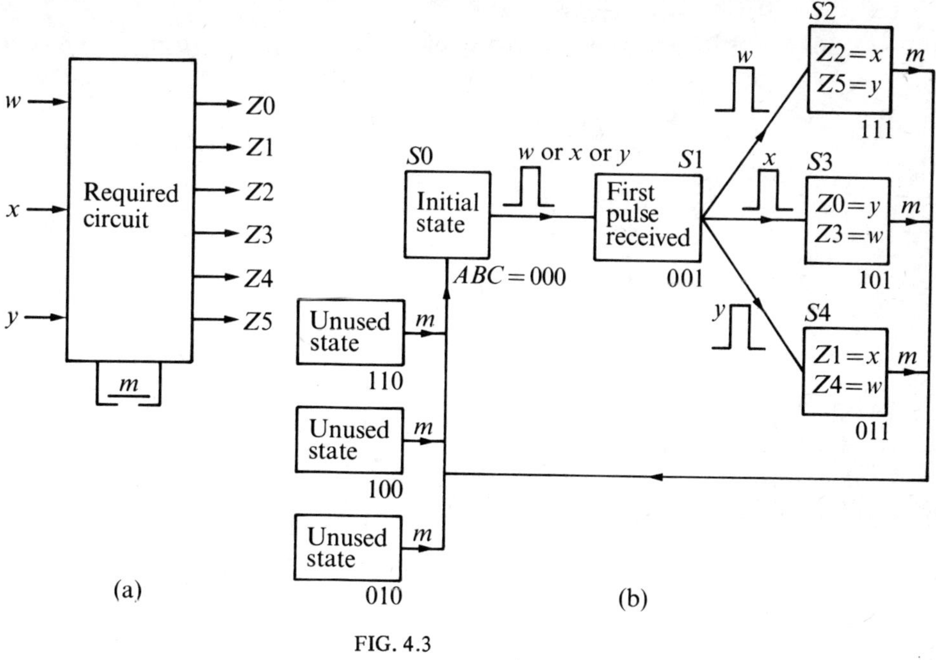

FIG. 4.3

Step 3 *State reduction*

The corresponding state table of our solution is shown in Figure 4.4. This is derived directly from the state diagram in Figure 4.3 (b).

No merging of rows is possible – see Section 10 in Chapter 1. We therefore introduce at this stage the three unused states.

	w	x	y
S0	S1	S1	S1
S1	S2	S3	S4
S2		(S2) Z2 = 1	(S2) Z5 = 1
S3	(S3) Z3 = 1		(S3) Z0 = y
S4	(S4) Z4 = 1	(S4) Z1 = 1	

FIG. 4.4

Step 4 *Circuit implementation*

Arbitrarily chosen codes for our eight states are shown in Figure 4.3(b). By direct reference to this diagram, we obtain

$$c_A = S1\,.(w + x)$$
$$= ABC(w + x)$$

$$c_B = S1\,(w + y)$$
$$= ABC(w + y)$$

$$c_c = S0\,.(w + x + y)$$
$$= \overline{ABC}(w + x + y)$$

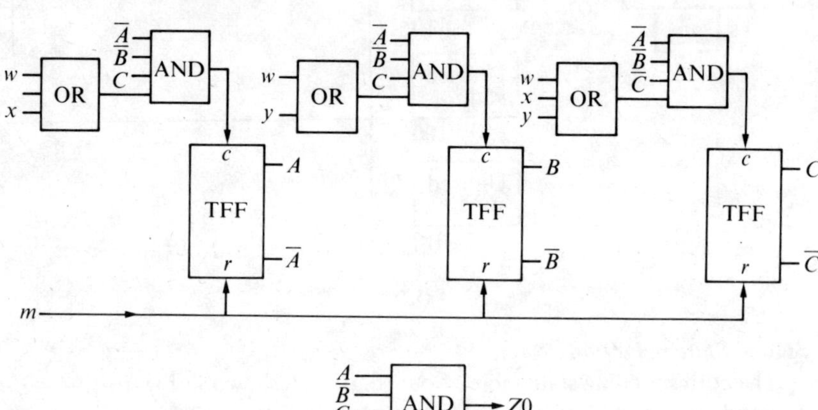

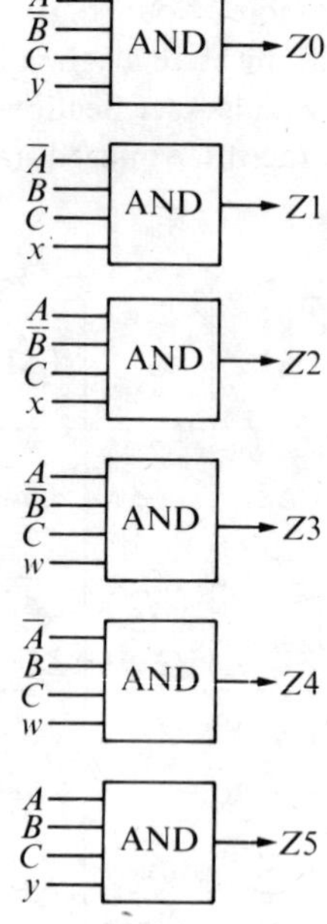

FIG. 4.5

$$
\begin{aligned}
r_A &= r_B = r_c = m \\
Z0 &= S3\,.\,y = A\bar{B}Cy \\
Z1 &= S4\,.\,x = \bar{A}BCx \\
Z2 &= S3\,.\,x = A\bar{B}Cx \\
Z3 &= S3\,.\,w = A\bar{B}Cw \\
Z4 &= S4\,.\,w = \bar{A}BCw \\
Z5 &= S2\,.\,y = ABCy.
\end{aligned}
$$

The corresponding circuit is shown in Figure 4.5. Clearly the six AND gates may be replaced by a demux discussed in section 1.4.

4.4 MULTI-MODE SEQUENTIAL CIRCUITS

The design and implementation of event-driven (unclocked), clock-driven (clocked), and pulse-driven circuits have been treated separately in Chapters 2, 3, and 4 respectively. Below we demonstrate by means of an example how sequential circuits can be designed and implemented intuitively as multi-mode devices. Formalized methods for their design and implementation are currently being developed by the author.

DESIGN EXAMPLE: *One Shot Circuit*

High frequency clock pulses are presented at input terminal c in Figure 4.6(a). Each activation of manual switch m is to allow one complete clock pulse to be output at terminal k, as shown in Figure 4.6(b).

Design a suitable circuit.

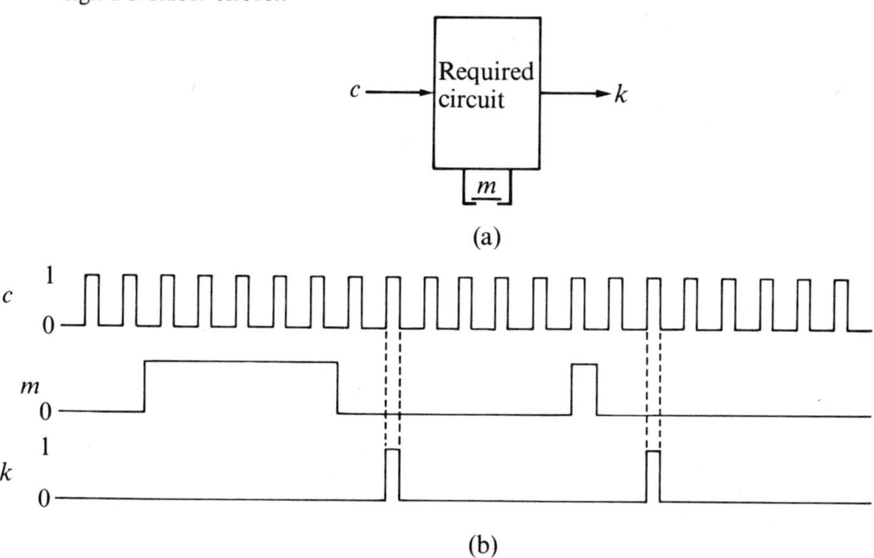

FIG. 4.6

SOLUTION

See problem entitled 'One shot circuit' in Chapters 2 and 3 for its implementation as an event-driven and as a clock-driven circuit.

Step 1 *External (I/O) characteristics*

As specified.

Step 2 *Internal characteristics*

The internal state diagram of a suitable circuit is shown in Figure 4.7.

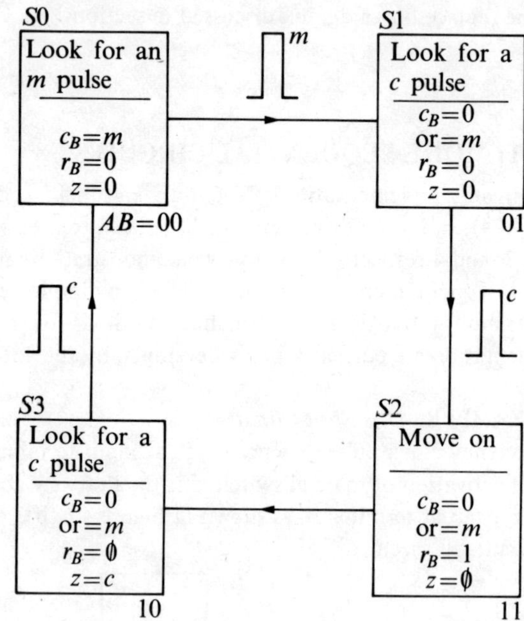

FIG. 4.7

Step 3 *State reduction*

At this stage of development we shall omit this step.

Step 4 *Circuit implementation*

By direct reference to the state diagram in Figure 4.7, we obtain

$$S_A = S1 = \bar{A}.B, \qquad \text{Therefore, } J_A = B$$

$$R_A = S3 = A.\bar{B}, \qquad \text{Therefore } K_A = \bar{B}$$

$$c_B = S0.m + (S3.m) + (S1.m) + (S2.m) = m$$

$$r_B = S2 + (S3) = A.B + (A.\bar{B}) = A$$

$$Z = S3 . c + (S2)$$
$$= A . \bar{B} . c + (A . B)$$
$$= A . c.$$

The corresponding circuit is shown in Figure 4.8. Note that the AND gate may be omitted if the duration of the output pulse can be extended to a clock period.

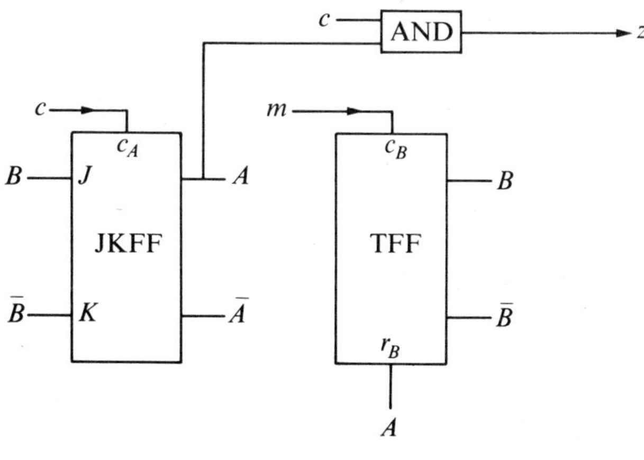

FIG. 4.8

4.5 PROBLEMS AND SOLUTIONS

In this section we shall illustrate the design and implementation of pulse-driven sequential circuits by means of selected problems and solutions.

PROBLEM 1: *Pulse Sequence Detector*

Non-overlapping pulses from three sensors arrive randomly on terminals w, x, and y in Figure (a). Design and implement a circuit that will generate a pulse on the output terminal z each time three pulses arrive consecutively on terminals w, x, and y. The circuit is to reset with signal A.

SOLUTION:

Step 1 *External (I/O) characteristics*

The conditions under which an output pulse will be generated are shown diagrammatically in Figure (b).

Step 2 *Internal characteristics*

A suitable internal state diagram is shown in Figure (c). Ignore state $S3$ at this stage.

Step 3 *State reduction*

The state table of our solution derived directly from Figure (c) is shown in Figure (d). Reference to it shows that no rows can be merged.

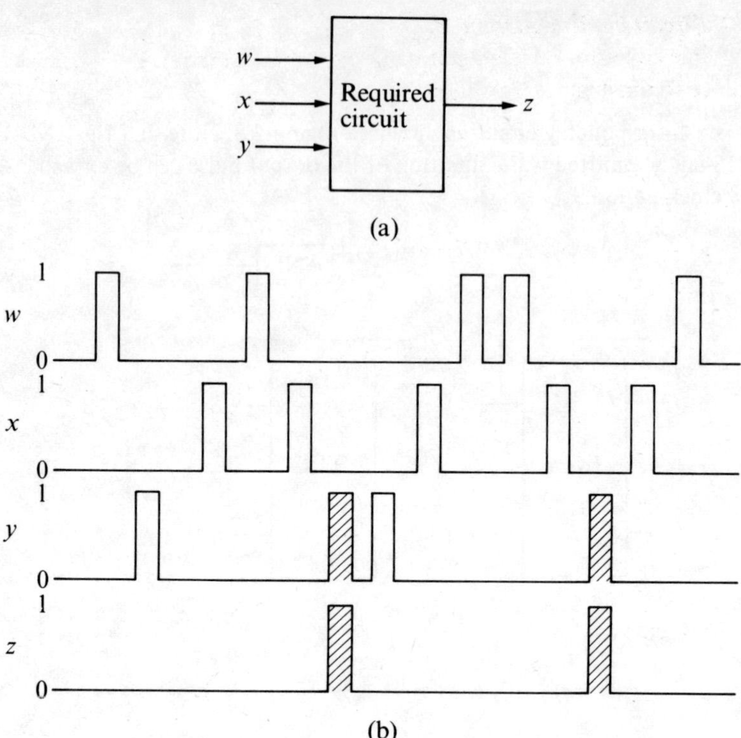

(a)

(b)

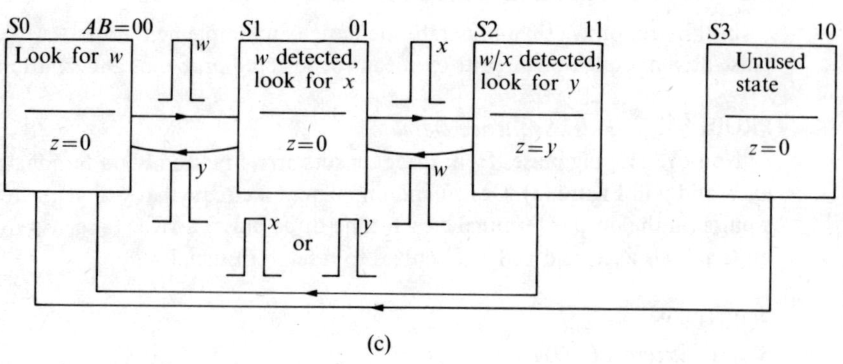

(c)

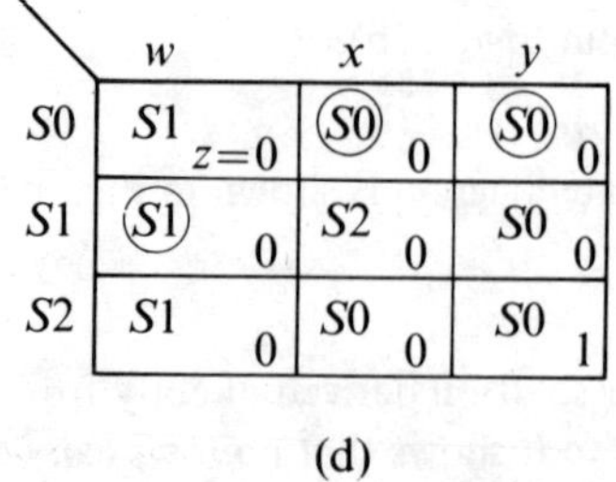

	w	x	y
S0	S1 z=0	(S0) 0	(S0) 0
S1	(S1) 0	S2 0	S0 0
S2	S1 0	S0 0	S0 1

(d)

Step 4 *Circuit implementation*

Suitable codes for our four states are shown in Figure (c). By direct reference to this Figure, we obtain

$$
\begin{aligned}
C_A &= S1\,.\,x + S2\,.\,w + S2\,.\,x + S2\,.\,y \\
&= \bar{A}Bx + ABw + ABx + ABy \\
&= Bx + ABw + ABy.
\end{aligned}
$$

$$
\begin{aligned}
r_A &= \text{System reset} + S3 + (S0) \\
&= R + A\bar{B} + (\bar{A}\bar{B}) \\
&= R + \bar{B}.
\end{aligned}
$$

$$
\begin{aligned}
C_B &= S0\,.\,w + S1\,.\,y + S2\,.\,x + S2\,.\,y \\
&= \bar{A}\bar{B}w + \bar{A}By + ABx + ABy \\
&= By + \bar{A}\bar{B}w + ABx.
\end{aligned}
$$

$$
r_B = R.
$$

$$
\begin{aligned}
z &= S2\,.\,y \\
&= ABy.
\end{aligned}
$$

The corresponding circuit implemented with NAND gates and TFFs is shown in Figure (e).

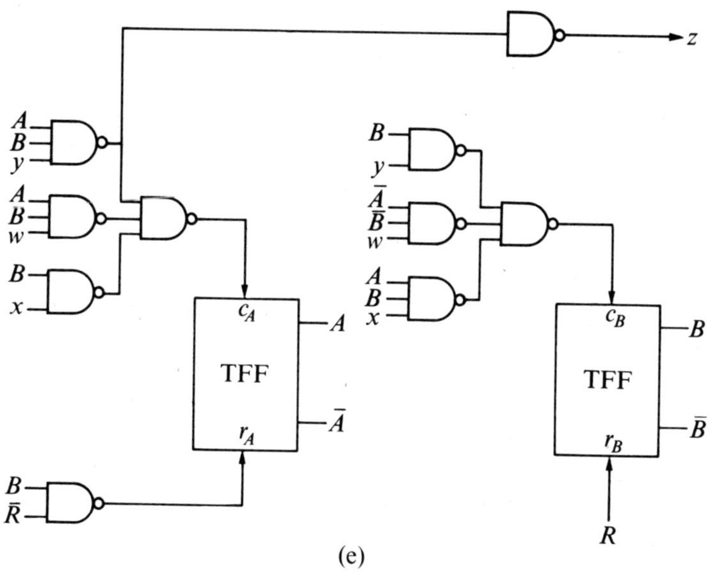

(e)

PROBLEM 2: *An Electronic Padlock*

Design a logic circuit that unlocks a door when three specified keys on a key-board are activated in sequence. If the wrong key is pressed at any time, the buzzer is to turn on. Activating the keys in the correct sequence when the buzzer is on is to turn off the buzzer and unlock the door; this allows the circuit to accommodate genuine mistakes.

SOLUTION:

Clearly there exist many variations of electronic padlocks, depending on the level of security desired and the circuit complexity that is acceptable. The circuit we shall design is very simple to construct and allows the user to change the combination at any time, either manually or electronically from a central station, with no reference to the supplier.

Step 1 *External (I/O) characteristics*

To make our solution general, we shall denote three keys that are to be activated in sequence by variables *w*, *x*, and *y*, as shown in Figure (a) - the block diagram of our solution. Signal *z* is generated when any other key on the keyboard is pressed. Signal *d*, when equal to 1, unlocks the door. Note that the door in our case must be opened while the third key in our sequence is being pressed. Signal *D* is generated when the door is open.

Step 2 *Internal characteristics*

A suitable internal state diagram is shown in Figure (b). Its operation is self-explanatory.

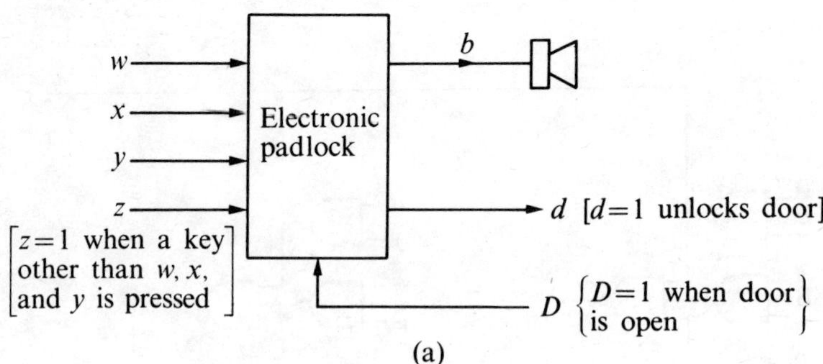

(a)

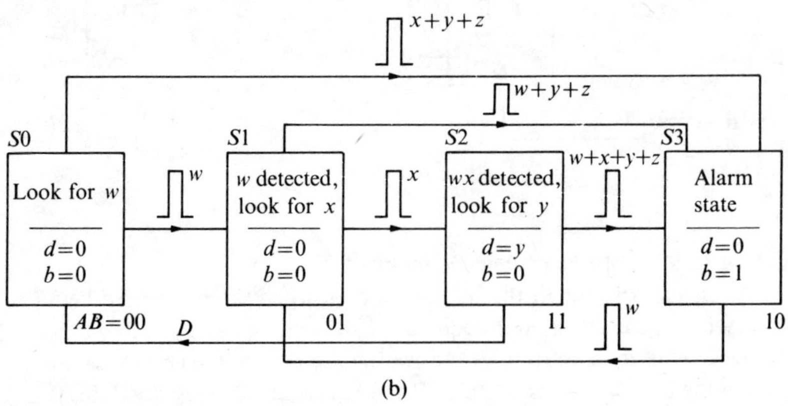

(b)

Step 3 *State reduction*

In this step we translate our internal state diagram into a state table and we attempt to merge rows in accordance with the rules stated in Section 10 of Chapter 1. Our state table is shown in Figure (c). Clearly no merging of rows is possible in this case.

	w	x	y	z
S0	S1 $d,b=0,0$	S3 0,0	S3 0,0	S3 0,0
S1	S3 0,0	S2 0,0	S3 0,0	S3 0,0
S2	S3 0,0	S3 0,0	(S2) $d,b=y,0$	S3 0,0
S3	S1 0,1	(S3) 0,1	(S3) 0,1	(S3) 0,1

Note that $D=1$ unconditionally resets the circuit

(c)

Step 4 *Circuit implementation*

Suitable codes for our four states are shown in Figure (b). By direct reference to this Figure, we obtain

$$
\begin{aligned}
c_A &= S0\,.\,(x+y+z) + S1\,.\,(w+x+y+z) + S3\,.\,w \\
&= \overline{A}\overline{B}(x+y+z) + \overline{A}B(w+x+y+z) + A\overline{B}w \\
&= \overline{A}(x+y+z) + \overline{A}Bw + A\overline{B}w \\
&= \overline{A}(x+y+z+Bw) + A\overline{B}w
\end{aligned}
$$

$$
\begin{aligned}
r_A &= S2\,.\,D + (\overline{S2}\,.\,D) \\
&= D.
\end{aligned}
$$

$$
\begin{aligned}
c_B &= S0\,.\,w + S1\,.\,(w+y+z) + S2\,.\,(w+x+z) + S3\,.\,w \\
&= \overline{A}\overline{B}w + \overline{A}B(w+y+z) + AB(w+x+z) + A\overline{B}w \\
&= w(\overline{A}\overline{B} + \overline{A}B + AB + A\overline{B}) + ABx + \overline{A}By + (\overline{A}B + AB) \\
&= w + ABx + \overline{A}By + Bz
\end{aligned}
$$

$$
\begin{aligned}
r_B &= S2\,.\,D + (\overline{S2}\,.\,D) \\
&= D.
\end{aligned}
$$

$$
\begin{aligned}
d &= S2\,.\,y \\
&= ABy.
\end{aligned}
$$

$$
\begin{aligned}
b &= S3 \\
&= A\overline{B}.
\end{aligned}
$$

The equivalent circuit implemented with TFFs and NAND gates is shown in Figure (d).

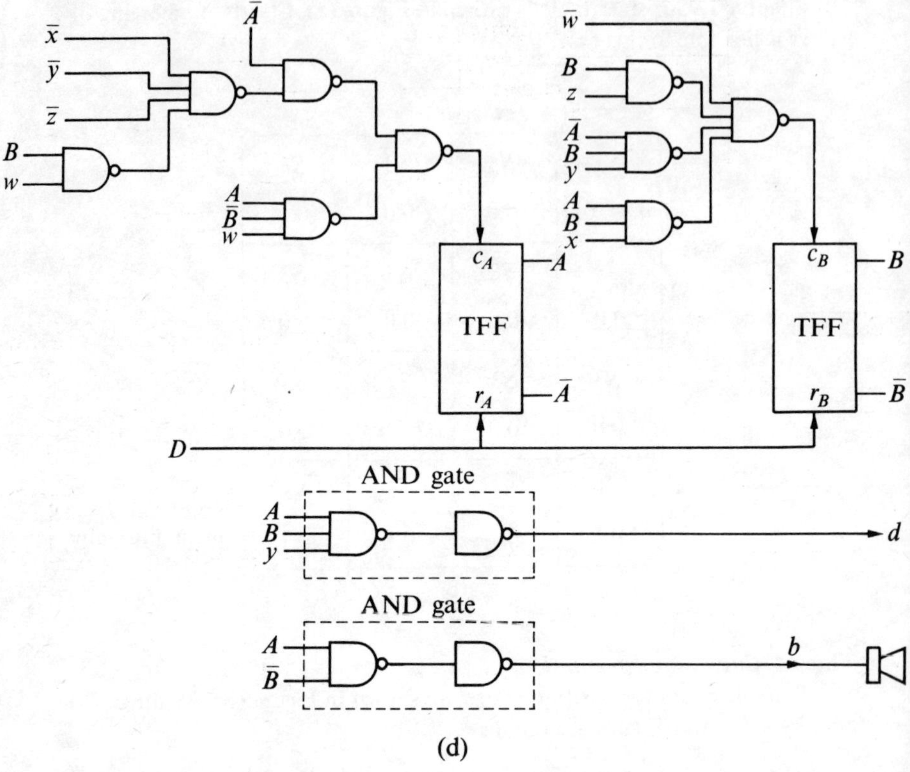

(d)

PROBLEM 3: *A Motor Control*

Design a control circuit that allows a motor to start by activating four push-buttons, w, x, y, and z, in sequence. Should the 'wrong' button be pressed, the motor control circuit is to be automatically disabled and a flag signal, f, is to be generated to indicate to a central station incorrect activation of the switches.

The control circuit is to reset by signal r, generated from the central station.

The motor starts by applying a pulse on its terminal m – see Figure (a). Ignore at this stage the presence of the AND gate and of signal D.

SOLUTION

Step 1 *External (I/O) characteristics*

The block diagram of our solution is shown in Figure (a). Activation of the 'wrong' push-button will set a disable flip-flop D. By ANDing the motor pulse m' with $\bar{D}$, we ensure that no pulse can be generated on

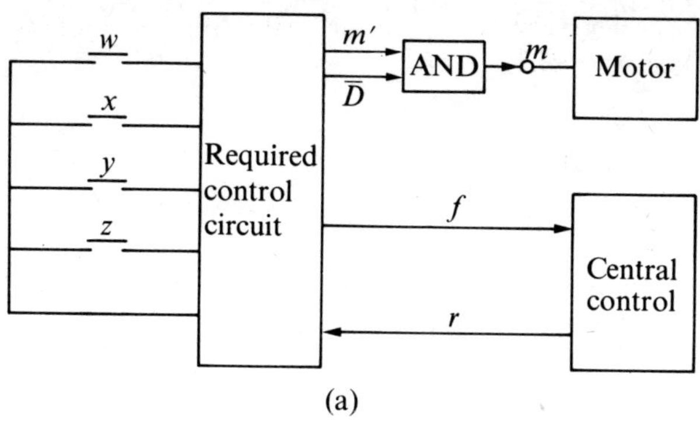

(a)

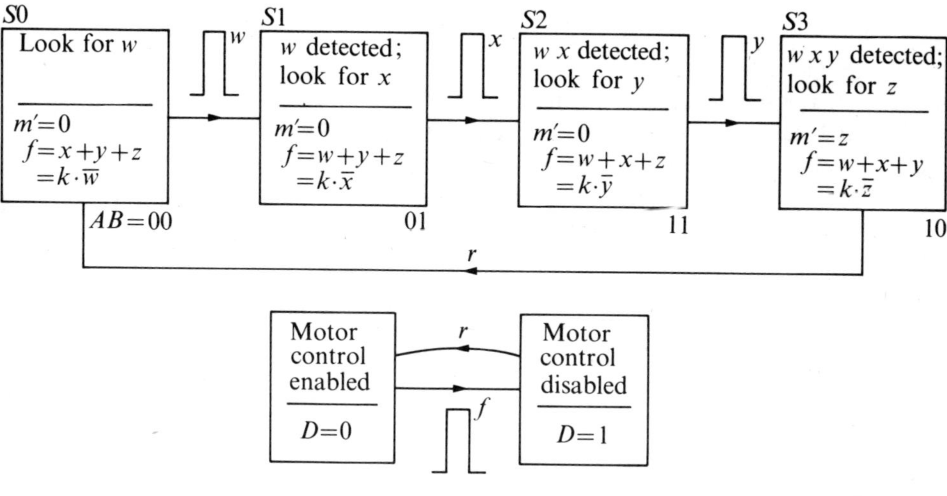

(b)

terminal m while signal D is present. We shall reset the disable flip-flop with reset signal r, which as we already mentioned is generated from the central control station.

Step 2 *Internal characteristics*

A suitable internal state diagram for our solution is shown in Figure (b). Signal k is the OR function of push-button signals w, x, y, and z; that is

$$k = w + x + y + z.$$

The fault signal generated in each state is

$$\begin{aligned} f &= x + y + z \\ &= \overline{w}.(w + x + y + z) \\ &= \overline{w}.k \qquad \textit{in state S0}, \end{aligned}$$

$$
\begin{aligned}
f &= w + y + z \\
&= \bar{x}.(w + x + y + z) \\
&= \bar{x}.k \qquad \textit{in state S1},
\end{aligned}
$$

$$
\begin{aligned}
f &= w + x + z \\
&= \bar{y}.(y + w + x + z) \\
&= \bar{y}.k \qquad \textit{in state S2}, \text{ and}
\end{aligned}
$$

$$
\begin{aligned}
f &= w + x + y \\
&= \bar{z}.(w + x + y + z) \\
&= k \qquad \textit{in state S3.}
\end{aligned}
$$

Therefore,

$$f = S0.\bar{w}.k + S1.\bar{x}.k + S2.\bar{y}.k + S3.\bar{z}.k \;\ldots \qquad (4.1)$$

Step 3 *State reduction*

The state table of our solution, derived directly from the state diagram in Figure (b), is shown in Figure (c). No merging of rows is possible according to the rules given in Chapter 1 (Section 10).

	w	x	y	z
$S0$	$S1$	($S0$) $f=1$	($S0$) $f=1$	($S0$) $f=1$
$S1$	($S1$) $f=1$	$S2$	($S1$) $f=1$	($S1$) $f=1$
$S2$	($S2$) $f=1$	($S2$) $f=1$	$S3$	($S2$) $f=1$
$S3$	($S3$) $f=1$	($S3$) $f=1$	($S3$) $f=1$	($S3$) $m'=1$

Zero outputs not shown

(c)

Step 4 *Circuit implementation*

To avoid race-hazards (unwanted signal spikes) on the flag line f, we use a race-free code for our four states in Figure (b). Substituting the state variables in equation 4.1 above, we obtain

$$
\begin{aligned}
f &= S0.\bar{w}.k + S1.\bar{x}.k + S2.\bar{y}.k + S3.\bar{z}.k \\
&= \bar{A}\bar{B}\bar{w}k + \bar{A}B\bar{x}k + AB\bar{y}k + A\bar{B}\bar{z}k.
\end{aligned}
$$

Signal k is generated by ORing the four push-button signals w, x, y, and z, as shown in Figure (d). The most straightforward method of generating signal f is to use a multiplexor (MUX) in a manner shown in Figure (d).

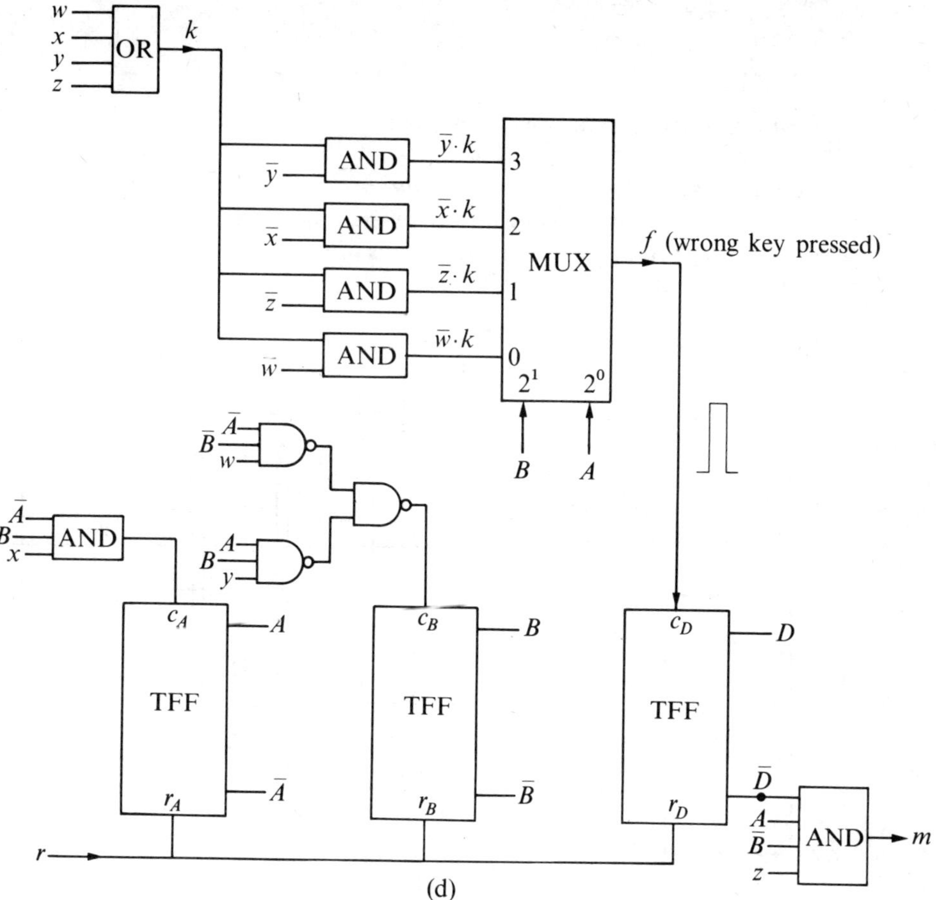

(d)

By direct reference to our state diagram in Figure (b), we obtain

$$\begin{aligned} m' &= S3\,.\,z \\ &= A\,.\,\bar{B}\,.\,z. \end{aligned}$$

Therefore,

$$\begin{aligned} m &= m'.\bar{D} \text{ (see Figure (a))} \\ &= A\,.\,\bar{B}\,.\,z\,.\,\bar{D}. \end{aligned}$$

Finally, our flip-flop equations, derived also by reference to Figure (b), are

$$\begin{aligned} c_A &= S1\,.\,x \\ &= \bar{A}Bx, \end{aligned}$$

$$r_A = r$$

$$\begin{aligned} c_B &= S0\,.\,w + S2\,.\,y \\ &= \bar{A}\bar{B}w + ABy, \end{aligned}$$

$r_B = r,$
$c_D = f,$ and
$r_D = r.$

Their circuit implementation is shown in Figure (d).

PROBLEM 4: *Up/down control of counters*

Given signals X and Y in Figure (a), generate signals R and c. Pulses X and Y are non-overlapping. For applications of this circuit see up/down control of counters on page 00.

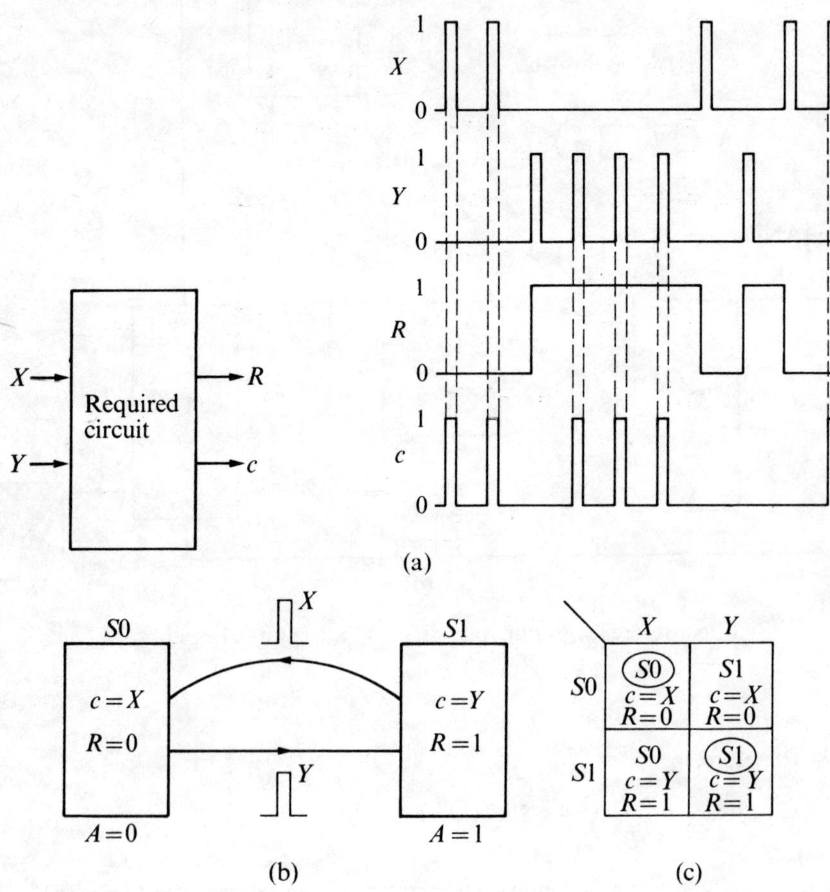

(a)

(b)

	X	Y
S0	(S0) c=X R=0	S1 c=X R=0
S1	S0 c=Y R=1	(S1) c=Y R=1

(c)

SOLUTION:

Step 1 *External (I/O) characteristics*

As specified in Figure (a).

Step 2 *Internal characteristics*

A suitable internal state diagram is shown in Figure (b).

Step 3 *State reduction*

The state table of our solution is shown in Figure (c). It is derived directly from the state diagram shown in Figure (b). According to the rules stated in Section 10 of Chapter 1, its rows cannot be merged.

Step 4 *Circuit implementation*

We use variable A to code the two states in Figure (b).

By direct reference to this diagram, we obtain

$$C_A = S0\,.\,Y + S1\,.\,X$$
$$= \bar{A}Y + AX,$$

$$R = S1$$
$$= A,$$

$$c = S0\,.\,X + S1\,.\,Y$$
$$= \bar{A}X + AY.$$

Their multiplexor implementation is shown in Figure (d).

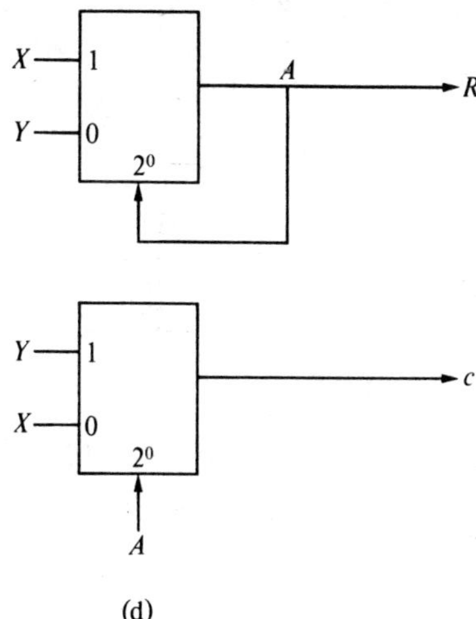

(d)

5 *Counters*

The functional characteristics, properties and design of the most commonly used counters are discussed in this chapter.

5.1 INTRODUCTION

Counters are cyclic circuits* whose output in a specified code gives the number of changes of the input signal or the number of the input pulses received since the circuit was in its initial state. Counters are being used extensively in industrial plants for such functions as controlling the position of a machine tool or for packing a specified number of items in a box. They are also widely used in laboratory environments for such functions as counting frequency, recording time, speed and acceleration.

5.2 CODES

The most commonly used codes in electronic counters are:

1. True binary (1-2-4-8) codes,
2. Gray codes,
3. B-C-D codes, and
4. Johnson codes.

The true binary code, often referred to simply as the 'binary code', is the most straightforward code because each digit is represented in a conventional binary system. Gray codes are codes in which adjacent numbers differ in one bit only. This eliminates races which arise when two or more bits attempt to change simultaneously. The race-free diagram on page 9, can be used to derive Gray codes. Examples of Gray codes are:

000	000	000	000
100	010	100	001
110	110	101	101
010	100	111	111
011	101	110	011
111	111	010	010
101	011	011	110
001	001	001	100

*** These are sequential circuits that return to their initial state after a specified number of changes in the input state.**

In the b-c-d (binary-coded-decimal) codes, each of the ten decimal digits, 0 to 9, is represented by a binary code, usually the 1-2-4-8 code. For example the b-c-d representation of 456 is 0010 1010 0110. B-c-d codes provide a useful link between the counting systems used by the machines and that used by humans.

The *Johnson codes* for two, three, four and five bits are listed below. Counters using this code are called Johnson counters or twisted-ring counters.

AB	*ABC*	*ABCD*	*ABCDE*
00	000	0000	00000
10	100	1000	10000
11	110	1100	11000
01	111	1110	11100
	011	1111	11110
	001	0111	11111
		0011	01111
		0001	00111
			00011
			00001

Codes can be made *error-correcting* by the addition of extra bits, whose function is to 'point' to the bit position of a corrupted digit. This allows the error to be corrected automatically. The most important codes of this kind are the *Hamming codes*, an example of which is given below.

X	p_1	p_2	1	p_4	2	4	8
0	0	0	0	0	0	0	0
1	1	1	1	0	0	0	0
2	1	0	0	1	1	0	0
3	0	1	1	1	1	0	0
4	0	1	0	1	0	1	0
5	1	0	1	1	0	1	0
6	1	1	0	0	1	1	0
7	0	0	1	0	1	1	0
8	1	1	0	1	0	0	1
9	0	0	1	1	0	0	1

Here we have a weighted code of four bits augmented by three parity bits p_1, p_2, and p_4, which are chosen to give even parity with the bits weighted '1, 2, 8', '1, 4, 8', and '2, 4, 8', respectively.

As an illustration, suppose it is necessary to check and correct the received character 1100000. A parity check between p_1 and bits 1, 2 and 8, viz. '1000', reveals an error. The bit position of the error is indicated by the values of $p_1p_2p_4$ - in our case $110 \equiv 3$. That is, the correct character is 1110000.

Binary codes are classified as *weighted* or *non-weighted.* In weighted codes a value or 'weight' is given to each digit according to its position in the code. For example the true binary code (1-2-4-8) is a weighted code because a 1 in the first position has a weight of 1, whereas a 1 in the third position has a weight of 4. Clearly the Gray and Johnson codes are non-weighted codes.

5.3 THE DESIGN STEPS

The design of pulse counters consist of

(i) drawing a state diagram,

(ii) coding the states according to the selected code, and

(iii) deriving the flip-flop equations.

The implementation of the design steps is demonstrated in the following sections.

We shall use variable X for pulses to be counted up and variable Y for pulses to be counted down, unless otherwise specified.

In practical systems, counters are usually used to synchronize the operation of other circuits. Therefore if a non-maximum length counter assumes an *unused state*, this is a clear indication that it has got out of step with the rest of the system. The corrective action in such a case must obviously be taken with reference to the actual system. In the absence of a specific system, our corrective action will consist of suppressing the input pulses and tripping an alarm. If we use variable F to denote collectively the unused states, the block diagram of a suitable arrangement is shown in Figure 4.1. Since we suppress the input pulses when an unused state is assumed, we can use their codes as optional products to reduce the J and K flip-flops equations.

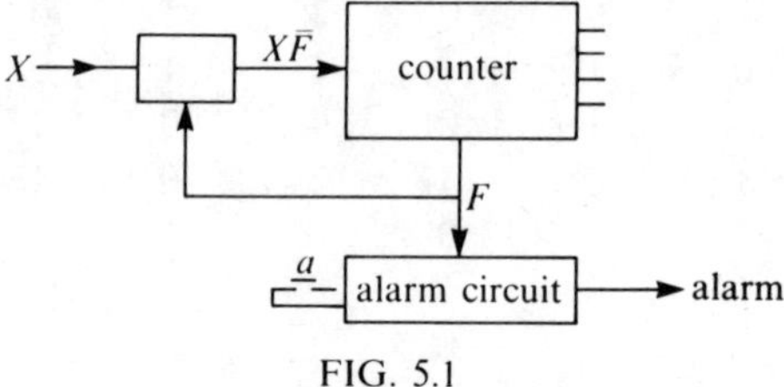

FIG. 5.1

5.4 SYNCHRONOUS 'UP' BINARY COUNTERS (MAXIMUM LENGTH)

For the sake of consistency we shall assign variable A to the 2^0 bit, B to the 2^1 bit, C to the 2^2 bit and so on. In deriving the general form of binary counters, we shall make use of the fact that the addition of higher order counting stages does not affect the lower order counting stages. This, of course, is also the case in conventional decimal counters, – for example the 'units' and 'tens' of a car milometer change at the end of every one and ten miles travelled, irrespective of the size of the milometer.

We shall next use the three design steps, mentioned in the previous section, to derive the *JK* flip-flop equations of binary counters.

Scale-2 'Up' Counter

State diagram and codes - see Figure 5.2(a).

Flip-flop equations:

$$S_A = S0 = \bar{A} \qquad \text{Therefore, } J_A = 1$$
$$R_A = S1 = A \qquad \text{Therefore, } K_A = 1.$$

The corresponding circuit is shown in Figure 5.2(b).

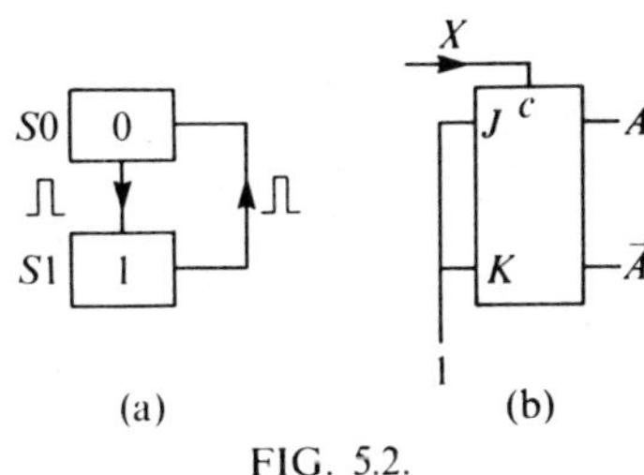

FIG. 5.2.

Scale-4 'Up' Counter

$J_A = K_A = 1$, as for scale-2 counter. State diagram and codes - see Figure 5.3(a).

Flip-flop equations:

$$S_B = S1 + (S2) = A\bar{B} \qquad \text{Therefore, } J_B = A$$
$$R_B = S3 + (S0) = AB \qquad \text{Therefore, } K_B = A.$$

The corresponding circuit is shown in Figure 5.3(b).

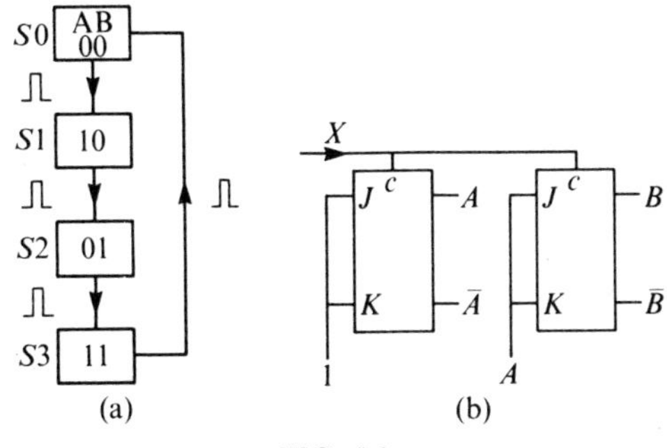

FIG. 5.3.

Scale-8 'Up' Counter

$J_A = K_A = 1$ and $J_B = K_B = A$, as for scale-4 counter. State diagram and codes - see Figure 5.4(a).

Flip-flop equations:

$$S_C = S3 + (S4) + (S5) + (S6) = AB\overline{C} \qquad \text{Therefore, } J_C = AB$$
$$R_C = S7 + (S0) + (S0) + (S1) = ABC \qquad \text{Therefore, } K_C = AB.$$

The corresponding circuit is shown in Figure 5.4(b).

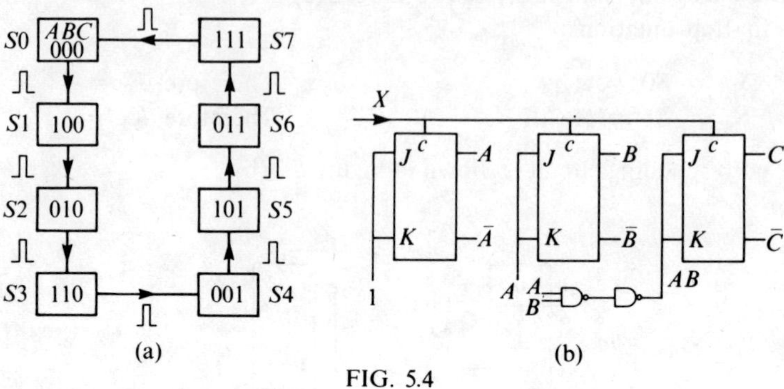

FIG. 5.4

Scale-2^n 'Up' Counter

By observation, the flip-flop equations are:

$$J_A = K_A = 1$$
$$J_B = K_B = A$$
$$J_C = K_C = AB = B\,J_B$$
$$J_D = K_D = ABC = C\,J_C$$

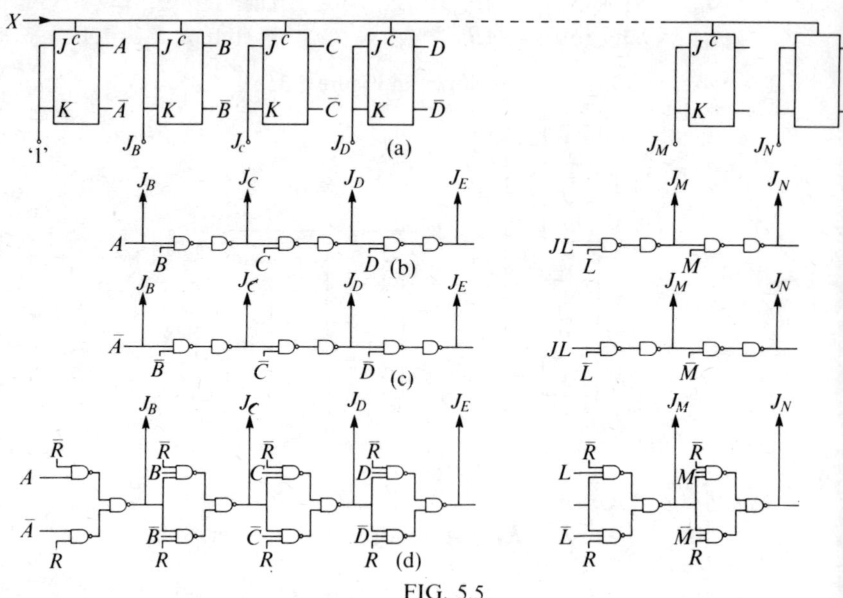

FIG. 5.5.

$$
\begin{aligned}
J_E &= K_E = ABCD = D\,J_D \\
J_M &= K_M = ABC\ldots K_L = L\,J_L \\
J_N &= K_N = ABC\ldots L_M = M\,J_M
\end{aligned}
$$

The circuit implementation is shown in Figure 5.5(a) and (b). (Large input gates must be used to implement directly the functions in the third column, if speed is essential.)

5.5 SYNCHRONOUS ‘DOWN’ BINARY COUNTERS (MAXIMUM LENGTH)

A ‘down’ counter is designed by referring to the state diagram of the corresponding ‘up’ counter but moving in the opposite direction to the arrows.

Scale-2 ‘Down’ Counter

State diagram and codes – see Figure 5.2(a).

Flip-flop equations:

$S_A = S0 = \overline{A}$ Thereforc, $J_A = 1$

$R_A = S1 = A$ Therefore, $K_A = 1$.

Scale-4 ‘Down’ Counter

State diagram and codes – see Figure 5.3(a).

Flip-flop equations:

$J_A = K_A = 1$, as for scale-2 ‘down’ counter.

$S_B = S0 + (S3) = \overline{A}\overline{B}$ Therefore, $J_B = \overline{A}$

$R_B = S2 + (S1) = \overline{A}B$ Therefore, $K_B = \overline{A}$.

Scale-8 ‘Down’ Counter

State diagram and codes – see Figure 5.4(a).

Flip-flop equations:

$J_A = K_A = 1$ and $J_B = K_B = \overline{A}$, as for scale-4 ‘down’ counter.

$S_C = S0 = (S4) = (S5) = (S6) = \overline{A}\overline{B}\overline{C}$ Therefore, $J_C = \overline{A}\overline{B}$

$R_C = S4 = (S1) = (S2) = (S3) = \overline{A}\overline{B}C$ Therefore, $K_C = \overline{A}\overline{B}$.

Scale-2^n ‘Down’ Counter

From the expressions derived so far, it is clear that for ‘down’ counters the flip-flop signals are the same as those for ‘up’ counters, but in their inverted form. Therefore,

$$
\begin{aligned}
J_A &= K_A = 1 \\
J_B &= K_B = \overline{A} \\
J_C &= K_C = AB = \overline{B}J_B \\
J_D &= K_D = \overline{A}\overline{B}\overline{C} = \overline{C}J_C
\end{aligned}
$$

$$J_E = K_E = \overline{A}\overline{B}\overline{C}\overline{D} = \overline{D}J_D$$

.

.

.

$$J_M = K_M = \overline{A}\overline{B}\overline{C}\ldots\overline{K}\overline{L} = \overline{L}J_L$$
$$J_N = K_N = \overline{A}\overline{B}\overline{C}\ldots\overline{K}\overline{L}\overline{M} = \overline{M}J_M.$$

The corresponding circuit is shown in Figures 5.4(a) and (c).

Note that in the case of binary counters it is possible to use a scale-up counter to count down by monitoring the inverted flip-flop signals, as shown below. Clearly, this method cannot be used for up/down (reversible) counters.

A	B	C	Decimal	$\overline{A}$	$\overline{B}$	$\overline{C}$	Decimal
0	0	0	0	1	1	1	7
1	0	0	1	0	1	1	6
0	1	0	2	1	0	1	5
1	1	0	3	0	0	1	4
0	0	1	4	1	1	0	3
1	0	1	5	0	1	0	2
0	1	1	6	1	0	0	1
1	1	1	7	0	0	0	0

5.6 SYNCHRONOUS 'UP' GRAY COUNTERS (MAXIMUM LENGTH)

Gray counters, as explained earlier, are counters in which the codes of adjacent numbers differ in one bit only.

The reader's attention is drawn to the following two facts relating to the implementation of Gray counters specifically and to Gray-coded cyclic circuits generally.

1. The unreduced J and K values of the flip-flops in one direction are the same as the K and J values of the flip-flops in the reverse direction, i.e. to reverse the circuit direction we need only interchange the J and K inputs of each flip-flop.
2. Optional products defined by unused states can be used to reduce the J and K values with no restrictions. However, this is not the case for S and R expressions.

Scale-2 Gray 'Up' Counter

Circuit diagram and codes – see Figure 5.2(a).

Flip-flop equations:

$$S_A = S0 = \overline{A} \qquad \text{Therefore, } J_A = 1$$
$$R_A = S1 = A \qquad \text{Therefore, } K_A = 1.$$

The corresponding circuit is shown in Figure 5.2(b).

Scale-4 Gray 'Up' Counter

State diagrams and codes – see Figure 5.6(a).

Flip-flop equations:

$$S_A = S0 = \overline{B} \qquad \text{Therefore, } J_A = \overline{B}$$
$$R_A = S2 = B \qquad \text{Therefore, } K_A = B$$
$$S_B = S1 = A \qquad \text{Therefore, } J_B = A$$
$$R_B = S3 = \overline{A} \qquad \text{Therefore, } K_B = \overline{A}.$$

The corresponding circuit is shown in Figure 5.6(b).

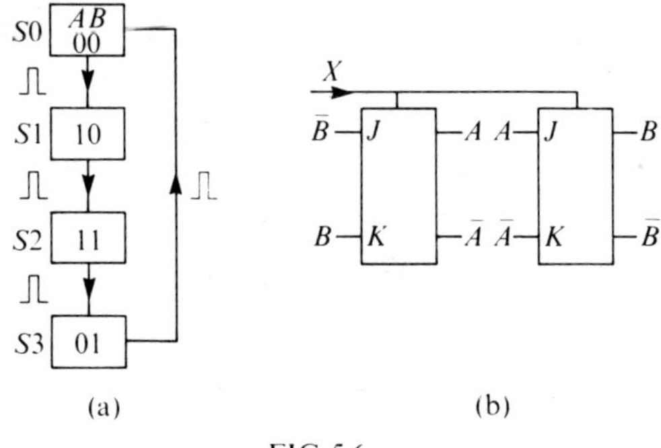

FIG.5.6.

Scale-8 Gray 'Up' Counter

State diagram and codes – see Figure 5.7(a).

Flip-flop equations:

$$S_A = S0 + S4 = \overline{A}\overline{B}\overline{C} + \overline{A}BC \qquad \text{Therefore, } J_A = BC + \overline{B}\overline{C}$$
$$R_A = S2 + S6 = AB\overline{C} + A\overline{B}C \qquad \text{Therefore, } K_A = B\overline{C} + \overline{B}C = \overline{J}_A$$

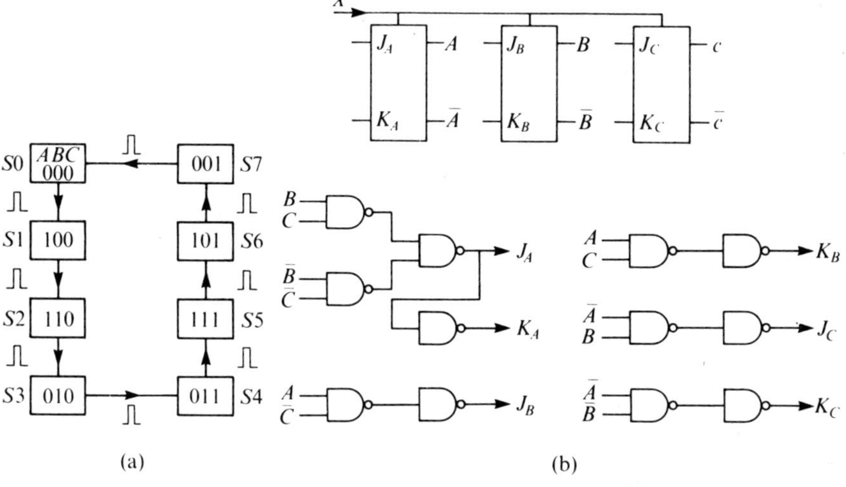

FIG.5.7.

$$S_B = S1 = A\bar{B}\bar{C} \qquad \text{Therefore, } J_B = A\bar{C}$$
$$R_B = S5 = ABC \qquad \text{Therefore, } K_B = AC$$
$$S_C = S3 = \bar{A}B\bar{C} \qquad \text{Therefore, } J_B = \bar{A}B$$
$$R_C = S7 = \bar{A}\bar{B}C \qquad \text{Therefore, } K_C = \bar{A}\bar{B}.$$

The corresponding circuit is shown in Figure 5.7(b).

Scale-16 Gray 'Up' Counter

State diagram and codes - see Figure 5.8(a).

Flip-flop equations:

$$S_A = S0 + S4 + S8 + S12 = \bar{A}\bar{B}\bar{C}\bar{D} + \bar{A}BC\bar{D} + \bar{A}\bar{B}CD + \bar{A}B\bar{C}D$$
$$\text{Therefore, } J_A = BC\bar{D} + \bar{B}\bar{C}\bar{D} + \bar{B}CD + B\bar{C}D$$
$$R_A = S2 + S6 + S10 + S14 = AB\bar{C}\bar{D} + A\bar{B}C\bar{D} + ABCD + A\bar{B}\bar{C}D$$
$$\text{Therefore, } K_A = B\bar{C}\bar{D} + \bar{B}C\bar{D} + BCD + \bar{B}\bar{C}D = \bar{J}_A$$
$$S_B = S1 + S9 = A\bar{B}\bar{C}\bar{D} + A\bar{B}CD$$
$$\text{Therefore, } J_B = A\bar{C}\bar{D} + ACD$$
$$R_B = S5 + S13 = ABC\bar{D} + AB\bar{C}D$$
$$\text{Therefore, } K_B = AC\bar{D} + A\bar{C}D$$
$$S_C = S3 = \bar{A}BC\bar{D}$$
$$\text{Therefore, } J_C = \bar{A}B\bar{D}$$
$$R_C = S11 = \bar{A}BCD$$
$$\text{Therefore, } K_C = \bar{A}BC$$
$$S_D = S7 = \bar{A}\bar{B}CD$$
$$\text{Therefore, } J_D = \bar{A}\bar{B}C$$
$$R_D = S15 = \bar{A}\bar{B}\bar{C}D$$
$$\text{Therefore, } K_D = \bar{A}\bar{B}\bar{C}.$$

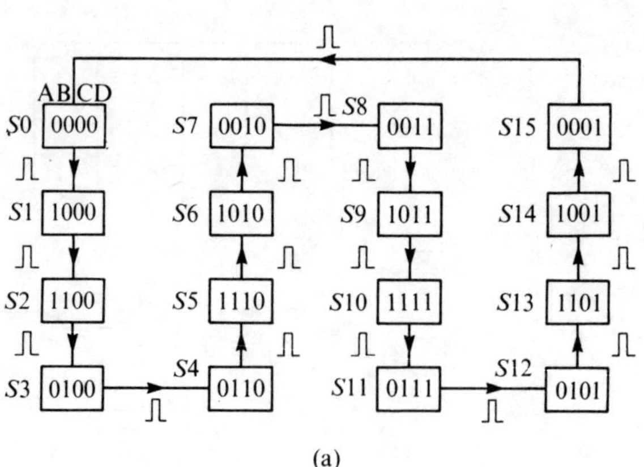

(a)

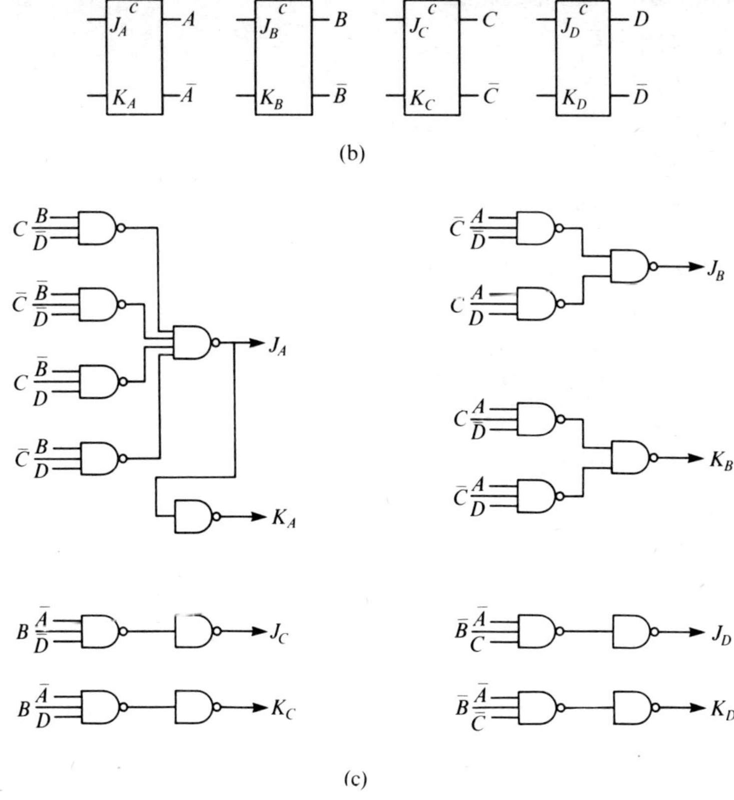

FIG. 5.8

5.7 SYNCHRONOUS 'DOWN' GRAY COUNTERS (MAXIMUM LENGTH)

Interchange the J and K values for each flip-flop in the corresponding 'up' Gray counter.

Scale-2 Gray 'Down' Counter

$$J_A = 1$$
$$K_A = 1.$$

Scale-4 Gray 'Down' Counter

$$J_A = B$$
$$K_A = \bar{B}$$
$$J_B = \bar{A}$$
$$K_B = A.$$

Scale-8 Gray 'Down' Counter

$$\begin{aligned}
J_A &= \bar{K}_A \\
K_A &= BC + \bar{B}\bar{C} \\
J_B &= AC \\
K_B &= A\bar{C} \\
J_C &= \bar{A}\bar{B} \\
K_C &= \bar{A}B.
\end{aligned}$$

Scale-16 Gray 'Down' Counter

$$\begin{aligned}
J_A &= \bar{K}_A \\
K_A &= BC\bar{D} + \bar{B}\bar{C}\bar{D} + \bar{B}CD + B\bar{C}D \\
J_B &= AC\bar{D} + A\bar{C}D \\
K_B &= A\bar{C}\bar{D} + ACD \\
J_C &= \bar{A}BD \\
K_C &= \bar{A}B\bar{D} \\
J_D &= \bar{A}\bar{B}\bar{C} \\
K_D &= \bar{A}\bar{B}\bar{C}.
\end{aligned}$$

5.8 UP/DOWN CONTROL

Physically up/down counters are counters in which the pulse count is stepped up or stepped down by each input pulse according to whether the value of an external control signal B is 0 or 1. Now, in practice the pulses that are to step the counter up or down appear on two separate lines X and Y, as shown in Figure 5.9. It is therefore necessary for the designer to generate

(i) the clock pulses that will drive the counter flip-flops and
(ii) the up/down control signal, B. We shall assume that step-up and step-down pulses in practice do not appear simultaneously.

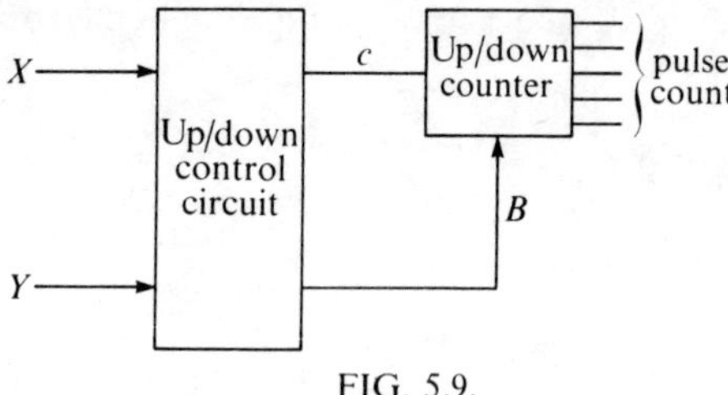

FIG. 5.9.

In up/down counters, as in any multi-mode circuit, the control signal must not be allowed to change during the presence of input data. Since in our case the control signal, of necessity, must be generated from input data, we can avoid this race condition by using the first pulse in each pulse train to change the value of B but not to generate a clock pulse, as shown in Figure 5.10. Since each time we change the value of B an input pulse is not counted, this method results in a maximum count error of 1 for an odd number of changes in B and no error for an even number of changes in B.

The reader's attention is drawn to the fact that this up/down control circuit can be used for all types of counters.

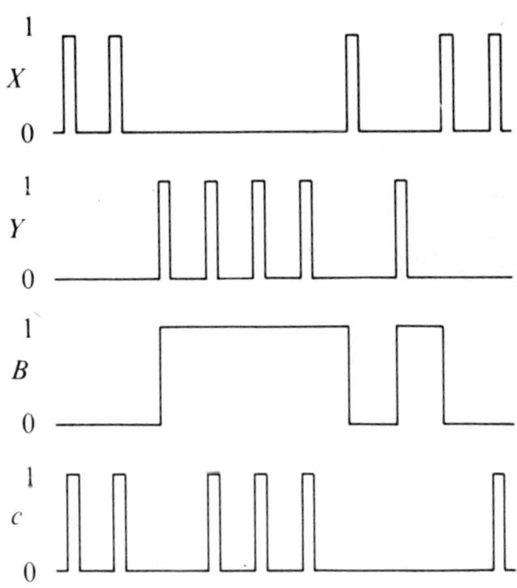

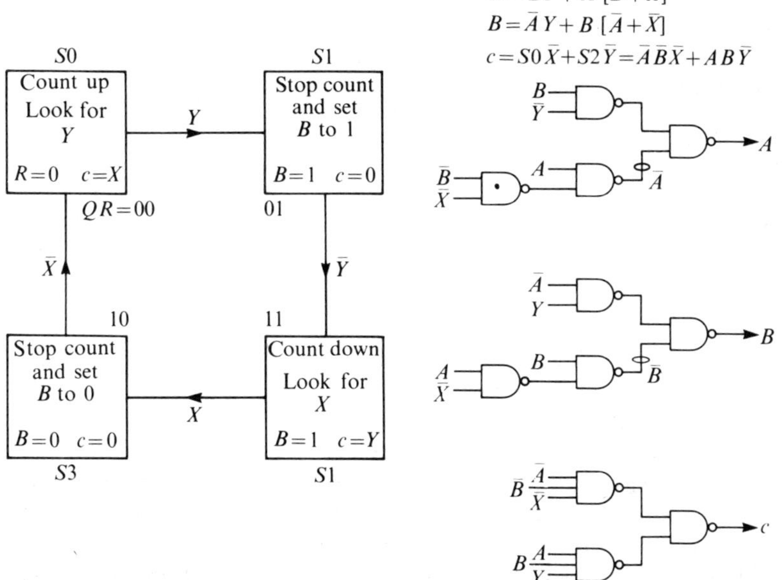

FIG. 5.10.

5.9 SYNCHRONOUS 'UP/DOWN' BINARY COUNTERS

Combining the flip-flop equations for 'up' counts when $R = 0$ and for 'down' counts when $R = 1$ in Table 5.1, we obtain:

$$\begin{aligned}
J_A &= K_A = 1\\
J_B &= K_B = A\bar{B} + \bar{A}R\\
J_C &= K_C = J_B\,(B\bar{R} + \bar{B}R)\\
J_D &= K_D = J_C\,(C\bar{R} + \bar{C}R)\\
&\;\;\vdots\\
J_M &= K_M = J_L\,(L\bar{R} + \bar{L}R)\\
J_N &= K_N = J_M(M\bar{R} + \bar{M}R).
\end{aligned}$$

The corresponding circuit implementation is shown in Figures 5.5(a) and (d).

5.10 SYNCHRONOUS 'UP/DOWN' GRAY COUNTERS

If we use variables J' and K' to denote the flip-flop inputs in the up/down mode, we obtain the following equations:

$$\begin{aligned}
J_A' &= J_A\,\bar{R} + K_A R\\
K_A' &= K_A\,\bar{R} + J_A R\\
J_B' &= J_B\,\bar{R} + K_B R\\
K_B' &= K_B\,\bar{R} + J_B R\\
J_C' &= J_C\,\bar{R} + K_C R\\
K_C' &= K_C\,\bar{R} + J_C R \quad \text{and so on.}
\end{aligned}$$

The flip-flop equations for the 'up' and 'down' binary counters are tabulated for convenience in Table 5.1.

5.11 ASYNCHRONOUS (RIPPLE–THROUGH) BINARY COUNTERS*

This is a popular counter configuration particularly when speed is not a critical factor in its operation. For counts of powers of 2 (2, 4, 8, 16, 32 . . .) the basic arrangement derived empircally consists of TFFs (T flip-flops) connected in cascade, as shown in Figure 5.11(a). As can be seen from the diagram the output of each flip-flop provides the clock signal of the next flip-flop; the input signal is used as the clock of the first flip-flop. We shall now describe a formal design procedure for this type of counter arrangement.

* From the switching point of view the relative response times of the flip-flops is known and precautionary action can be taken.

	SYNCHRONOUS 1-2-4-8 BINARY COUNTERS				SYNCHRONOUS GRAY COUNTERS									
	2^n 'up'	2^n 'down'	decade 'up'	decade 'down'	scale 2 'up'	scale 4 'up'	scale 8 'up'	decade 'up'	scale 16 'up'	scale 2 'down'	scale 4 'down'	scale 8 'down'	decade 'down'	scale 16 'down'
J_A	1	1	1	1	1	$\bar{B}$	$BC + \bar{B}\bar{C}$	$BC + \bar{B}\bar{C}\bar{D}$	$BC\bar{D} + \bar{B}\bar{C}\bar{D} + \bar{B}CD$ $B\bar{C}D$	1	B	$\bar{J}_A$	$B\bar{C} + \bar{B}C\bar{D}$	$\bar{J}_B$
K_A	1	1	1	1	1	B	$\bar{J}_A$	$B\bar{C} + \bar{B}\bar{C}\bar{D}$	$\bar{J}_A$	1	$\bar{B}$	$BC + \bar{B}\bar{C}$	$BC\bar{D} + \bar{B}\bar{C}\bar{D}$	$BC\bar{D} + \bar{B}\bar{C}\bar{D} + \bar{B}CD + B\bar{C}D +$
J_B	A	$\bar{A}$	$A\bar{D}$	$\bar{A}C + \bar{A}D$		A	$A\bar{C}$	$A\bar{C}$	$A\bar{C}\bar{D} + ACD$		$\bar{A}$	AC	AC	$AC\bar{D} + A\bar{C}D$
K_B	A	$\bar{A}$	$\bar{A}$	$\bar{A}$		$\bar{A}$	AC	AC	$AC\bar{D} + A\bar{C}D$		A	$A\bar{C}$	$A\bar{C}$	$A\bar{C}\bar{D} + ACD$
J_C	AB	$\bar{A}\bar{B}$	$\bar{A}\bar{B}$	$\bar{A}D$			$\bar{A}B$	$\bar{A}B$	$\bar{A}B\bar{D}$			$\bar{A}\bar{B}$	D	$\bar{A}BD$
K_C	AB	$\bar{A}\bar{B}$	$\bar{A}\bar{B}$	$\bar{A}\bar{B}$			$\bar{A}\bar{B}$	D	$\bar{A}BD$			$\bar{A}B$	$\bar{A}B$	$\bar{A}B\bar{D}$
J_D	ABC	$\bar{A}\bar{B}\bar{C}$	$\bar{A}\bar{B}\bar{C}$	$\bar{A}\bar{B}\bar{C}$				$\bar{A}\bar{B}C$	$\bar{A}B\bar{C}$				$\bar{A}\bar{B}\bar{C}$	$\bar{A}\bar{B}\bar{C}$
K_D	ABC	$\bar{A}\bar{B}\bar{C}$	AD	$\bar{A}\bar{B}\bar{C}$				$\bar{A}\bar{B}\bar{C}$	$\bar{A}\bar{B}\bar{C}$				$\bar{A}\bar{B}C$	$\bar{A}\bar{B}C$

TABLE 5.1

Let us denote by $c0, c1, c2, c3, \ldots$ the clock signals of flip-flops $A, B, C, D, \ldots$. As before the flip-flops are given from left to right the weights $2^0, 2^1, 2^2, 2^3$, respectively. Since a TFF changes state upon receipt of a clock pulse, the design procedure consists essentially of generating a clock pulse for a flip-flop each time we wish it to change state. For example, flip-flop C changes state twice in a scale-8 count cycle – see Figure 4.4(a). This implies that we need to generate two clock pulses during the complete cycle, the trailing edges of which must coincide with leaving states $S3$ and $S7$. Since the leading edge of a clock pulse clearly must not coincide with the trailing edge of the previous clock pulse, and because the switching of a flip-flop is independent of the width of the clock pulse, the leading edge of the first clock pulse may be generated on entering either state $S2$ or state $S1$ or when $X = 1$ in state $S0$. Similarly in the case of the second clock pulse, its leading edge may be generated at either $S6$ or $S5$ or when $X = 1$ in state $S4$.

Referring to Figure 4.4(a), we obtain:

$$c0 = S0X + S1X + S2X + S3X + S4X + S5X + S6X + S7X = (S0 + S1 + S2 + S3 + S4 + S5 + S6 + S7)X = X.$$

$$c1 = (S1 \text{ or } (S1 + S0X)) + (S3 \text{ or } (S3 + S2X)) + (S5 \text{ or } (S5 + S4X)) + (S7 \text{ or } (S7 + S6X) = (A\bar{B}\bar{C} \text{ or } (A\bar{B}\bar{C} + \bar{A}\bar{B}\bar{C}\bar{X})) + (AB\bar{C} \text{ or } (AB\bar{C} + \bar{A}B\bar{C}X)) + (A\bar{B}C \text{ or } (A\bar{B}C + \bar{A}\bar{B}CX)) + (ABC \text{ or } (ABC + \bar{A}BCX)) = A\bar{B}\bar{C} + A\bar{B}C + AB\bar{C} + ABC = A.$$

$$c2 = (S3 \text{ or } (S3 + S2) \text{ or } (S3 + S2 + S1) \text{ or } (S3 + S2 + S1 + S0X)) + (S7 \text{ or } (S7 + S6) \text{ or } (S7 + S6 + S5) \text{ or } (S7 + S6 + S5 + S4X)) = (AB\bar{C} \text{ or } B\bar{C} \text{ or } (A\bar{C} + B\bar{C}) \text{ or } (B\bar{C} + A\bar{C} + \bar{C}X)) + (ABC \text{ or } BC \text{ or } (AC + BC) \text{ or } (BC + AC + CX)) = BC + BC = B.$$

For counting cycles that are not a power of 2 the unconditional reset signal r described in the next section is used.

Down Counts

Using the same reasoning as above, we obtain:

$$c0 = X \qquad c1 = \bar{A}\ A \qquad c2 = \bar{B} \qquad c3 = \bar{C} \text{ and so on.}$$

Up/Down Counts

The flip-flop equations are:

$$c0 = X$$
$$c1 = A\bar{R} + \bar{A}R$$
$$c2 = B\bar{R} + \bar{B}R$$
$$c3 = C\bar{R} + \bar{C}R$$

.
.
.

$$c11 = L\overline{R} + \overline{L}R$$
$$c12 = M\overline{R} + \overline{M}R$$ and so on. See Figure 5.11(b).

As an exercise, try to explain why the counter, when implemented, would malfunction. Show that in general up/down ripple-through binary counters cannot be implemented.

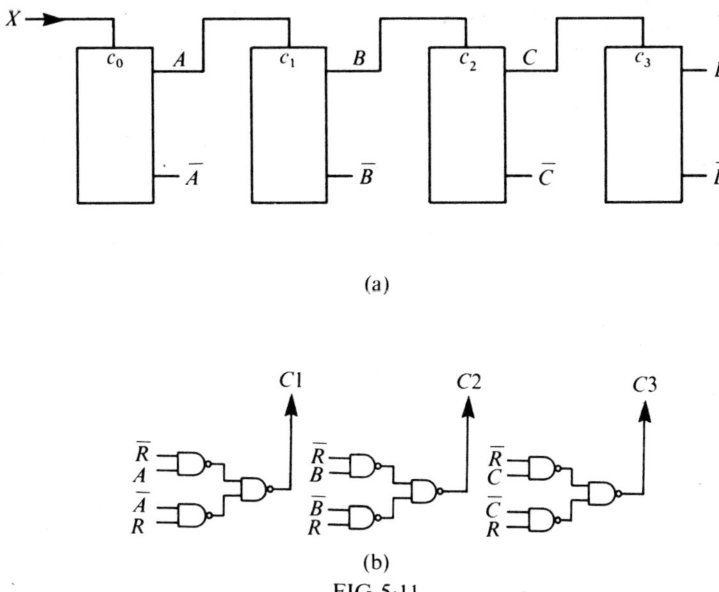

(b)
FIG 5·11

5.12 RESETTABLE COUNTERS

Pulse counters of scale-m, where m is not a power of 2, can be implemented either by skipping the unused state, as shown in Figure 5.12(a), or by resetting unconditionally the flip-flops when the counter assumes the $(m + 1)$th state, as shown in Figure 5.12(b).

There are no special problems associated with the design of counters that do not use the unconditional reset facility of the flip-flops. Their design is straightforward, as it is demonstrated in the problems and solutions section at the end of this chapter.

In the case of counters using the unconditional reset facility two problems may arise in practice. The first problem occurs when an AND gate is used to generate the reset signal, r. Should, in such a case, one of the flip-flops reset much faster than the other(s), the reset signal will switch to 0 (i.e. it will be removed) before the other flip-flop(s) are reset, in which

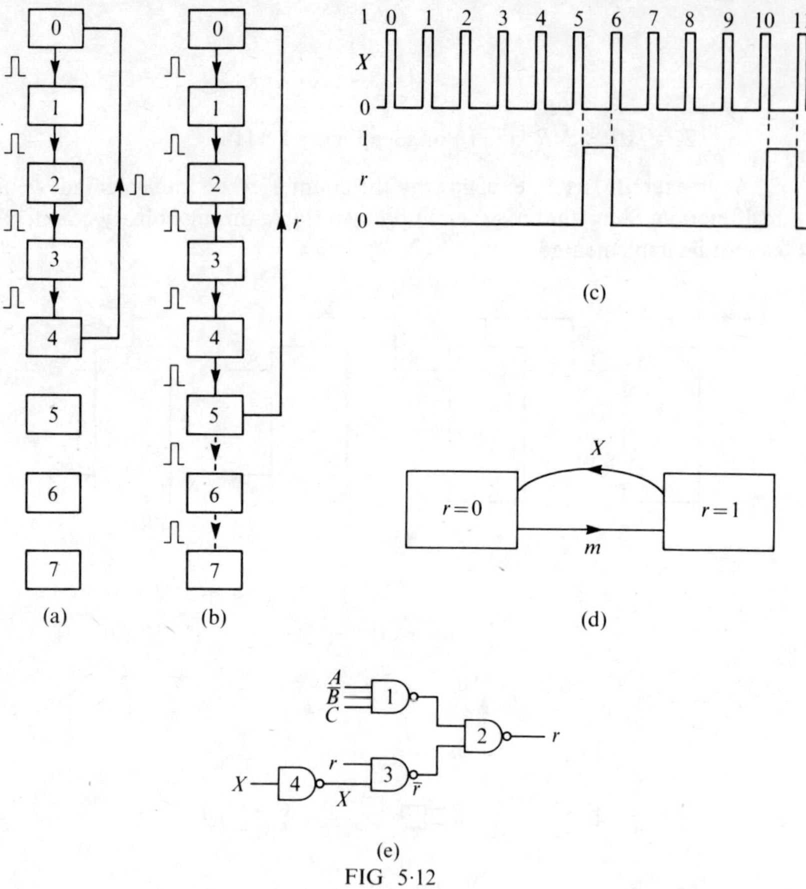

FIG 5·12

case we may fail to reset all of the flip-flops. This can be avoided in practice by maintaining the reset signal on until the leading edge of the next clock pulse. In Figure 5.12(c) we show the duration of r for $m = 5$.

In Figure 5.12(d) the state diagram of the reset circuit is shown. From it, we obtain $r = m + r\overline{X}$. Its corresponding circuit implementation is shown in Figure 5.12(e). The inputs to gate 1 are the factors in the product defining m. For example for a decade binary counter $m = 10$, defined by $\overline{A}B\overline{C}D$ or simply BD. Therefore the inputs to gate 1 in such a case would be B and D.

The second problem arises when non-Gray codes are used i.e. when transitions may involve the change of state of more than one flip-flop. During such a transition signal m may be generated for a short time, which could generate the reset signal prematurely.

Generally speaking the counter configuration shown in Figure 5.12(a) is best suited for fixed counts, whereas the resettable configuration is more suitable for variable-scale (programmable) counters.

Example

A decade 'up' binary counter can be implemented by resetting all four flip-flops as soon as the 10th pulse has been recorded, i.e.

$$r = \bar{A}B\bar{C}D + (ABD) + (CD) = BD.$$

Similarly a decade 'down' binary counter can be implemented by resetting flip-flops B and C immediately the first pulse has been recorded, i.e.

$$r = ABCD + (BC\bar{D}) + (\bar{A}CD) + (\bar{B}CD) = BC.$$

5.13 DECADE COUNTERS

The design of resettable decade counters has been discussed in the previous section. In this section we shall therefore concentrate on the design of non-resettable decade counters using the binary (1-2-4-8) and Gray codes.

Decade Binary 'Up' Counter

State diagram and codes – see Figure 5.13(a). Unused states: $BD + CD$.

Flip-flop equations are the same as for the scale-16 'up' binary counter, viz. $J_A = K_A = 1, J_B = K_B = A, J_C = K_C = AB$, and $J_D = K_D = ABC$, with the modifications shown below, which are required to inhibit the $S0$ to $S10$ transition and initiate the $S9$ to $S0$ transition.

$$S_B = AB.S9 = AB(A + D) = ABD$$
$$(S9 = ABCD + (BD) + (CD) = AD) \quad \text{Therefore, } J_B = AD$$

$$R_D = ABCD + S9 = ABCD + AD = AD \quad \text{Therefore, } K_D = A.$$

The corresponding circuit is shown in Figure 4.13(b).

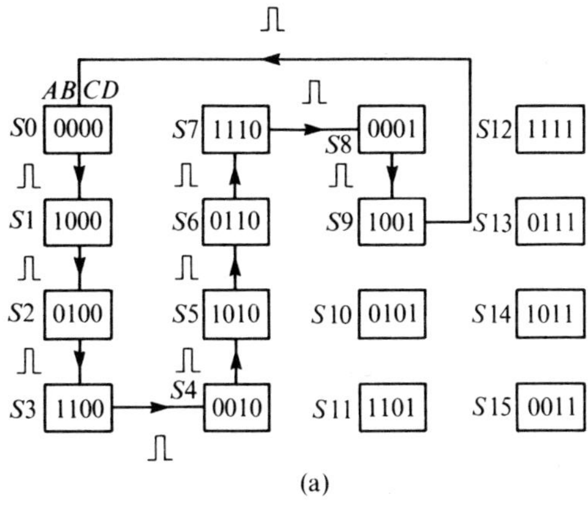

(a)

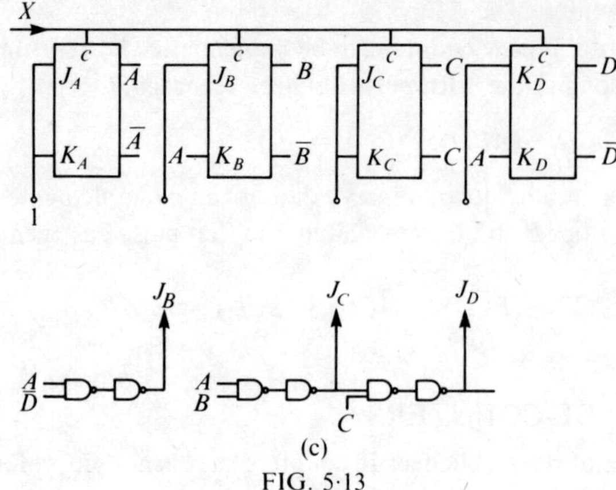

(c)

FIG. 5·13

Decade Binary 'Down' Counter

State diagrams and codes – see Figure 4.14 (a). Unused states: $BD + CD$.

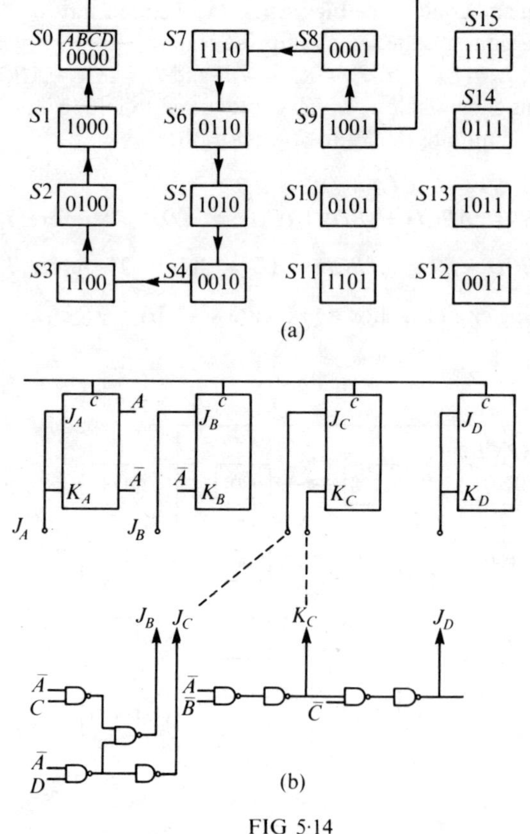

(b)

FIG 5·14

Flip-flop equations are the same for the scale-16 'down' binary counter viz. $J_A = K_A = 1, J_B = K_B = \bar{A}, J_C = K_C = \overline{A}\overline{B}$ and $J_D = K_D = \overline{A}\overline{B}\overline{C}$, with the modifications shown below which are required to inhibit the $S0$ to $S15$ transition and to initiate the $S0$ to $S9$ transition.

$$S_B = \overline{A}\overline{B}\overline{S0} = \overline{A}\overline{B}(A + B + C + D) + (BD) + (CD) = \overline{A}\overline{B}C + \overline{A}D$$
$$\text{Therefore, } J_B = \overline{A}C + \overline{A}D$$

$$S_C = \overline{A}\overline{B}\overline{C}.\overline{S0} = \overline{A}\overline{B}\overline{C}(A + B + C + D) + (BD) + (CD) = \overline{A}\overline{B}\overline{C}D + (BD) + (CD) = \overline{A}D$$
$$\text{Therefore, } J_C = \overline{A}D$$

The corresponding circuit is shown in Figure 5.14(b).

5.14 B-C-D COUNTERS

The general configuration of a binary-coded-decimal counter is shown in Figure 5.15(a). The decade counters are arranged in cascade. Each counter is driven by a pulse generated from the previous counter except

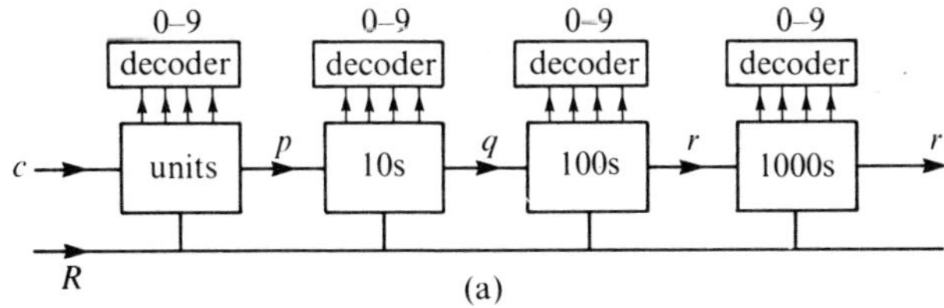

(a)

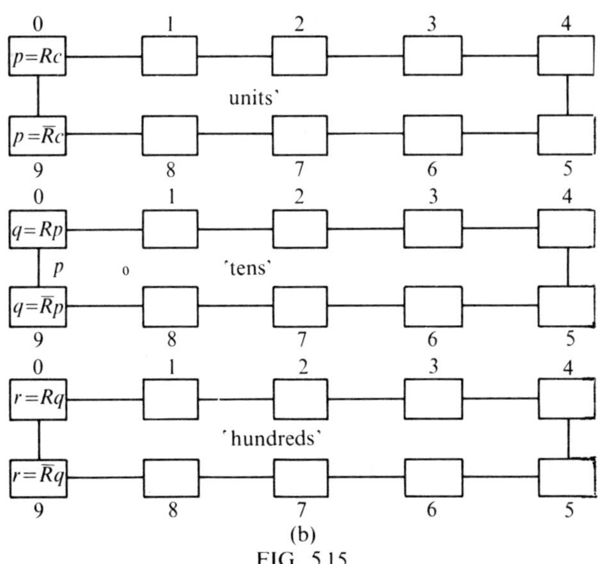

(b)

FIG. 5.15.

for the first stage which is driven directly by the input pulse train. The up/down mode is determined by signal R. In the case of 'up' counts the output of each counter stage is the pulse that reverts the counter to its initial state, whereas in the case of 'down' counts it is the pulse that moves the counter out of its initial state.

The implementation of each decade stage has been discussed in detail in previous sections. A binary to decimal decoder is used with each stage if a decimal read-out is required.

5.15 JOHNSON COUNTERS

It is evident from the table listing the Johnson code in section 5.2 that it is not necessary to use a systematic design procedure for Johnson counters by observing that they can be implemented using D flip-flops in a conventional shift register arrangement in which the complement of the last flip-flop, l, is introduced into the first flip-flop, A. These considerations lead directly to the JK circuit shown in Figure 5.16.

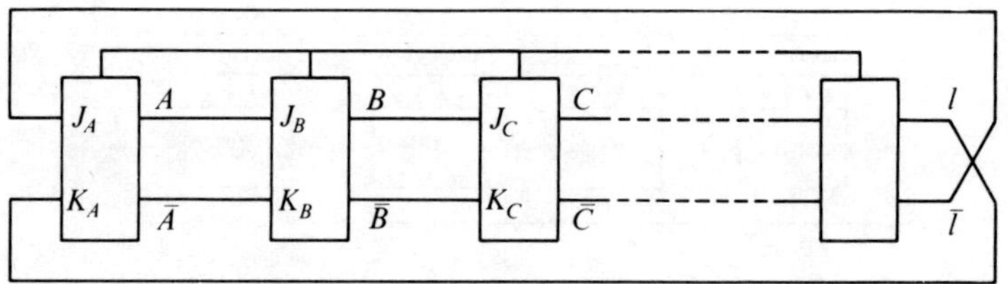

FIG. 5.16

Note that N flip-flops are required for a counting cycle of $2N$, which leaves $2^N - 2N$ unused states. If the clock is not suppressed when an unused state is assumed, the counter behaviour is easily determined by noting that on receipt of the next clock pulse each flip-flop assumes the value of the flip-flop to its left, with the exception of the first flip-flop which assumes the inverted value of the last flip-flop. For example if in a scale-6 Johnson counter unused state 010 is assumed in error, on receipt of the next clock the state of the flip-flops will be $\bar{0}01 = 101$ - that is it moves to the second unused state. On the following clock pulse the flip-flops assume the values $\bar{1}10 = 010$. That is, if an unused state is assumed in a scale-6 Johnson counter, it will oscillate between the two unused states.

5.16 PROBLEMS AND SOLUTIONS

A set of problems and solutions illustrating the design of various types of counters follows.

PROBLEM 1: *Binary Counters*

Derive the flip-flop equations (i) for a scale-5 and (ii) for a scale-6 synchronous binary 'up' counters. The flip-flops cannot be unconditionally reset.

SOLUTION

The state diagrams, appropriately coded, of the scale-5 and scale-6 counters are shown in Figures (a) and (b). If an unused state is assumed, we shall suppress the clock pulses and, if necessary, trip an alarm – as explained in Section 5.3. This allows us to use the codes of the unused states as algebraically optional products.

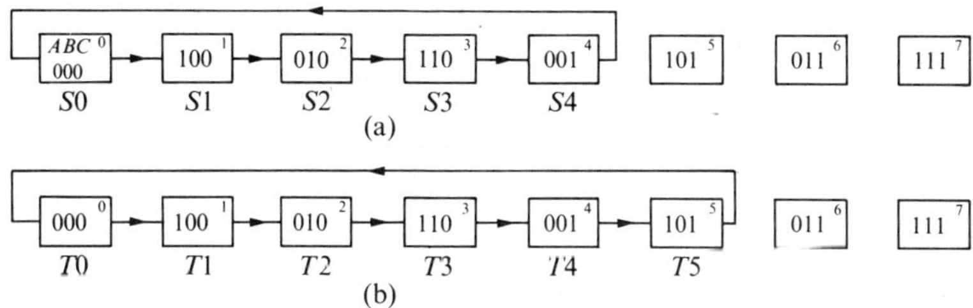

(i) Optional products due to unused states: AC and BC. By direct reference to Figure (a), we obtain:

$$\begin{aligned}
S_A &= \bar{A}\bar{B}\bar{C} + \bar{A}B\bar{C} + (AC) + (BC) = \bar{A}\bar{C} && \text{Therefore, } J_A = \bar{C}\\
R_A &= A\bar{B}\bar{C} + A\bar{B}C + (AC) + (BC) = A && \text{Therefore, } K_A = 1\\
S_B &= A\bar{B}\bar{C} + (\bar{A}B\bar{C}) + (AC) + (BC) = A\bar{B} && \text{Therefore, } J_B = A\\
R_B &= AB\bar{C} + (\bar{A}\bar{B}\bar{C}) + (\bar{A}\bar{B}C) + (AC) + (BC) = AB && \\
& && \text{Therefore, } K_B = A\\
S_C &= AB\bar{C} + (\bar{A}\bar{B}C) + (AC) + (BC) = AB && \text{Therefore, } J_C = AB\\
R_C &= \bar{A}\bar{B}C + (AC) + (BC) = C && \text{Therefore, } K_C = 1.
\end{aligned}$$

(ii) Optional products due to unused states: BC. By direct reference to Figure (b), we obtain:

$$\begin{aligned}
S_A &= \bar{A}\bar{B}\bar{C} + \bar{A}B\bar{C} + \bar{A}\bar{B}C + (BC) = A && \text{Therefore, } J_A = 1\\
R_A &= A\bar{B}\bar{C} + AB\bar{C} + A\bar{B}C + (BC) = A && \text{Therefore, } K_A = 1\\
S_B &= A\bar{B}\bar{C} + (\bar{A}B\bar{C}) + (BC) = A\bar{B}\bar{C} && \text{Therefore, } J_B = A\bar{C}\\
R_B &= AB\bar{C} + (\bar{A}\bar{B}C) + (\bar{A}\bar{B}\bar{C}) + (BC) = AB && \text{Therefore, } K_B = A\\
S_C &= AB\bar{C} + (\bar{A}\bar{B}C) + (BC) = ABC && \text{Therefore, } J_C = AB\\
R_C &= A\bar{B}C + (\bar{A}\bar{B}\bar{C}) + (A\bar{B}\bar{C}) + (\bar{A}B\bar{C}) = BC && \text{Therefore, } K_C = A.
\end{aligned}$$

PROBLEM 2: *Programmable Counters*

Design a binary counter whose scale changes from eight to six when an external control signal m is present – see Figure (a).

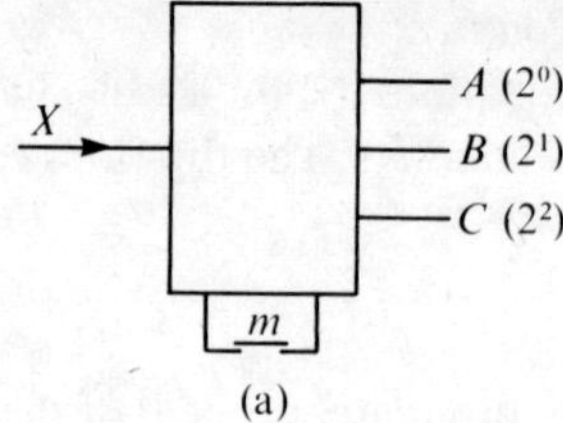

(a)

SOLUTION

The corresponding state diagram is shown in Figure (b). We shall consider first its implementation with non-resettable counters and second its implementation with resettable counters.

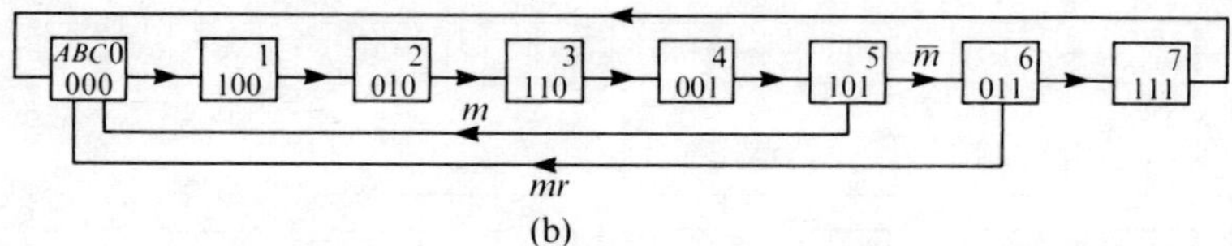

(b)

(i)

$$
\begin{aligned}
S_A &= \bar{A}\bar{B}\bar{C}+\bar{A}B\bar{C}+\bar{A}\bar{B}C+\bar{A}BC=\bar{A} && \text{Therefore, } J_A = 1\\
R_A &= A\bar{B}\bar{C}+AB\bar{C}+A\bar{B}C+ABC=A && \text{Therefore, } K_A = 1\\
S_B &= A\bar{B}\bar{C}+A\bar{B}C\bar{m} = A\bar{B}\bar{C}+A\bar{B}\bar{m} && \text{Therefore, } J_B = A(\bar{c}+\bar{m})\\
R_B &= AB\bar{C}+ABC = AB && \text{Therefore, } K_B = A\\
S_C &= AB\bar{C} && \text{Therefore, } J_C = AB\\
R_C &= A\bar{B}Cm+ABC = ACm+ABC && \text{Therefore, } K_C = AB+Cm.
\end{aligned}
$$

(ii)

$$
\begin{aligned}
r &= ABCm + r\bar{X}\\
&= BCm + r\bar{X}.
\end{aligned}
$$

In Figure (c) we show the implementation in case (ii) using the ripple-through counter configuration.

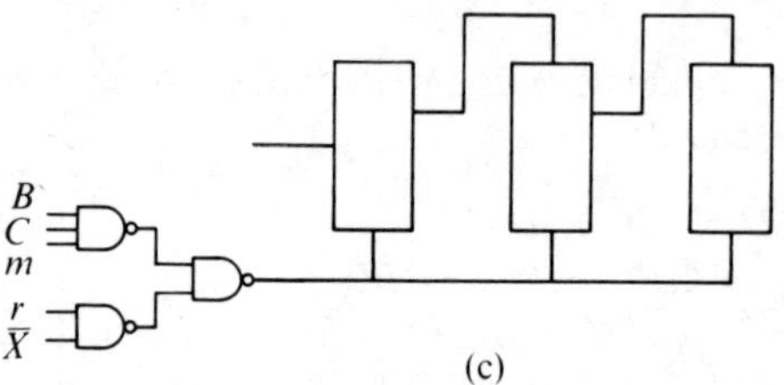

(c)

PROBLEM 3: *A Self-Locking Counter*

Design a binary pulse counter that locks automatically after a pulse count of five has been recorded. The next counting cycle is reinitiated by activating switch m in Figure (a).

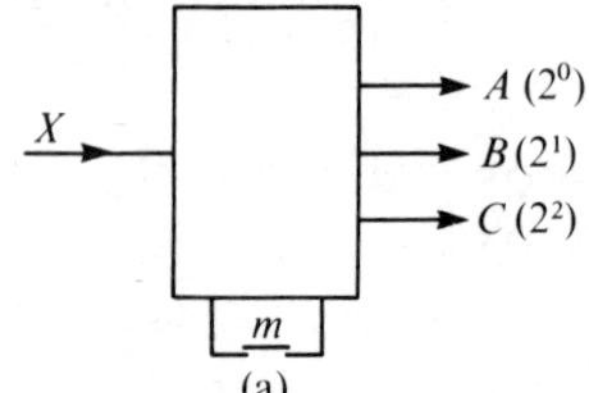

(a)

SOLUTION

Our solution consists of suppressing the incoming pulses, X, after a pulse count of five has been recorded – see Figure (b). Signal c is a pulse train of five pulses. A suitable state diagram of the control circuit is shown in Figure (c). The circuit equations, derived directly from it, are:

$$K = L\overline{X} + K(L + m)$$
$$L = \overline{K}m + L(\overline{K} + \overline{A} + \overline{C})$$
$$c = KLX.$$

The corresponding NAND circuit is shown in Figure (d).

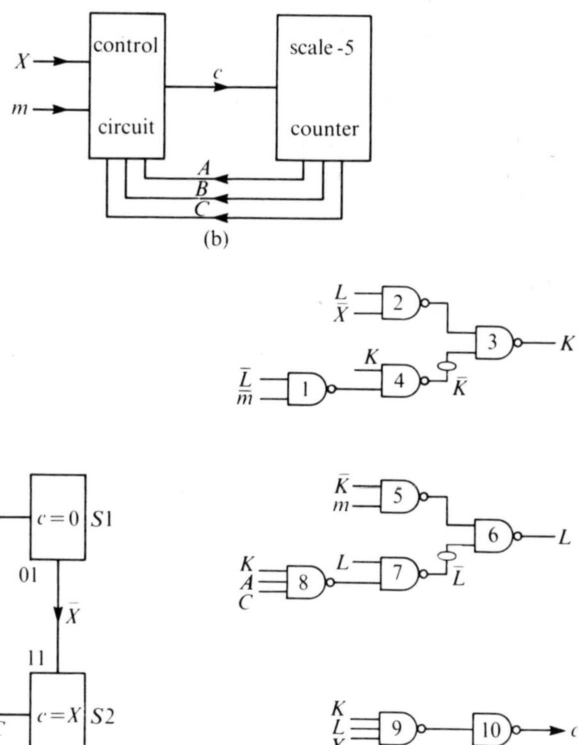

(b)

(c)

(d)

PROBLEM 4: *Pulse Trains*

Design a circuit that allows a pulse train of predetermined length to be output on terminal Z each time switch m is activated. Complete pulses only to be output.

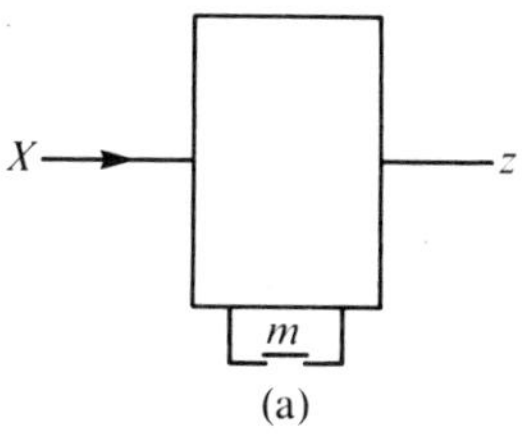

(a)

SOLUTION

The block diagram of our solution is shown in Figure (b). The counter is used to count the pulses on the output line. $K = 0$ indicates that the pulse count is 0, otherwise $K = 1$. Its operation is described by the state diagram in Figure (c). By direct reference to this diagram, we obtain the circuit's equations:

$$
\begin{aligned}
A &= B\bar{X} + A(B + m + K) \\
B &= \bar{A}m + B(\bar{A} + \bar{K}) \\
Z &= ABX + A\bar{B}KX = ABX + AKX.
\end{aligned}
$$

The corresponding circuit is shown in Figure (d).

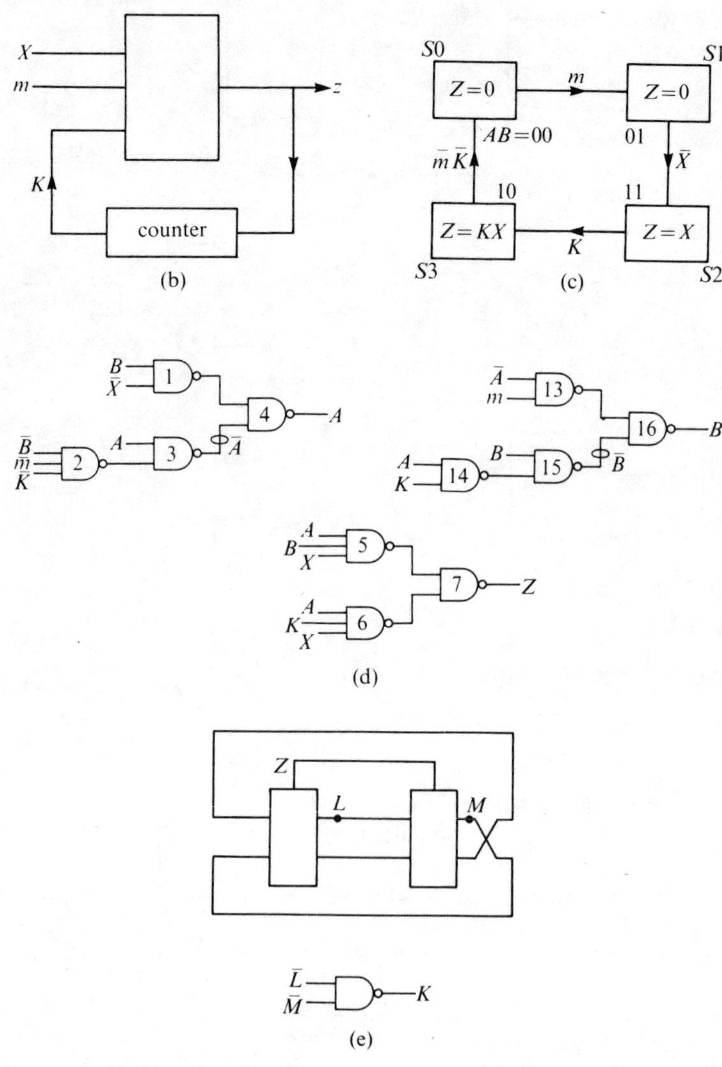

(b) (c) (d) (e)

Example

For a pulse train of four pulses $K = L + M$, where L and M are the flip-flop signals of the scale-4 counter in Figure (e).

PROBLEM 5: *Gray Up/Down Counter*

Derive the flip-flop equations for a scale-6 Gray up/down counter.

SOLUTION

Because in Gray counters the values of the J and K flip-flop signals in the 'up' mode are the same as the K and J values respectively in the 'down' mode, it is only necessary to derive the flip-flop equations for the 'up' mode, shown in Figure (a) - see Section 4.6. As in Problem 1, we shall suppress the clock pulses if one of the unused states $S6$ or $S7$ is assumed - this allows us to use AB as an optional product.

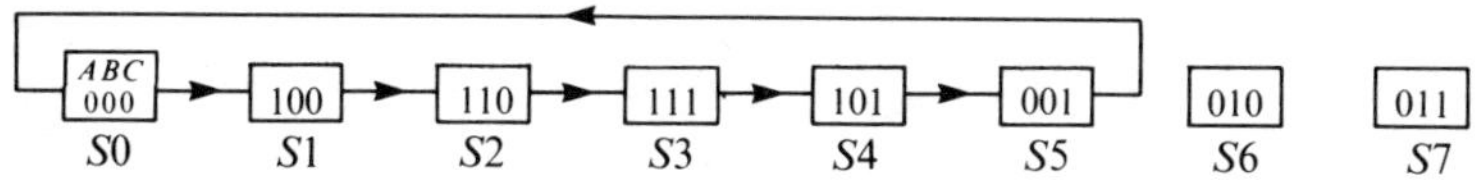

By direct reference to Figure (a), we obtain:

$$
\begin{aligned}
S_A &= S0 = \bar{A}\bar{B}\bar{C} & \text{Therefore, } J_A &= \bar{B}\bar{C} + (\bar{A}B) = \bar{B}\bar{C} \\
R_A &= S4 = A\bar{B}C & \text{Therefore, } K_A &= BC + (\bar{A}B) = \bar{B}C \\
S_B &= S1 = A\bar{B}\bar{C} & \text{Therefore, } J_B &= A\bar{C} + (\bar{A}B) = A\bar{C} \\
R_B &= S3 = ABC & \text{Therefore, } K_B &= AC + (\bar{A}B) = AC \\
S_C &= S2 = AB\bar{C} & \text{Therefore, } J_C &= AB + (\bar{A}B) = B \\
R_C &= S5 = \bar{A}\bar{B}C & \text{Therefore, } K_C &= \bar{A}\bar{B} + (\bar{A}B) = \bar{A}.
\end{aligned}
$$

Therefore, for the up/down count, the JKFF equations are:

$$
\begin{aligned}
J_A &= \bar{B}\bar{C}\bar{R} + \bar{B}CR \\
K_A &= \bar{B}C\bar{R} + \bar{B}\bar{C}R \\
J_B &= A\bar{C}\bar{R} + ACR \\
K_B &= AC\bar{R} + A\bar{C}R \\
J_C &= B\bar{R} + \bar{A}R \\
K_C &= \bar{A}\bar{R} + BR
\end{aligned}
$$

- the required result.

PROBLEM 6: *Gray Up/Down Decade Counter*

Design a Gray-coded decade up/down counter.

SOLUTION

A suitable state diagram is shown in Figure (a). Should one of the unused six states, specified by $A\bar{C} + \bar{B}\bar{C}$, be assumed, we shall suppress the incoming pulses, c. This is achieved, as explained in the text, by ANDing c with $\overline{A\bar{C} + \bar{B}\bar{C}}$, namely $c(C + \bar{A}B)$, which allows us to use the Boolean products $A\bar{C}$ and $\bar{B}\bar{C}$ as algebraically-optional products.

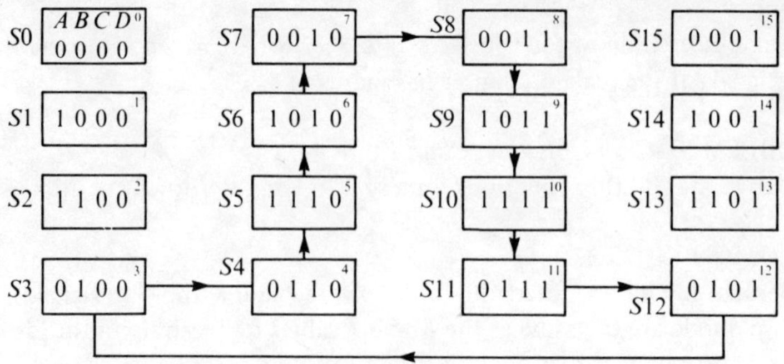

Up Mode

By direct reference to Figure (a), we obtain:

$$S_A = S4 + S8 = \overline{A}BC\overline{D} + \overline{A}\overline{B}CD$$

$$+ \quad \text{Therefore, } J_A = BC\overline{D} + \overline{B}CD + (\overline{B}\overline{C}) = BC\overline{D} + \overline{B}D$$

$$R_A = S6 + S10 = A\overline{B}C\overline{D} + ABCD$$

$$\text{Therefore, } K_A = \overline{B}C\overline{D} + BCD + (\overline{B}\overline{C}) = BCD + \overline{B}\overline{D}$$

$$S_B = S9 = A\overline{B}CD$$

$$\text{Therefore, } J_B = ACD + (A\overline{C}) = AD$$

$$R_B = S5 = ABC\overline{D}$$

$$\text{Therefore, } K_B = AC\overline{D} + (A\overline{C}) = AD$$

$$S_C = S3 = \overline{A}B\overline{C}\overline{D}$$

$$\text{Therefore, } J_C = \overline{A}B\overline{D}$$

$$R_C = S11 = \overline{A}BCD$$

$$\text{Therefore, } K_C = \overline{A}BD$$

$$S_D = S7 = \overline{A}\overline{B}C\overline{D}$$

$$\text{Therefore, } J_D = \overline{A}\overline{B}C + (\overline{B}\overline{C}) = \overline{A}\overline{B}$$

$$R_D = S12 = \overline{A}B\overline{C}D$$

$$\text{Therefore, } K_D = \overline{A}B\overline{C} + (A\overline{C}) + (\overline{B}\overline{C}) = \overline{C}.$$

Down Mode

As explained in Section 5.6, the flip-flop equations for the 'down' mode are obtained by interchanging the J and K values for the 'up' mode. Thus $J_D = \overline{C}$ and $K_D = \overline{A}\overline{B}$.

PROBLEM 7: *B-C-D 'Up' Counters*

Design a b-c-d 'up' counter to count up to 999 . . . pulses. The pulse count is to be displayed as a decimal number on seven-segment light displays.

SOLUTION

A suitable block diagram of the required solution is shown in Figure (a). The state diagram for three stages (counting range 0 to 999) is shown in Figure (b). By direct reference to Figure (b), we obtain:

a = input pulses (X)
$b = D$
$c = H.$

A circuit implementation using ripple-through counters is shown in Figure (c).

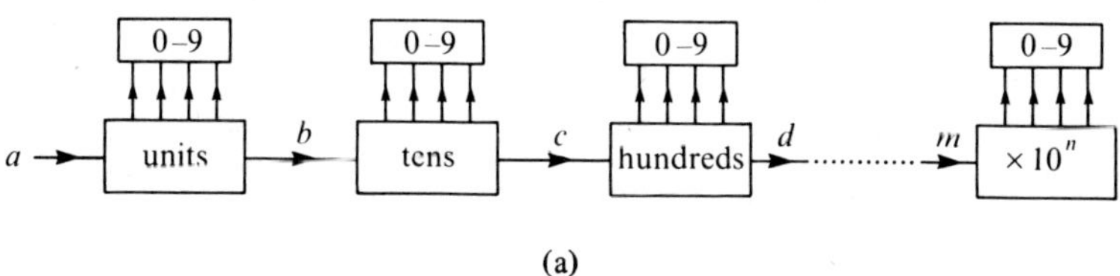

(a)

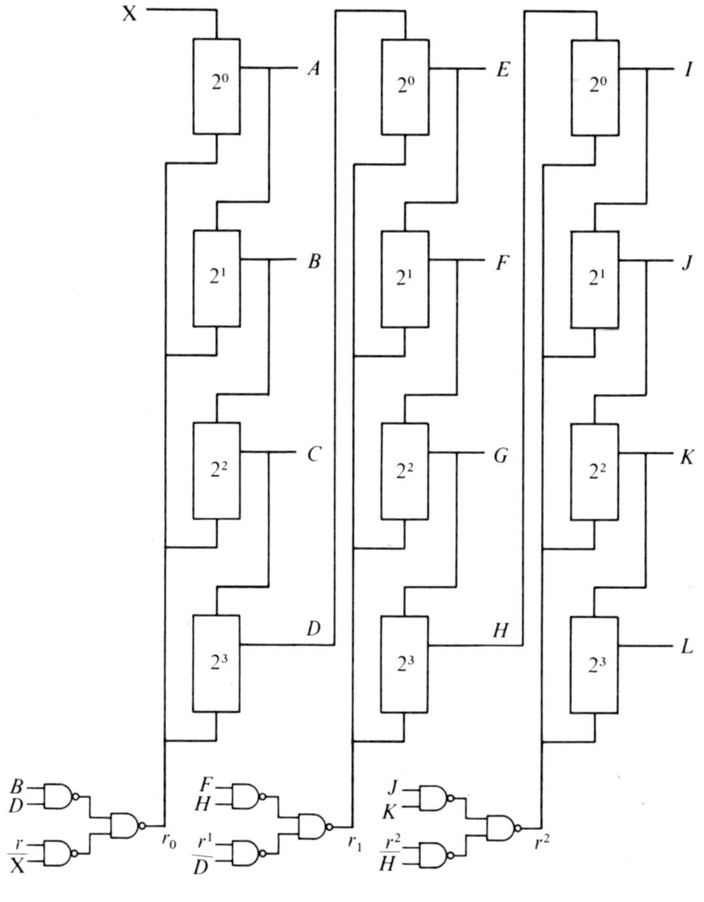

(b)

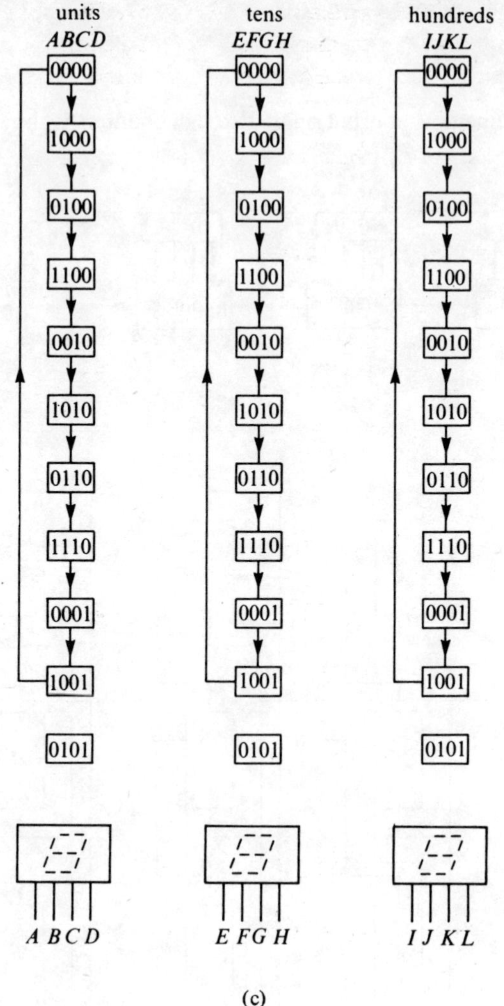

(c)

PROBLEM 8: *Divide By 60 Circuit*

Design and implement a circuit which is intended to receive 60 pulses per second on terminal *a* and to output one pulse per second on terminal *s* in Figure (a). (Signal *a* may be generated from a 60 Hz domestic power supply, by means of an isolating step-down transformer and a pulse shaping circuit).

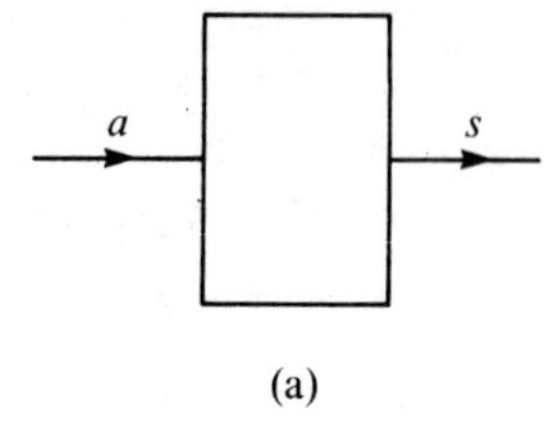

(a)

SOLUTION

A sixty-state cyclic circuit is required to divide the incoming frequency by 60. Because of the relatively low frequency of the incoming pulses, possibly the simplest implementation consists of six flip-flops in a ripple-through arrangement to be unconditionally reset immediately following the 60th input pulse – see Figure (b). By direct reference to this figure, we obtain:

$$s = S59\,.\,a = AB\overline{C}DEFa = ABDEFa.$$

The flip-flop reset signal is

$$r = S60 = \overline{A}\overline{B}CDEF = CDEF.$$

The corresponding circuit is shown in Figure (c).

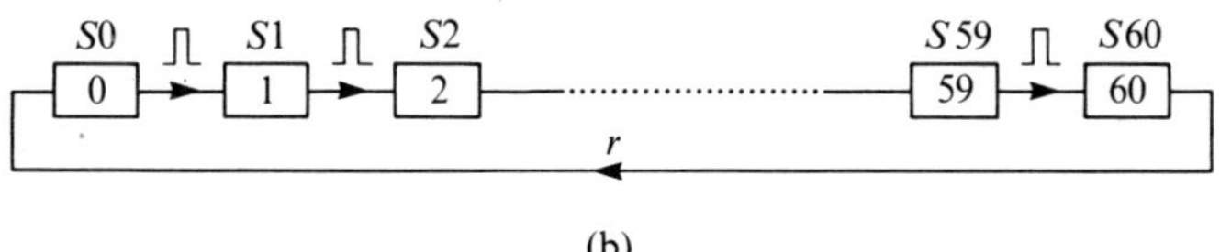

(b)

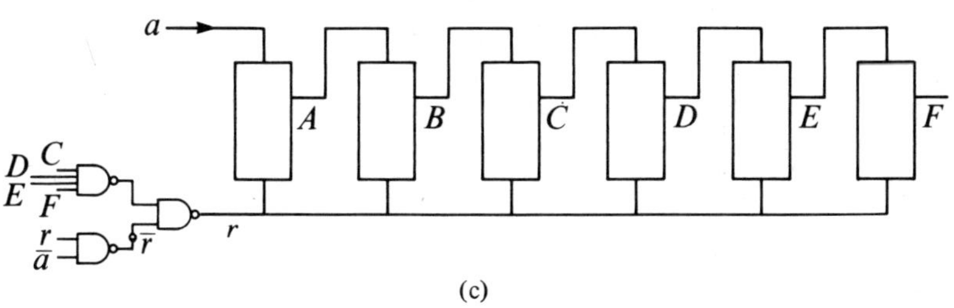

(c)

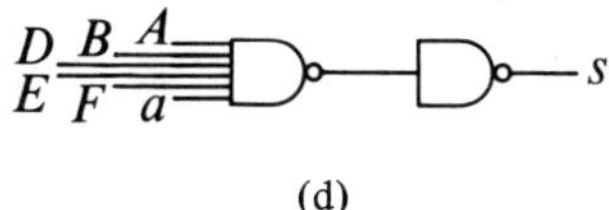

(d)

PROBLEM 9: *A 60-Minute Clock*

Design and implement a 60-minute digital clock, that is a clock which is intended to receive one pulse per minute on terminal m in Figure (a) and displays the minute count 0 to 59 on two seven-segment displays.

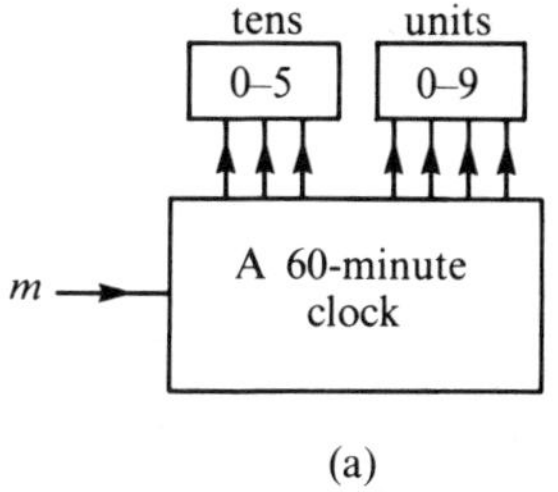

(a)

SOLUTION

Suitable state diagrams for resettable counters are shown in Figure (b). By direct reference to this figure, we obtain:

$$r1 = \overline{A}B\overline{C}D + (ABD) + (CD) = BD$$
$$r2 = \overline{E}FG + (EFG) = FG.$$

The ‘units’ counter is driven directly by the input signal, m, and the ‘tens’ counter by signal D.

A ripple-through implementation of Figure (b) is shown in Figure (c).

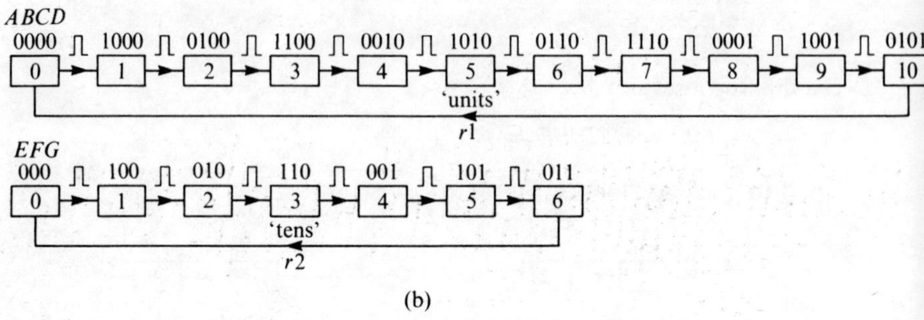

(b)

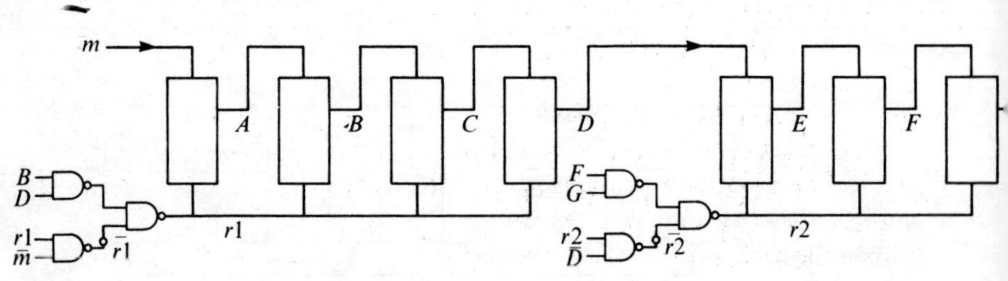

(c)

PROBLEM 10: *A 12-Hour Clock*

Design and implement a 12-hour clock, that is, a clock which is intended to receive one pulse per hour on terminal h in Figure (a) and displays the hour count 1 to 12 on two seven-segment light displays.

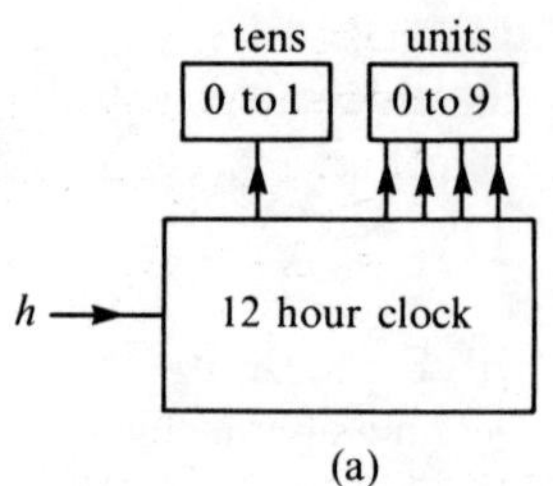

(a)

SOLUTION

Suitable state diagrams for resettable counters are shown in Figure (b).

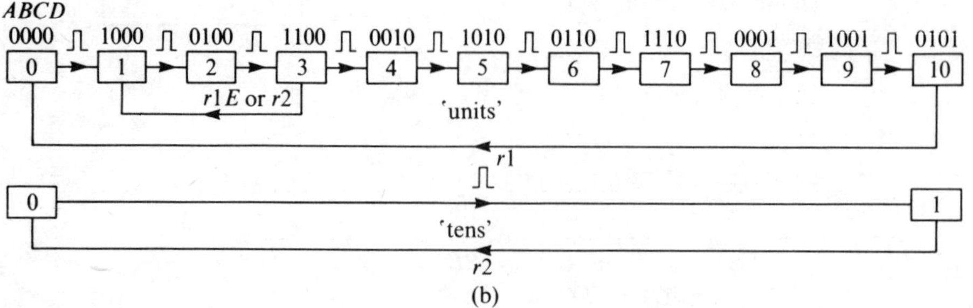

(b)

By direct reference to this figure, we obtain:

$$r1 = ABCDE + ABCDE = BD + ABE \quad \text{or} \quad r1 = BD + r2$$
$$r2 = AB \quad \text{or} \quad r2 = ABE.$$

The 'units' counter is driven directly by the input signal, h, and the 'tens' counter by signal D.

A ripple-through implementation of Figure (b) is shown in Figure (c).

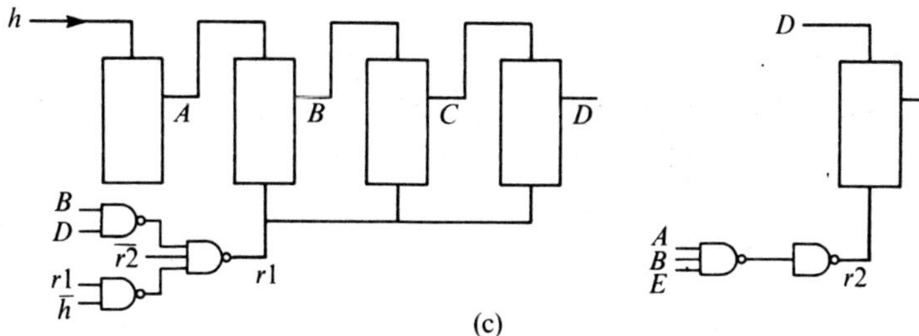

(c)

PROBLEM 11: *A 24-Hour Clock*

Design and implement a 24-hour digital clock, that is a clock which receives one pulse per hour on terminal h in Figure (a) and displays the hour count on two seven-segment light displays.

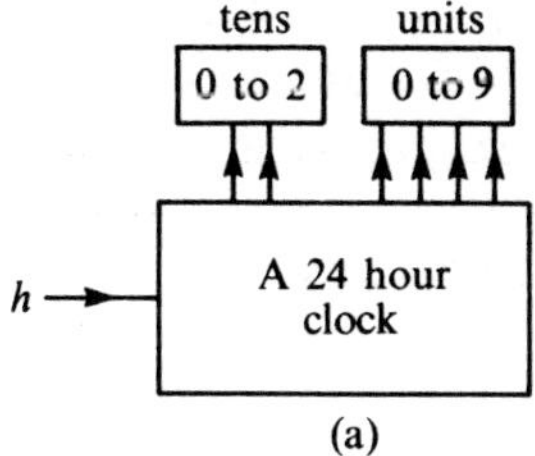

(a)

SOLUTION

Suitable state diagrams for resettable counters are shown in Figure (b). By direct reference to this figure, we obtain:

$$r1 = BD + ACF \quad \text{or} \quad r1 = BD + r2$$
$$r2 = AC \quad \text{or} \quad r2 = ACF.$$

The 'units' counter is driven directly by the input signal, h, and the 'tens' counter by signal D.

A ripple-through implementation of Figure (b) is shown in Figure (c).

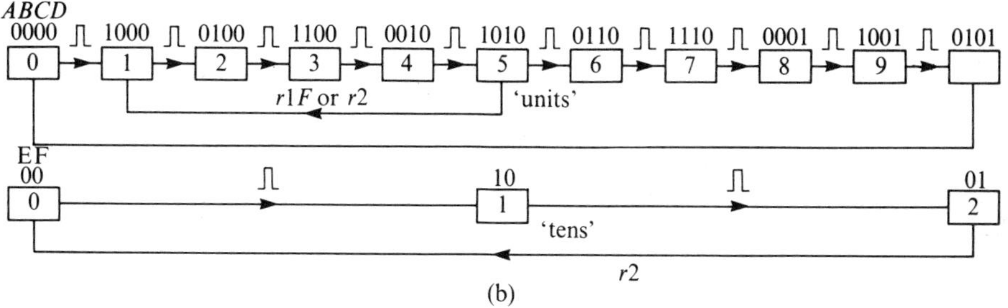

(b)

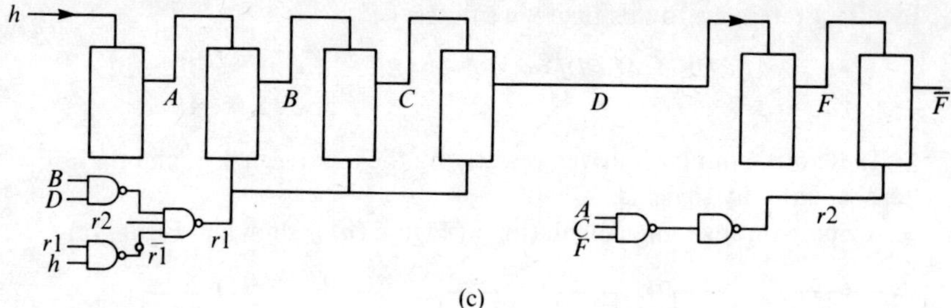

(c)

PROBLEM 12: *An Event Counter*

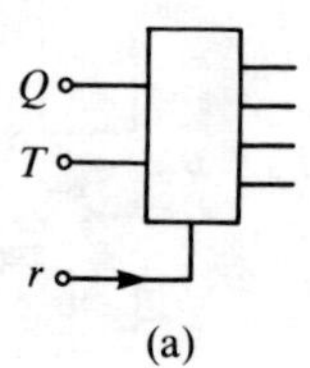

(a)

Events occuring in an experimental environment are recorded as square pulses on terminal Q in Figure (a). It is required to measure the time taken for six of these events to occur, following an initializing pulse on terminal r.

The events occur at a rate of not less than 100 per second. The time base is to be provided by a clock pulse generator on terminal T operating at 1 kHz (i.e. one thousand pulses per second). The result is to be displayed as a decimal number on a 2-digit seven-segment display.

SOLUTION

Maximum time to record six pulses = 6/100 = .06 seconds. Maximum number of clock pulses in .06 seconds = 1000 × .06 = 60. Our solution consists of using signal r to reset the 'clock' and event registers, shown in Figure (b). We prevent the registers from being reset during the presence

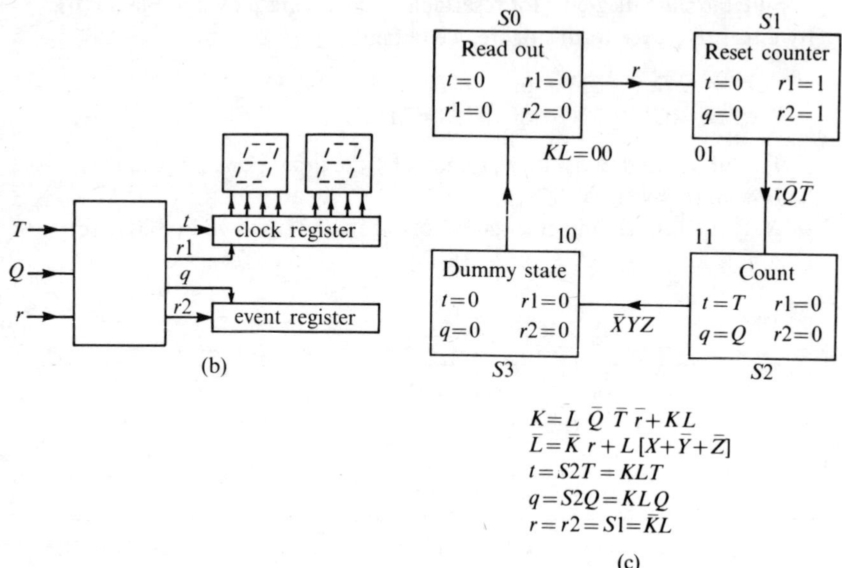

(b)

$$K = L\,\bar{Q}\,\bar{T}\,\bar{r} + KL$$
$$\bar{L} = \bar{K}\,r + L\,[X + \bar{Y} + \bar{Z}]$$
$$t = S2T = KLT$$
$$q = S2Q = KLQ$$
$$r = r2 = S1 = \bar{K}L$$

(c)

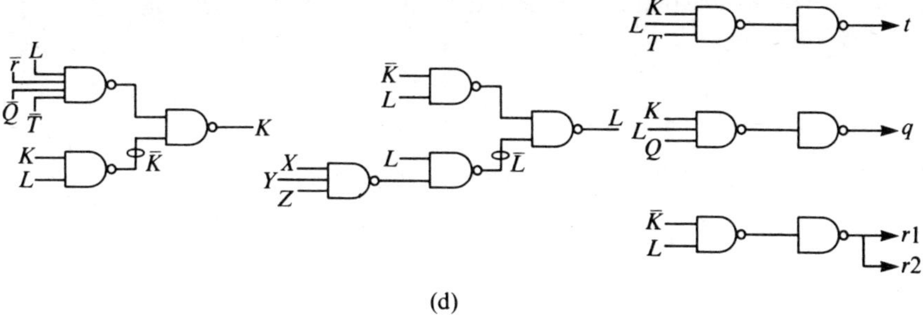

(d)

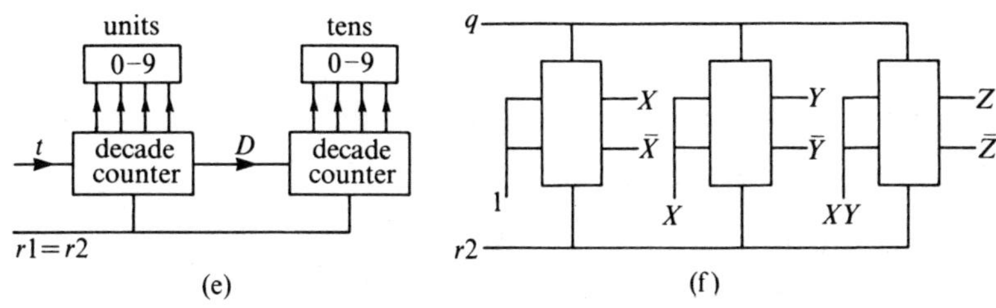

(e) (f)

of either an event or a clock pulse, by initiating the transition to state $S2$ in Figure (c) with signal $\bar{r}\bar{Q}\bar{T}$. When we get to state $S2$ we allow the input clock and event pulses to drive their corresponding registers shown in Figures (a) and (b). After six pulses have been recorded $XYZ = 011$, which automatically resets the control circuit by causing it to move from state $S2$ to state $S0$ (through dummy state $S1$).

PROBLEM 13: *A Digital Tachometer*

Design a digital tachometer, that is a digital circuit that counts the number of incoming pulses, d, during one second and displays the pulse count during the following second. A timing signal, t, which changes its logic level every one second is assumed available.

SOLUTION

Our solution consists of steering the incoming pulses into one of two counters, $R1$ and $R2$ in Figure (a), during consecutive seconds. While one counter is being driven the other can be read.

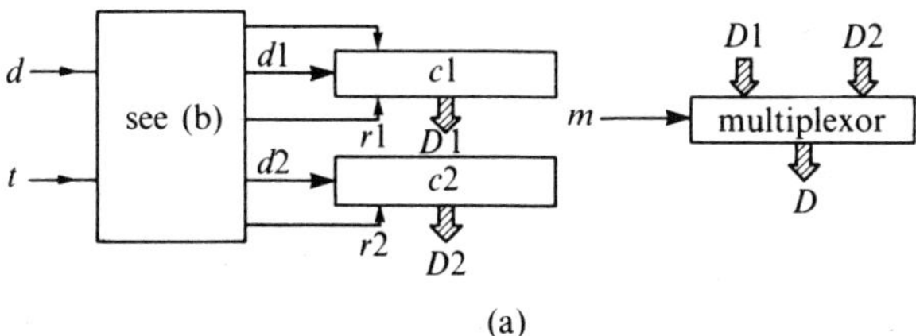

(a)

The state diagram of a suitable control circuit is shown in Figure (b). Its NAND equations are:

$$A = Bd + A(B + \overline{d}) \qquad d1 = S0d + (S3d) = \overline{B}d \qquad r1 = S3 = A\overline{B}$$
$$B = \overline{A}\overline{d}t + B(\overline{A} + d + t) \qquad d2 = S2d + (S1d) = Bd \qquad r2 = S1 = \overline{A}B$$

The corresponding circuit is shown in Figure (c).

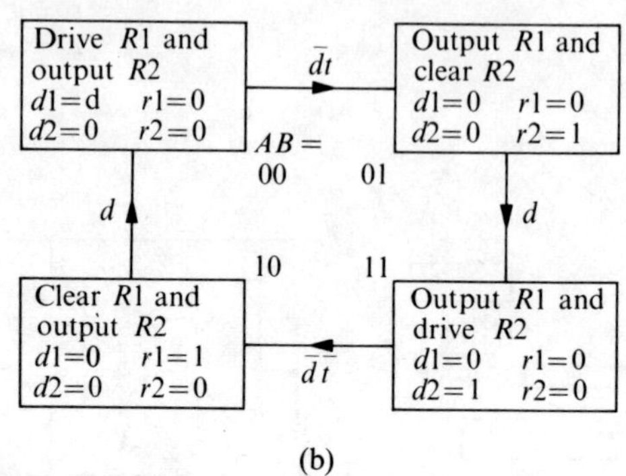

(b)

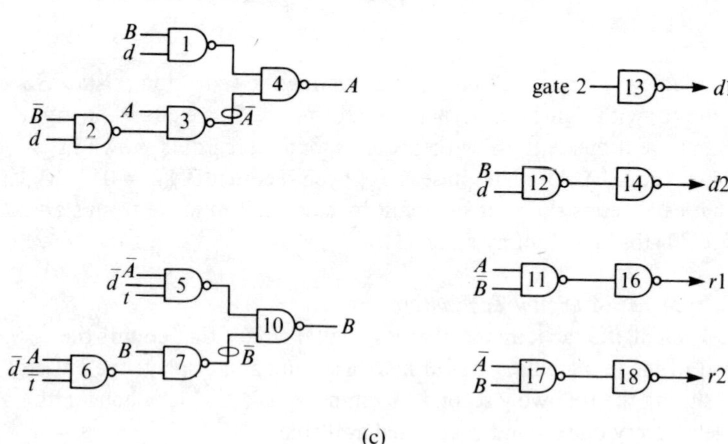

(c)

PROBLEM 14: *A Large Cycle Shift Register*

Design a shift register which has a cycle of 105 states. (Hint: 105 = 3 × 5 × 7).

SOLUTION

Our solution consists of connecting in cascade three shift registers of cycles 3, 5, and 7, as shown in Figure (a).

(i) *Three-state cycle* 00 - 10 - 01

$$J_A = \overline{B}$$
$$K_A = 1$$

(ii) *Five-state cycle* 000 - 100 - 110 - 011 - 001

$$J_C = \overline{E}$$
$$K_C = D$$

(iii) *Seven-state cycle* 000 - 100 - 010 - 101 - 110 - 110 - 011 - 001

$$J_F = K_F = \overline{H}.$$

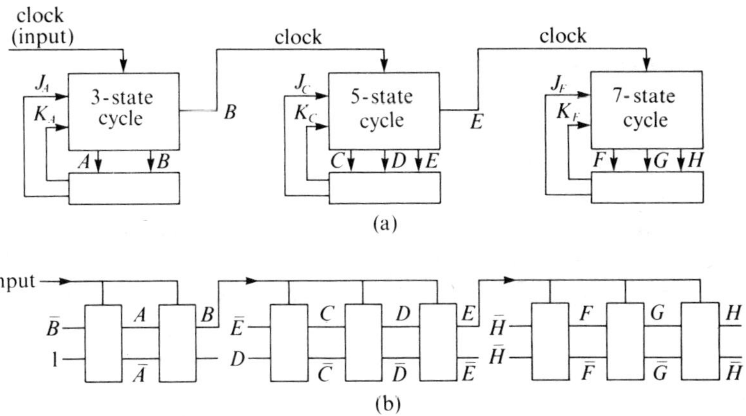

(a)

(b)

6 *Combinational Circuits*

In this chapter we describe steps for meeting fan-in restrictions and for designing hazard-free combinational circuits.

6.1 INTRODUCTION

Two of the most essential features that must be met in the design of logic circuits are the imposed gate *fan-in* restrictions and *hazard-free operation.* Gate fan-in is the number of input terminals provided in a gate, i.e. the maximum number of input signals to a gate. Race-hazards are unwanted transient signals (signal spikes), which under certain changes of an input signal and with certain relationships of circuit delays appear in a logic circuit. Figure 5.1 shows an example in which 'spikes' occur during a change of input signal A from 1 to 0 when $B = C = 1$. The cause of race hazards is that immediately following a change in a signal A, $A = \overline{A} =$ either 0 or 1. It follows that if the Boolean expression of a signal in a circuit reduces to either of the two forms $A + \overline{A}$ or $A \cdot \overline{A}$, a race-hazard exists at the output of the corresponding gate – otherwise the signal is hazard-free.

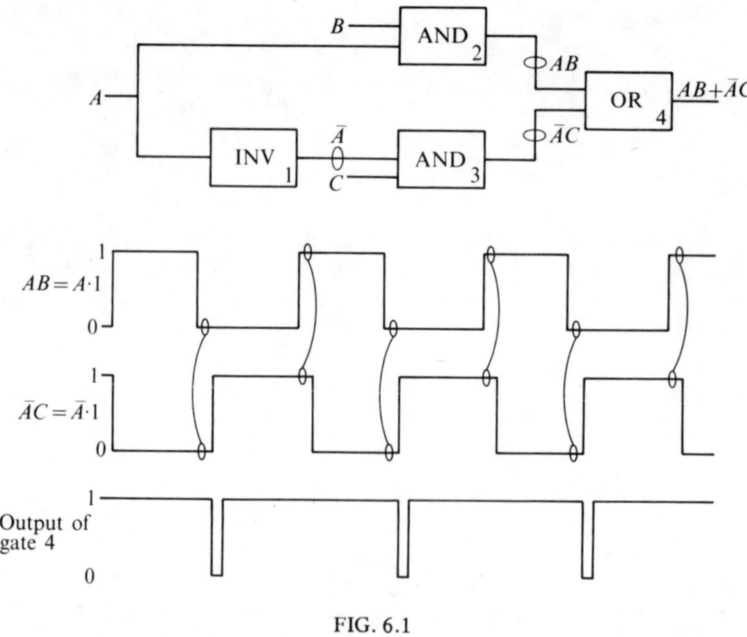

FIG. 6.1

Returning to our example in Figure 5.1, $f = AB + \overline{A}C$ which reduces to $A + \overline{A}$ when $B = C = 1$, revealing the existence of a race-hazard at the output of gate 4. Race-hazards in a circuit clearly can be suppressed by preventing its Boolean expression from reducing to either of the two forms $A + \overline{A}$ or $A \cdot \overline{A}$. This is readily achieved by means of Theorem 2 in Appendix 1, namely

$$AB + \overline{A}C = AB + \overline{A}C + BC$$

or

$$(A + B)(\overline{A} + C) = (A + B)(\overline{A} + C)(B + C).$$

The introduction of the third term prevents the first expression from being reduced to $A + \overline{A}$, since when $B = C = 1$, $AB + \overline{A}C + BC$ reduces to $A + \overline{A} + 1 = 1$. Similarly the second expression, when $B = C = 0$, reduces to $(A + 0)(\overline{A} + 0)(0 + 0) = A \cdot \overline{A} \cdot 0 = 0$.

The implication of a fan-in restriction on the implementation of a Boolean function is equivalent to imposing a restriction on the maximum size of the products and sums in the expression of the function to be implemented. For example, the Boolean function $p = AB + A\overline{C} + A\overline{D}$ cannot be implemented directly using two-input NAND gates, because it contains a sum of three products - see Figure 6.2(a). One method of meeting the fan-in restriction is simply to bracket two of the three-products. Bracketing the first two products, we obtain $p = (AB + A\overline{C}) + A\overline{D}$. Its two-input NAND implementation, shown in Figure 6.2(b), uses eight gates, that is two additional gates. Another possibility is to take a common factor, A, between two of the products. Taking a common factor between the first two products, we obtain $p = A(B + \overline{C}) + A\overline{D}$. Its corresponding circuit, shown in Figure 6.2(c), meets the fan-in restriction of two with no increase in the gate count. Had we, however, taken A as a common factor between the second and third products, we would have obtained $p = AB + A(\overline{C} + \overline{D})$, which can be implemented with two gates less than the original circuit - see Figure 6.2(d). Clearly, $p = AB + A(\overline{C} + \overline{D})$ is the optimal form of the expression to be implemented - even if the fan-in restriction of two were not imposed. The question therefore arises as to how one arrives in a systematic manner at the optimal expression of a logic function which is to be implemented with specified gates. Such a method exists and is based on the use of the merging table, described in the next section. For a detailed description of its derivation and its application to more complicated circuits, the interested reader is referred to Zissos, D. *Logic Design Algorithms*, Oxford University Press (1972), and Zissos, D. and Duncan, F. G. *Fan-in Restrictions in Logic Circuits*, Proc. IEE, Vol. 118, February 1971.

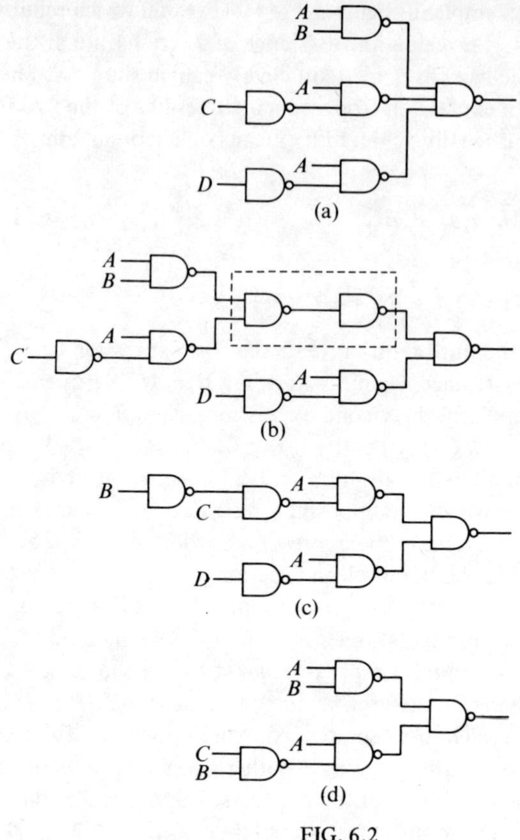

FIG. 6.2

6.2 THE MERGING TABLE

In the case of NAND circuits our starting point is an irredundant sum-of-products expression of the function to be implemented, e.g. $p = AB + A\bar{C} + A\bar{D}$.

Second we dualize the expression and number the brackets.

$$p^1 = (A+B)^1(A+\bar{C})^2(A+\bar{D})^3.$$

Third we determine the effect on the gate count, ΔN, of merging each pair of brackets individually. Merging is the process by which we use Theorem 4 in Appendix 1 to replace two brackets by a single bracket that contains the Boolean product of their contents. It is essential to note that merging does not affect terms which are present in both brackets. To derive the value of ΔN we count the components of the two brackets in the following manner:

- x is the number of terms in the smaller bracket, excluding common terms.

y is the number of terms in the larger bracket, excluding common terms.

n equals 1 if a group of terms in one bracket, called the head (see Theorem 4 in Appendix 1), is the complement of a group of terms in the other. n equals 0 otherwise.

l is the number of literals counted in x and y - a literal is a term consisting of one factor which is a true or an inverted variable.

t is the count of uninverted literals, such that for each
- *(i) its complement does not occur as a literal in any of the other brackets.
- *(ii) it does not occur in its uninverted form in a product within the expression.

i is the count of inverted literals such that for each
- *(i) it is not repeated in the expression (as an inverted literal)
- *(ii) it does not occur in its uninverted (true) form in a product within the expression.

N is the gate count and ΔN is the change in the value of N caused by merging two brackets.

The relevant quantities for each bracket pair are next tabulated and the value of ΔN read directly from the merging table - see Table 6.1. In the case of our example

$$p = (A + B)^1 (A + \overline{C})^2 (A + \overline{D})^3, \text{ we obtain}$$

b/p	n	x	y	r	t	$l - i$	ΔN
1/2	0	1	1	-	1	$2 - 1 = 1$	0
1/3	0	1	1	-	1	$2 - 1 = 1$	0
2/3	0	1	1	-	0	$2 - 1 = 0$	-2

The above tabulation reveals that merging bracket 1 with either bracket 2 or 3 will allow us to meet the fan-in restriction of two with no change in the gate count, whereas merging brackets 2 and 3 in addition to meeting the imposed fan-in restriction of two, reduces the gate count by 2. Merging 1/2, 1/3 and 2/3, we obtain:

$$\begin{aligned} p &= (A + B\overline{C})(A + \overline{D}) \\ &= (A + B\overline{D})(A + \overline{C}) \\ &= (A + B)(A + \overline{C}\overline{D}). \end{aligned}$$

Redualizing, we obtain:

$$\begin{aligned} p &= A(B + C) + AD \text{ - see Figure 5.2(c)} \\ &= A(B + D) + AC \\ &= AB + A(C + D) \text{ - see Figure 5.2(d)} \end{aligned}$$

We shall illustrate the use of the merging table by means of further examples.

* can be omitted with no disastrous effects. In such a case $l = t + i$.

Table 6.1. The merging table

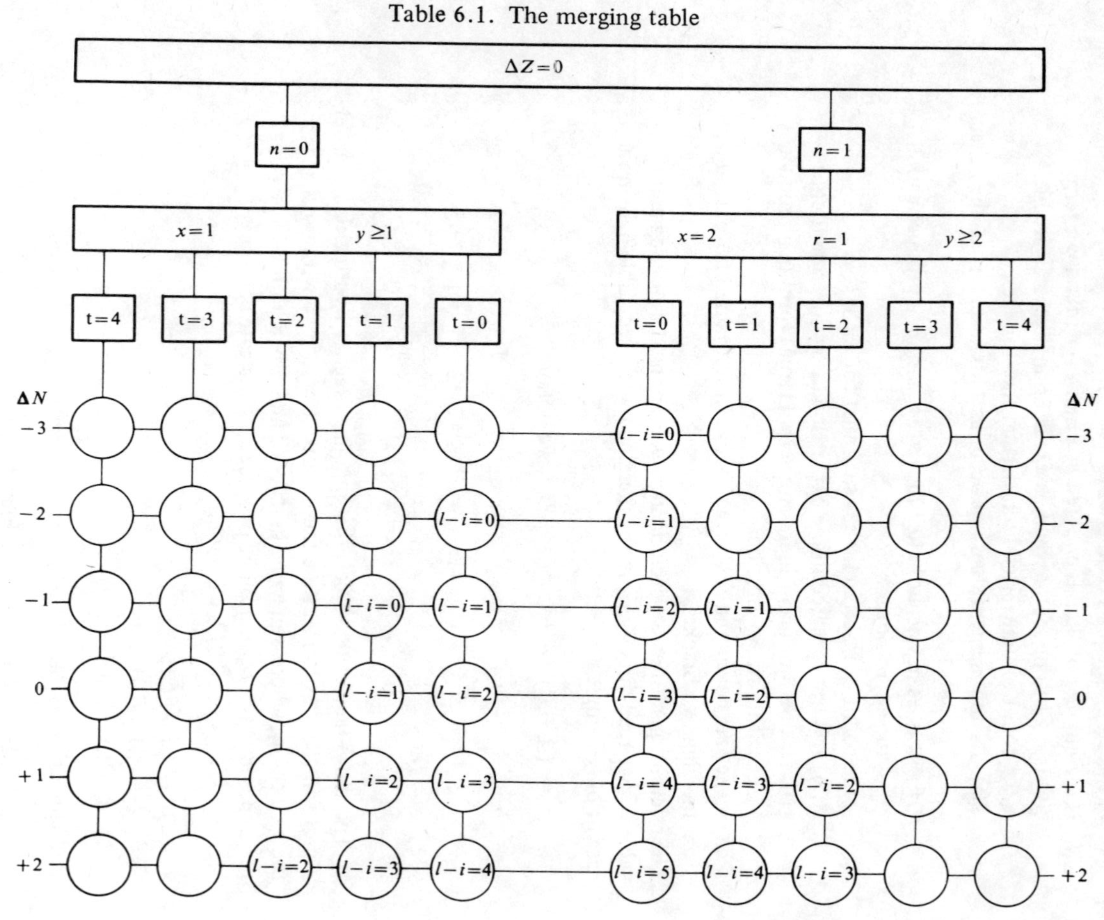

Example 1

Use two-input NAND gates to implement the Boolean function

$$f = A\overline{B} + \overline{A}C + CD + \overline{B}C.$$

SOLUTION

Reduce	$f = A\overline{B} + \overline{A}C + CD$						
Dualize	$f^1 = (A + \overline{B})^1 (\overline{A} + C)^2 (C + D)^3$						
Merge							
b/p	n	x	y	r	t	$l - i$	ΔN
1/2	1	2	2	1	2	$4 - 2 = 2$	+1
1/3	0	2	-	-	-	-	-
2/3	0	1	1	-	1	$2 - 1 = 1$	0

$$f^1 = (A + \overline{B})(C + \overline{A}D).$$

Redualize $f = A\overline{B} + C(\overline{A} + D)$.

The circuit implementations of the reduced and merged forms are shown in Figures 5.3 (a) and (b).

Brackets 1 and 3 do not qualify to merge using the merging table, because $n = 0$ and $x > 1$.

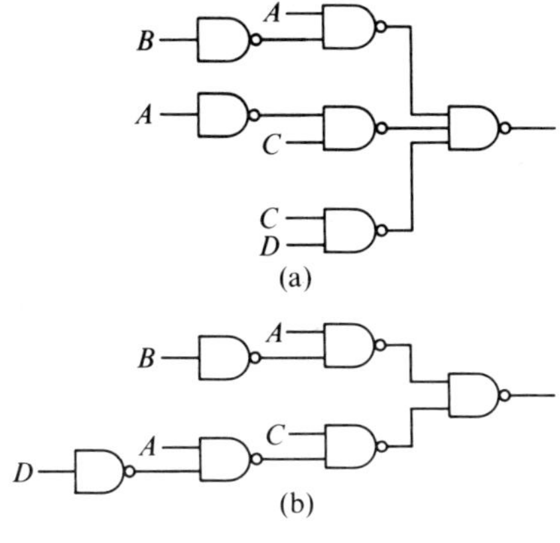

FIG. 6.3

Example 2

Use three-input NAND gates to implement the Boolean function

$$f = AB + \overline{A}\overline{C} + \overline{C}\overline{D} \text{ (reduced).}$$

SOLUTION

Clearly the given expression can be implemented directly without violating the fan-in restriction, as shown in Figure 5.4 (a). We would, however, attempt merging in case we can reduce the gate count of seven.

Dualize	$f^1 = (A+B)^1(\overline{A}+\overline{C})^2(\overline{C}+\overline{D})^3$						
Merge							
b/p	n	x	y	r	t	$l-i$	ΔN
1/2	1	2	2	1	2	$4-1=3$	+2
1/3	0	2	-	-	-	-	-
2/3	0	1	1	-	0	$2-2=0$	−2.

Merge 2 and 3 $\quad f^1 = (A+B)(\overline{A}\overline{D}+\overline{C})$

Redualize $\quad f = AB + \overline{C}(\overline{A}+\overline{D})$.

The above tabulated quantities indicate that implementing the merged form of the given function reduces the gate count by 2 - see Figure 5.4(b).

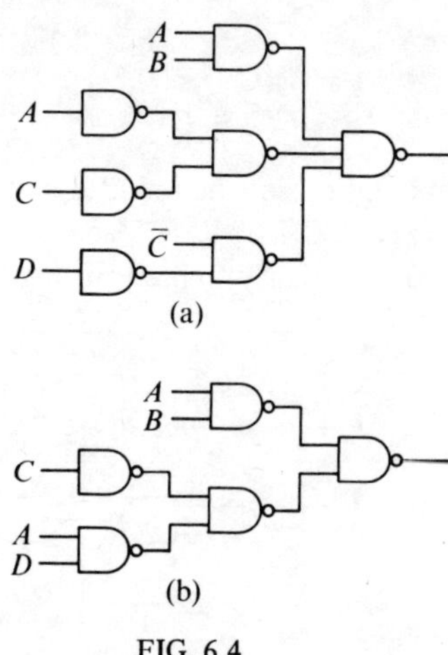

FIG. 6.4

6.3 PROBLEMS AND SOLUTIONS

The use of the procedures used for detecting race-hazards, for meeting fan-in restrictions and for designing hazard-free circuits is illustrated by the following set of problems and solutions.

PROBLEM 1: *Circuit Reduction*

Reduce the circuit shown in Figure (a).

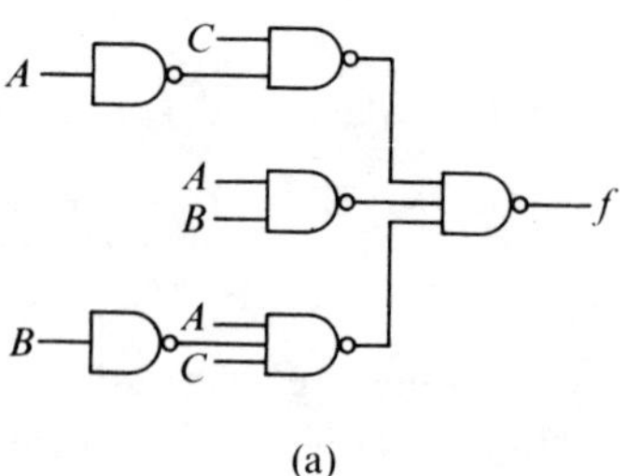

(a)

SOLUTION

By direct reference to the given circuit, we obtain:

$$f = C\overline{A} + AB + A\overline{B}C$$

Reduce

$$f = \overline{A}C + AB + A\overline{B}C$$

BC

AC

C - replaces parents $\overline{A}C$ and $A\overline{B}C$

$$= C + AB.$$

The corresponding circuit is shown in Figure (b).

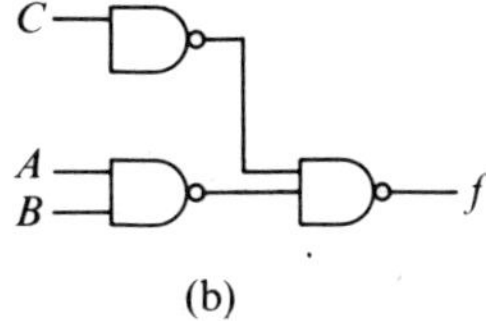

(b)

PROBLEM 2: *Circuit Reduction*

Reduce the circuit shown in Figure (a).

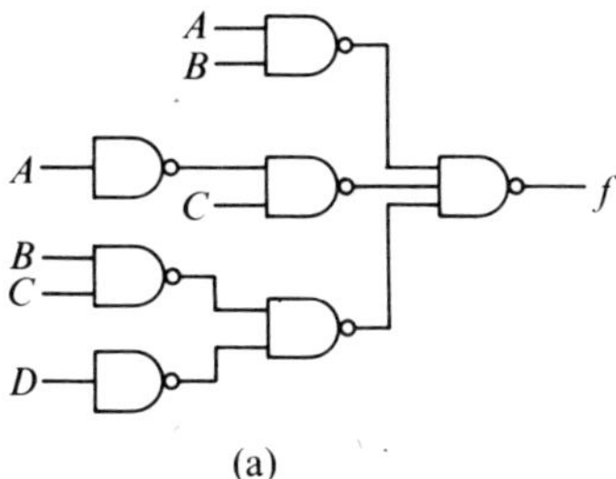

(a)

SOLUTION

By direct reference to the given circuit, we obtain:

$$f = AB + \overline{A}C + (\overline{B} + \overline{C})\overline{D}$$

Reduce

$$f = AB + \bar{A}C + \bar{B}\bar{D} + \bar{C}\bar{D}$$

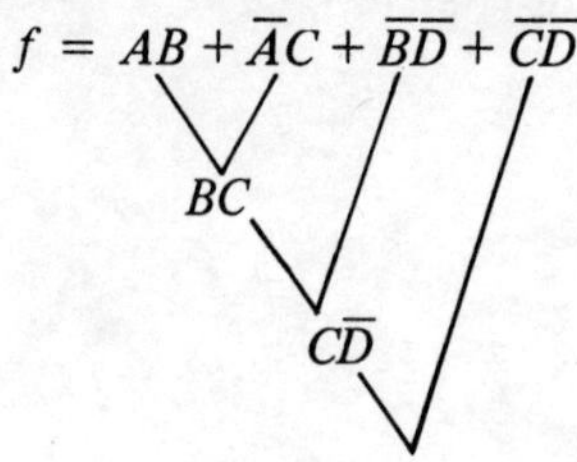

$\bar{D}$ - replaces parent products $\bar{B}\bar{D}$ and $\bar{C}\bar{D}$

$$= AB + \bar{A}C + \bar{D}.$$

The corresponding circuit is shown in Figure (b).

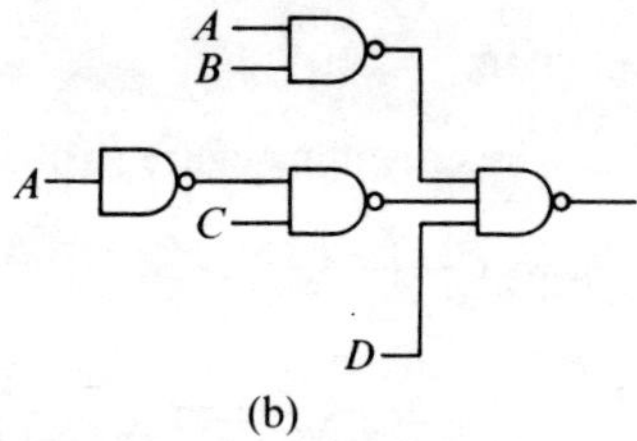

(b)

PROBLEM 3: *Minimal Design*

Use two-input NAND gates to implement minimally the following Boolean functions.

$$f = AB + AC$$
$$g = A\bar{B} + A\bar{C}.$$

SOLUTION

(a) Reduce $\quad f = AB + AC$

Dualize $\quad f' = (A+B)^1 (A+C)^2$

Attempt merging

b/p	n	x	y	r	t	$l-i$	ΔN
1/2	0	1	1	-	2	$2-0=2$	+2

Do not merge.

Redualize $\quad f = AB + AC.$

The corresponding circuit is shown in Figure (a).

(b) Reduce $\quad f = A\bar{B} + A\bar{C}$

$\quad f = A\bar{B} + A\bar{C}$

Dualize $\quad f' = (A+\bar{B})^1 (A+\bar{C})^2$

Attempt merging

b/p	n	x	y	r	t	$l-i$	ΔN
1/2	0	1	1	-	0	$2-2=0$	−2

Merge	$f' = A + BC$
Redualize	$f = A(\overline{B} + \overline{C})$.

The corresponding circuit is shown in Figure (b).

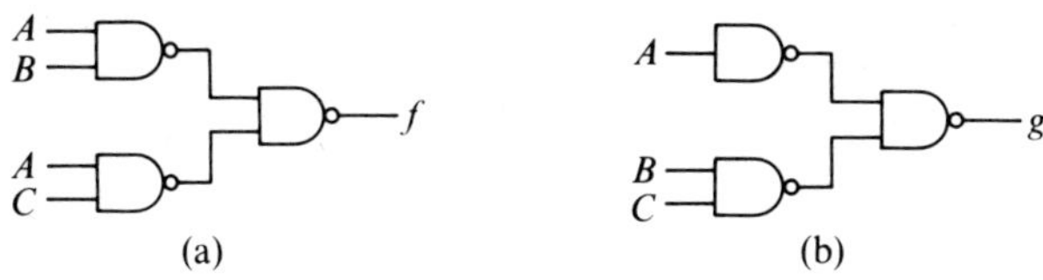

(a) (b)

PROBLEM 4: *Minimal Design*

Use two-input NAND gates to implement the following Boolean functions.

(a) $h = A\overline{B} + \overline{A}\overline{C}$

(b) $i = AB + \overline{A}\overline{C} + C\overline{D}$.

SOLUTION

(a) Reduce $h = A\overline{B} + \overline{A}\overline{C}$

Dualize $h' = (A + \overline{B})^1 (\overline{A} + \overline{C})^2$

Attempt merging

b/p	n	x	y	r	t	$l-i$	ΔN
1/2	1	2	2	1	1	$4-3=1$	-1

Merge	$h' = \overline{A}\overline{C} + A\overline{B}$
Redualize	$h = (\overline{A} + \overline{C})(A + \overline{B})$.

The corresponding circuit is shown in Figure (a).

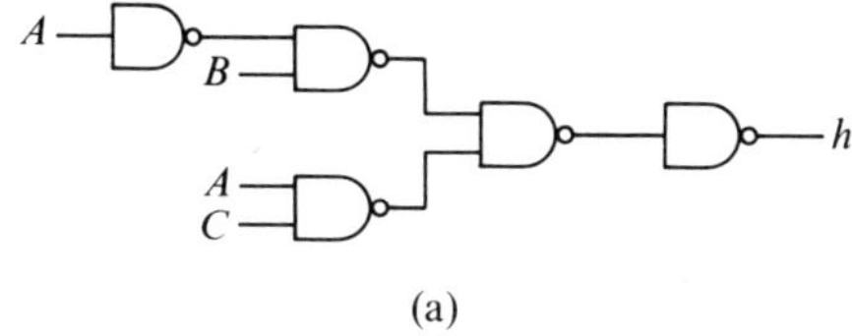

(a)

(b) Reduce $i = AB + \overline{A}\overline{C} + C\overline{D}$

Dualize $i' = (A + B)^1 (A + C)^2 (C + \overline{D})^3$

Attempt merging

b/p	n	x	y	r	t	$l-i$	ΔN
1/2	1	2	2	2	2	$4-2=2$	$+1$
1/3	0	2	-	-	-	4 -	-
2/3	1	2	2	1	1	$4-3=1$	-1

Merge 2 and 3	$i' = (A + B)(\overline{A}C + \overline{C}\overline{D})$
Redualize	$i = AB + (\overline{A} + C)(\overline{C} + \overline{D})$.

The corresponding circuit is shown in Figure (b).

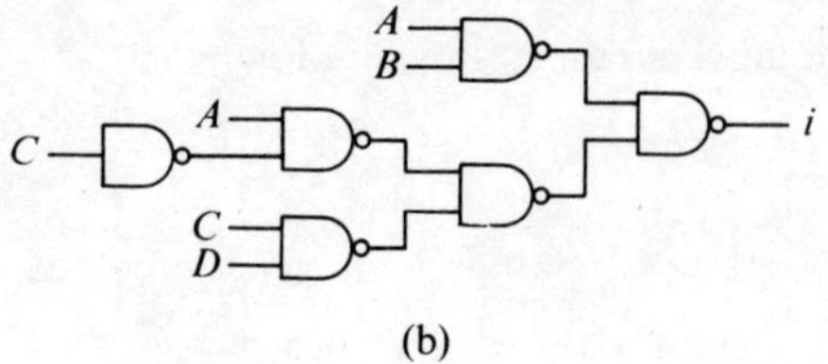

(b)

PROBLEM 5: *Minimal Design*

Use the smallest number of three-input NAND gates to implement the Boolean function

$$f = \overline{A}\overline{B}\overline{C} + \overline{A}\overline{C}D + ABD + ACD \text{ (irredundant).}$$

SOLUTION

Step 1 *Minimize**

Using the minimization tree, we obtain:

$(AB)D$ — $(\overline{A}\overline{C})D$; $(AB)D$ | $(AC)D$; $(\overline{A}\overline{B})\overline{C}$ | $(\overline{A}\overline{C})D$

$$f = ACD + B\overline{C}D + \overline{A}\overline{B}\overline{C}.$$

Step 2 *Merge*

Since fan-in restriction is not violated, we would only merge at negative levels on ΔN.

Dualize $\quad f' = (A + C + D)^1 (B + \overline{C} + D)^2 (\overline{A} + \overline{B} + \overline{C})^3$

Merge

b/p	n	x	y	r	t	$l-i$	ΔN
1/2	1	2	2	1	0	$4-0=4$	+1
1/3	1	3	-	-	-		-
2/3	1	2	2	1	2	$4-2=2$	+1

We do not merge. Therefore $f = ACD + B\overline{C}D + \overline{A}\overline{B}\overline{C}$ is the required expression. The corresponding circuit is shown in Figure (a).

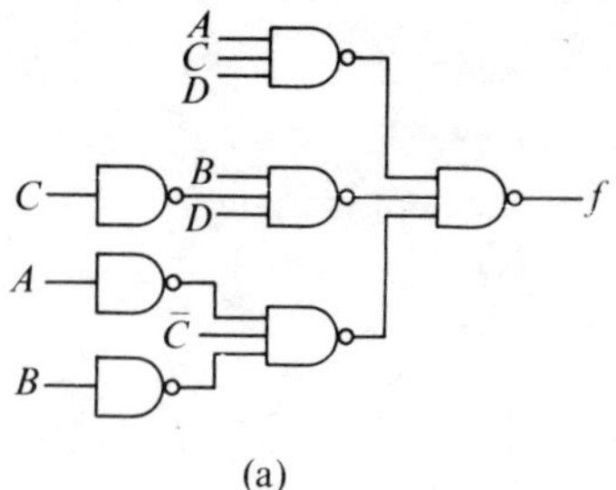

(a)

* See appendix 1 for minimization steps.

PROBLEM 6: *Race Hazards*

Show under what circumstances the direct NAND implementations of the Boolean functions listed below will produce a signal spike at their output.

(a) $f = AB + A\overline{C} + \overline{C}D$
(b) $g = AB + \overline{A}CD + BC$
(c) $h = (A + \overline{B})(\overline{A} + \overline{C})$.

SOLUTION

(a) Because no Boolean variable appears both in its inverted and uninverted form, no signal races exist in the circuit.

(b) As the expression does not reduce to $A + \overline{A}$, the signal spike due to a race in signals A and $\overline{A}$ is blanked out by signal BC.

(c) The expression reduces to $A \cdot \overline{A}$ when $B = C = 1$, revealing a spike when A changes from 0 to 1, as shown in Figure (a).

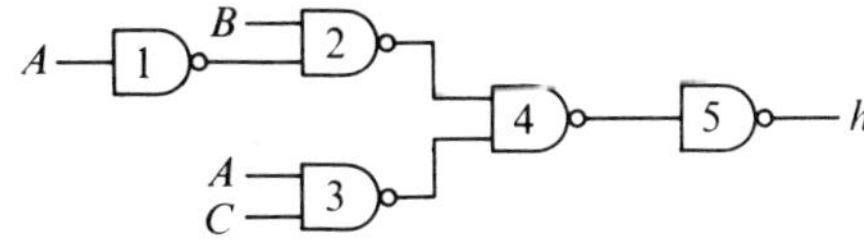

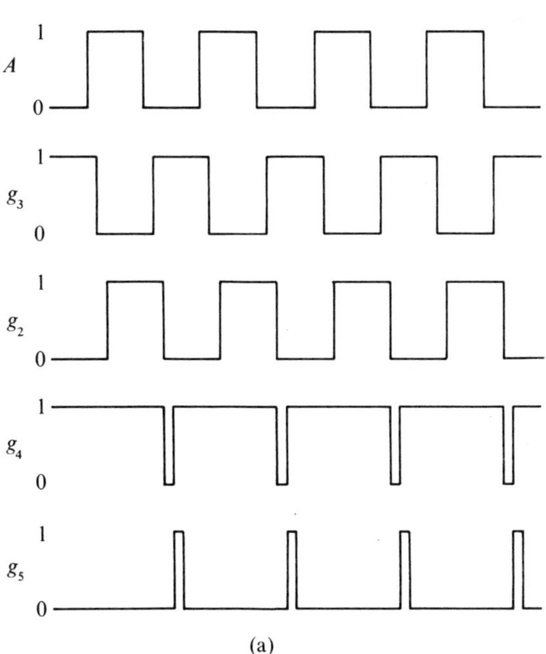

(a)

PROBLEM 7: *Hazard-free Design*

Consider the Boolean function, already expressed minimally, $f = AB + \overline{A}C$. Show under what circumstances its direct NAND realization will produce a spike at its output. Derive an equivalent hazard-free expression that can be implemented minimally using two input NAND gates.

SOLUTION

(a) A spike will be produced at the output of gate 2 in Figure (a) when $B = C = 1$ and A changes from 1 to 0.

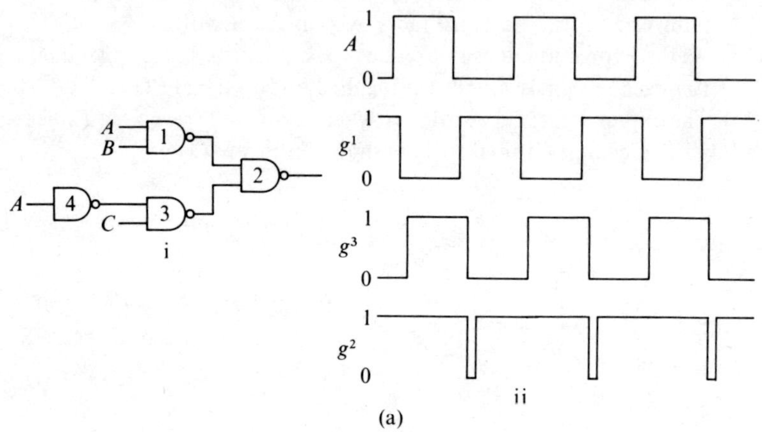

(a)

(b) $f = AB + \overline{A}C + BC$ - hazard-free expression.

Dualize $\quad f' = (A + B)^1(\overline{A} + C)^2(B + C)^3$

Attempt merging

b/p	n	x	y	r	t	$l - i$	ΔN
1/2	1	2	2	1	3	$4 - 1 = 3$	+3
1/3	0	1	1	-	1	$2 - 0 = 2$	+1
2/3	0	1	1	-	1	$2 - 1 = 1$	0

Merge 2/3 $\quad f' = (A + B)(\overline{A}B + C)$

Redualize $\quad f = AB + C(\overline{A} + B).$

The corresponding circuit is shown in Figure (b).

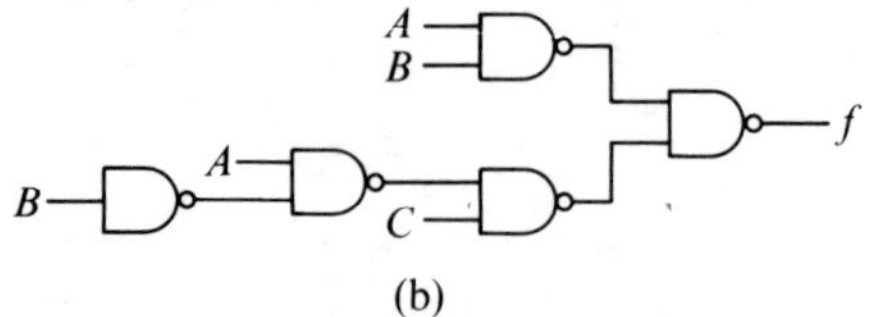

(b)

PROBLEM 8: *A Parity Circuit*

A four bit b-c-d (binary-coded-decimal) code is to be converted to a give-bit code by the addition of an odd parity bit - see Figure (a). Design minimally a suitable circuit using three-input NAND gates.

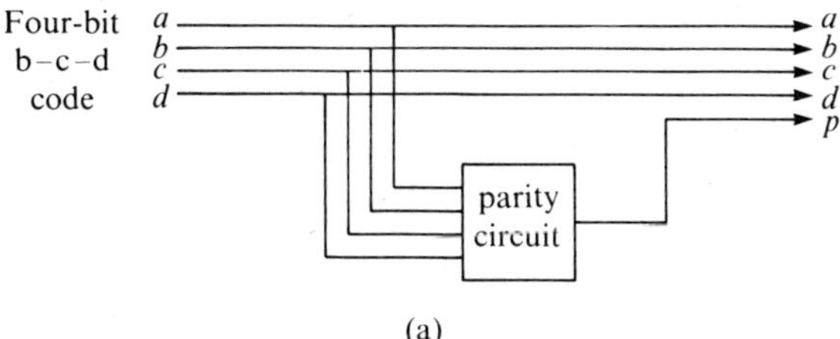

(a)

SOLUTION

$$\begin{aligned} p &= \bar{a}\bar{b}\bar{c}\bar{d} + \bar{a}b\bar{c}\bar{d} + \bar{a}\bar{b}c\bar{d} + a\bar{b}\bar{c}\bar{d} + \bar{a}bcd + a\bar{b}cd + ab\bar{c}d + abc\bar{d} \\ &= \bar{d}(a\bar{b}\bar{c} + \bar{a}b\bar{c} + \bar{a}\bar{b}c + abc) + d(\overline{a\bar{b}\bar{c} + \bar{a}b\bar{c} + \bar{a}\bar{b}c + abc}) \\ &= \bar{d}X + d\bar{X} \end{aligned}$$

now,

$$\begin{aligned} X &= a\bar{b}\bar{c} + \bar{a}b\bar{c} + \bar{a}\bar{b}c + abc \\ &= c(a\bar{b} + \bar{a}b) + c(\overline{a\bar{b} + ab}) \\ &= \bar{c}Y + c\bar{Y} \end{aligned}$$

and

$$Y = a\bar{b} + \bar{a}b \text{ - see Figure below.}$$

The corresponding circuit is shown in Figure (b).

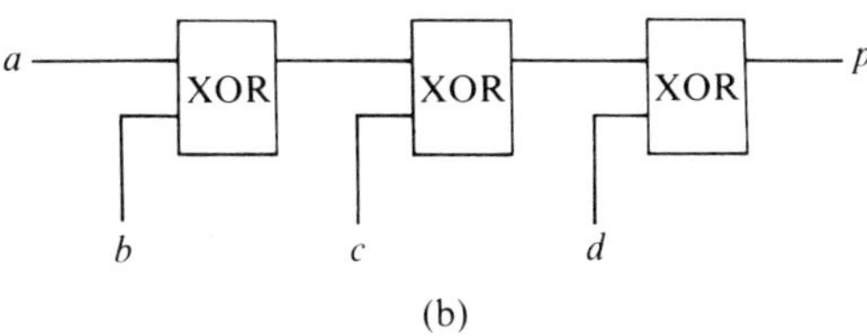

(b)

PROBLEM 9: *Two's Complement* Circuit*

Design a circuit to generate the two's complement of a given binary number - see Figure (a).

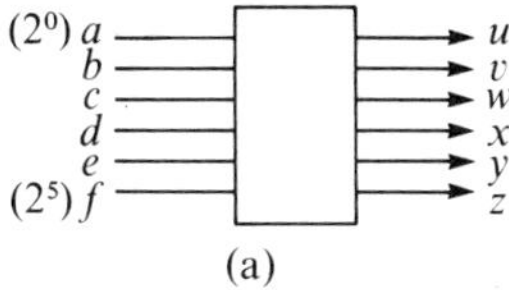

(a)

* The two's complement of a binary number can be formed as follows: starting from the least significant digit we output each digit uninverted up to and including the first '1' digit. The remainder digits are inverted, e.g. 010100 is output as 101100.

SOLUTION

The circuit equations are:

$$
\begin{aligned}
u &= a \\
v &= b\bar{a} + \bar{b}a \\
w &= c\bar{a}\bar{b} + \bar{c}(a+b) \\
x &= d\bar{a}\bar{b}\bar{c} + \bar{d}(a+b+c) \\
y &= e\bar{a}\bar{b}\bar{c}\bar{d} + \bar{e}(a+b+c+d) \\
z &= f\bar{a}\bar{b}\bar{c}\bar{d}\bar{e} + \bar{f}(a+b+c+d+e)
\end{aligned}
$$

The corresponding circuit is shown in Figure (b).

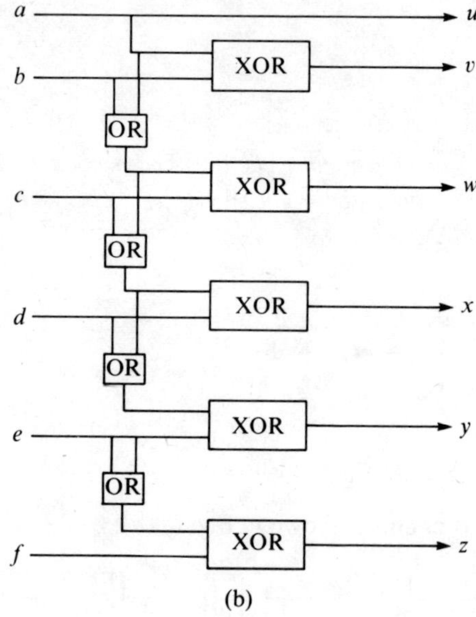

(b)

PROBLEM 10: *Seven Segment Display*

The standard arrangement for displaying a decimal digit on a seven segment display is shown in Figure (a).

a f g b e d c
0 1 2 3 4 5 6 7 8 9

(a)

Derive the input/output equations of a circuit (a decoder) that accepts the value of the decimal digit and outputs a '1' on each terminal for which the corresponding segment is to be illuminated.

SOLUTION

The I/O equations in this case are best derived by means of Karnaugh maps as shown in Figure (b). Blank entries are used as optionals.

CD \ AB	00	01	11	10
00	1	1	1	0
01	1			1
11				
10	0	1	1	1

a

CD \ AB	00	01	11	10
00	1	1	1	1
01	1			1
11				
10	1	0	1	0

b

CD \ AB	00	01	11	10
00	1	0	1	1
01	1			1
11				
10	1	1	1	1

c

CD \ AB	00	01	11	10
00	1	1	1	0
01	1			0
11				
10	0	1	0	1

d

CD \ AB	00	01	11	10
00	1	1	0	0
01	1			0
11				
10	0	1	0	0

e

CD \ AB	00	01	11	10
00	1	0	0	0
01	1			1
11				
10	1	1	0	1

f

CD \ AB	00	01	11	10
00	0	1	1	0
01	1			1
11				
10	1	1	0	1

g

(b)

$$
\begin{aligned}
a &= B + D + AC + \overline{A}\overline{C} \\
b &= C + \overline{A}\overline{B} + AB \\
c &= A + \overline{B} + C \\
d &= \overline{A}\overline{C} + B\overline{C} + \overline{A}B + A\overline{B}C \\
e &= \overline{A}\overline{C} + \overline{A}B \\
f &= \overline{A}\overline{B} + \overline{A}C + \overline{B}C + D \\
g &= D + B\overline{C} + \overline{A}C + \overline{B}C
\end{aligned}
$$

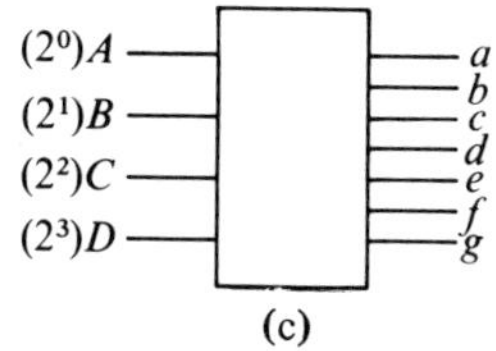

(c)

PROBLEM 11: *Encoders/Decoders**

Derive the input/output equations of

(a) a decimal to binary encoder, and

(b) a binary to decimal decoder.

Block diagrams of the encoder and decoder are shown in Figure (a).

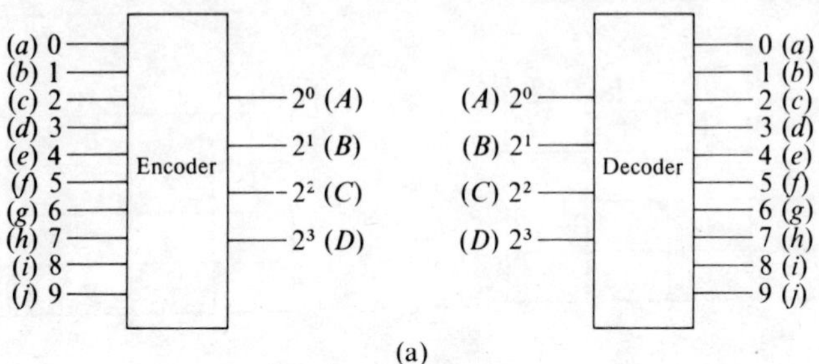

(a)

SOLUTION

(a) $A = b + d + f + h + j$

$B = c + d + g + h$

$C = e + f + g + h$

$D = i + j$

CD \ AB	00	01	11	10
00	$a=1$	$c=1$	$d=1$	$b=1$
01	$i=1$			$j=1$
11				
10	$e=1$	$g=1$	$h=1$	$f=1$

(b) By direct reference to the decoder's Karnaugh map, we obtain:

$a = \overline{A}\overline{B}\overline{C}\overline{D}$ $\quad c = \overline{A}B\overline{C}$ $\quad e = \overline{A}\overline{B}C$ $\quad g = \overline{A}BC$ $\quad i = \overline{A}D$

$b = A\overline{B}\overline{C}\overline{D}$ $\quad d = AB\overline{C}$ $\quad f = A\overline{B}C$ $\quad h = ABC$ $\quad j = AD$

PROBLEM 12: *Code Conversion (Natural Binary to Gray)*

Design a circuit to convert the true binary code to Gray code shown in the table below.

* A device that generates the binary representation of a decimal number is called a decimal to binary encoder (or more simply decimal to binary coder). By analogy a device that receives a given binary code and generates the equivalent decimal number is called a binary to decimal decoder (or more simply binary to decimal coder).

	Binary Code			Gray Code		
N	a	b	c	w	x	y
0	0	0	0	0	0	0
1	1	0	0	1	0	0
2	0	1	0	1	1	0
3	1	1	0	0	1	0
4	0	0	1	0	1	1
5	1	0	1	1	1	1
6	0	1	1	1	0	1
7	1	1	1	0	0	1

SOLUTION

The I/O equations in this case are best derived by means of Karnaugh maps. From the Karnaugh maps in Figure (a), we obtain:

$$w = ab + ab$$
$$x = bc + bc$$
$$y = c$$

The corresponding circuit is shown in Figure (b).

The circuit can clearly be expanded to accommodate larger word lengths.

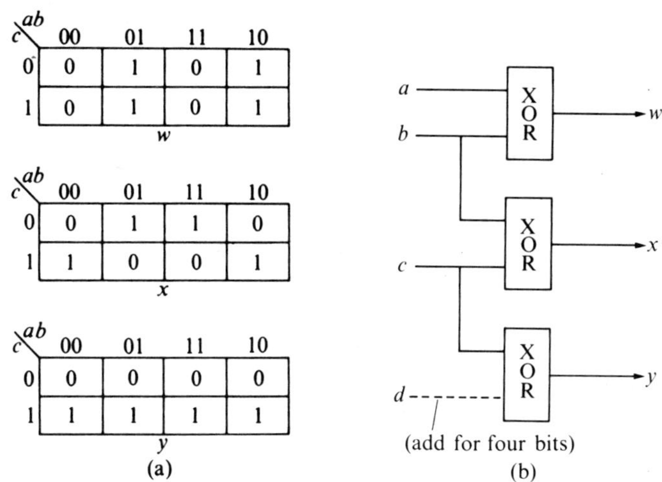

(a) (b)

PROBLEM 13: *NOR Circuit Design*

Use the smallest number of two-input NOR gates to implement the Boolean function $f = (A + \overline{B})(\overline{A} + B)(A + \overline{C})(\overline{A} + C)$. The given expression is irredundant.

SOLUTION

Applying the minimization steps described in Appendix 1, we obtain:

$$f = (A + \overline{B})(B + \overline{C})(\overline{A} + C).$$

We next apply the merging steps to reduce the number of brackets from three to two.

$$f = (A + \overline{B})^1 (B + \overline{C})^2 (\overline{A} + C)^3$$

b/p	n	x	y	r	t	$l-i$	ΔN
1/2	1	2	2	1	1	$4-2=2$	0
1/3	1	2	2	1	1	$4-2=2$	0
2/3	1	2	2	1	1	$4-2=2$	0

Merging 1 and 2, we obtain:

$$f = (AB + \overline{B}\overline{C})(\overline{A} + C).$$

The corresponding circuit is shown in Figure (a).

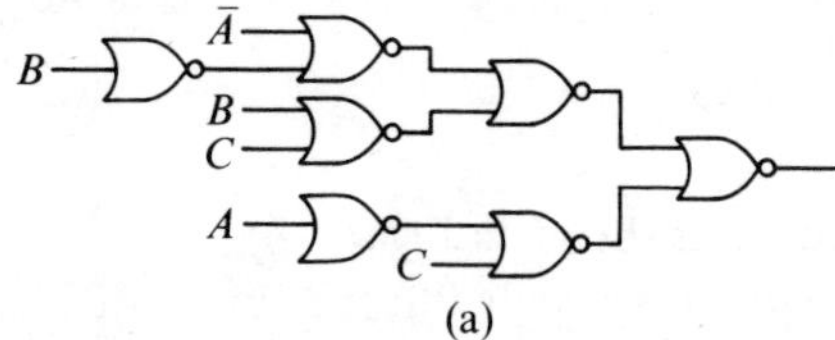

(a)

PROBLEM 14: *A Two-flag Sorter*

Design and implement a two-flag sorter.

SOLUTION

A flag sorter is a device that automatically detects and identifies the presence of a signal at its input. It is also referred to as a *priority encoder.* Eight-flag sorters are available commercially as i.c. chips. We shall refer to the input signals as flags. For definition of flag signals see Problem 13 in Chapter 2.

When more than one signal are simultaneously present at its input, a flag sorter generates a single address only, defining the incoming signal with the highest priority. For example if flags 2 and 3 are present, and flag 3 has higher priority than flag 2, the address generated by the flag sorter will be three. Unless we specify otherwise, we shall assume that the higher the flag number, the higher its priority.

In addition to the address signals, a flag sorter generates a signal, I, to indicate that one or more flags are present at its input, as shown in Figure (a). In an industrial environment signal I will be referred to as a

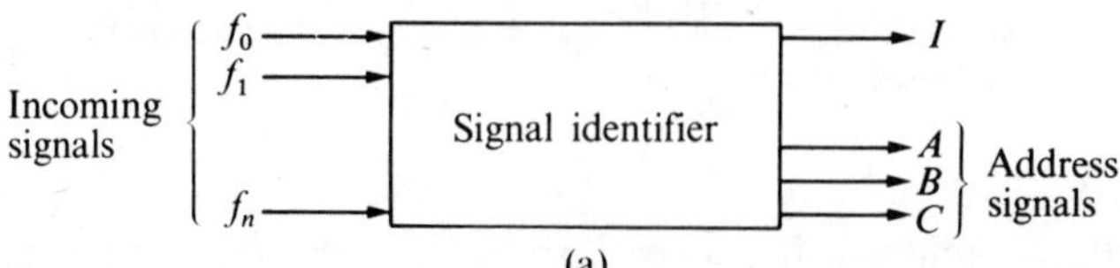

(a)

master alarm, whereas in a computer environment it is referred to as an *interrupt signal.* Signal I is generated by ORing the input signals, that is $I = f_0 + f_1 + f_2 + \ldots + f_n$.

Flag sorters are used extensively in automatic alarm detection systems, and in computer and microprocessor systems using the interrupt mode. The interested reader is referred to *System Design with Microprocessors* by D. Zissos, Academic Press, 1978.

The block diagram of a two-flag sorter is shown in Figure (b). Its I/O (input/output) signal relationship is shown in the form of a truth table in Figure (c). When no flag is present, interrupt signal I is zero. The address signal in this case may be 0 or 1, since the unit for which it is generated will not be reading it.

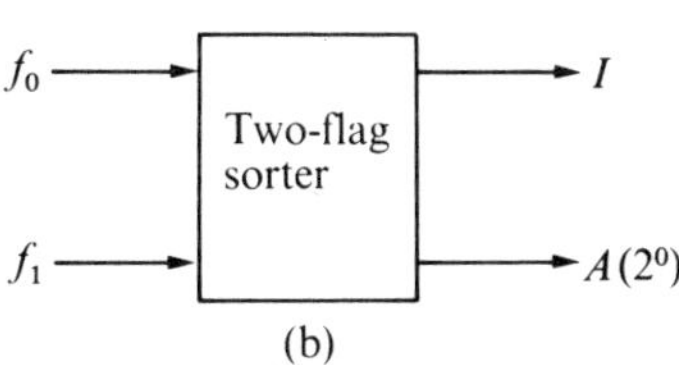

(b)

f_0	f_1	I	A
0	0	0	Ø
x	1	1	1
1	0	1	0

(c)

The second row is filled in the following manner. Our circuit first samples the highest-priority flag, in our case f_1. If $f_1 = 1$, it does not sample the other flag, since the address to be generated in this case is 1, whether f_0 is present or not. We indicate this by inserting x in the first column.

We next move to the third row of our truth table. Because $f_1 = 1$, our circuit samples the state of f_0. Finding $f_0 = 1$, it generates an interrupt signal, I, and address 0.

By direct reference to our truth table, we obtain

$$\begin{aligned} I &= f_0 + f_1, \text{ and} \\ A &= f_1 + (\bar{f}_0 \cdot \bar{f}_1) \\ &= f_1. \end{aligned}$$

That is, a two-flag sorter can be implemented with an OR gate, as shown in Figure (d).

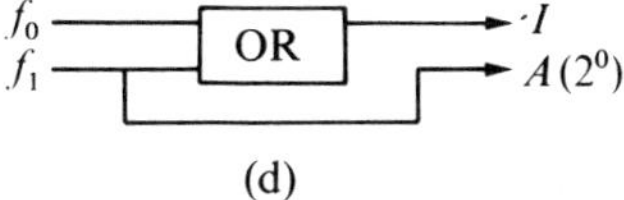

(d)

PROBLEM 15: *A Four-flag Sorter*

Design and implement a four-flag sorter.

SOLUTION

The block diagram of a four-flag sorter is shown in Figure (a). As in

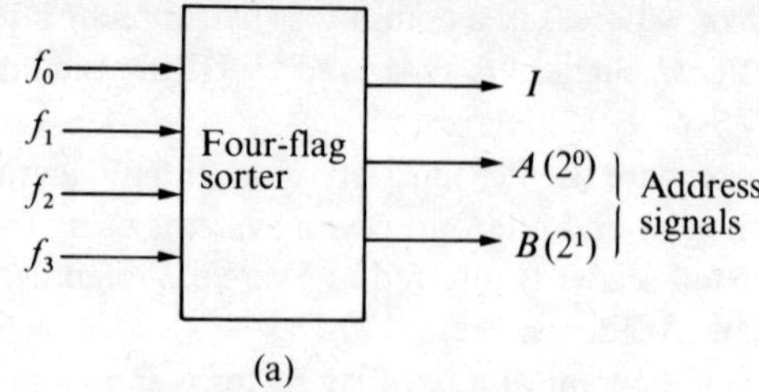

(a)

f_0	f_1	f_2	f_3	I	B	A
0	0	0	0	0	∅	∅
X	X	X	1	1	1	1
X	X	1	0	1	1	0
X	1	0	0	1	0	1
1	0	0	0	1	0	0

(b)

the previous problem we use a truth table to define the I/O (input/output) signal relationship – see Figure (b). It is derived using the method explained in the previous problem. By direct reference to this table, we obtain

$$I = f_0 + f_1 + f_2 + f_3$$

$$A = f_3 + \bar{f}_3 \bar{f}_2 f_1$$
$$= f_3 + \bar{f}_2 f_1$$

$$B = f_3 + \bar{f}_3 f_2$$
$$= f_3 + f_2$$

The corresponding NAND circuit is shown in Figure (c).

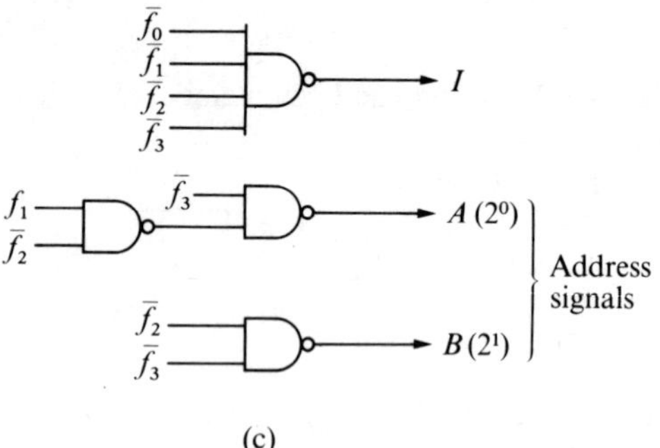

(c)

PROBLEM 16: *An Eight-flag Sorter*

Design and implement an eight-flag sorter.

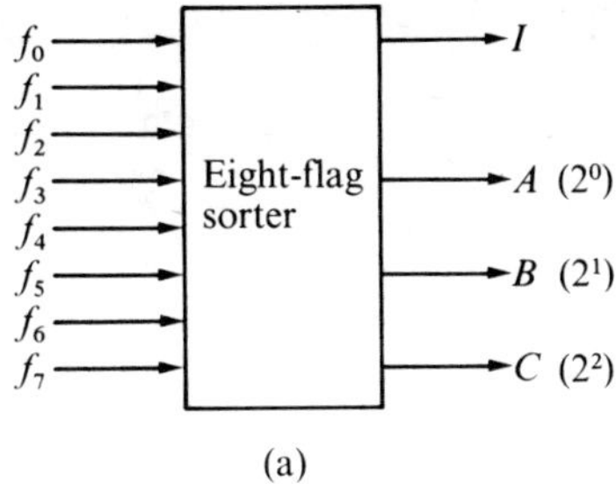

(a)

Inputs								Outputs			
f_0	f_1	f_2	f_3	f_4	f_5	f_6	f_7	I	C	B	A
0	0	0	0	0	0	0	0	0	∅	∅	∅
X	X	X	X	X	X	X	1	1	1	1	1
X	X	X	X	X	X	1	0	1	1	1	0
X	X	X	X	X	1	0	0	1	1	0	1
X	X	X	X	1	0	0	0	1	1	0	0
X	X	X	1	0	0	0	0	1	0	1	1
X	X	1	0	0	0	0	0	1	0	1	0
X	1	0	0	0	0	0	0	1	0	0	1
1	0	0	0	0	0	0	0	1	0	0	0

(b)

SOLUTION

The block diagram of an eight-flag sorter is shown in Figure (a). Its I/O relationship is shown in the form of a truth table in Figure (b). By direct reference to this table, we obtain the following equations:

$$1 = f_0 + f_1 + f_2 + f_3 + f_4 + f_5 + f_6 + f_7.$$

$$\begin{aligned} A &= f_7 + f_5 \bar{f}_6 \bar{f}_7 + f_3 \bar{f}_4 \bar{f}_5 \bar{f}_6 \bar{f}_7 + f_1 \bar{f}_2 \bar{f}_3 \bar{f}_4 \bar{f}_5 \bar{f}_6 \bar{f}_7 \\ &= f_7 + f_5 \bar{f}_6 + f_3 \bar{f}_4 \bar{f}_6 + f_1 \bar{f}_2 \bar{f}_4 \bar{f}_6. \end{aligned}$$

$$\begin{aligned} B &= f_7 + f_6 \bar{f}_7 + f_3 \bar{f}_4 \bar{f}_5 \bar{f}_6 \bar{f}_7 + f_2 \bar{f}_3 \bar{f}_4 \bar{f}_5 \bar{f}_6 \bar{f}_7 \\ &= f_7 + f_6 + f_3 \bar{f}_4 \bar{f}_5 + f_2 \bar{f}_4 \bar{f}_5. \end{aligned}$$

$$\begin{aligned} C &= f_7 + f_6 \bar{f}_7 + f_5 \bar{f}_6 \bar{f}_7 + f_4 \bar{f}_5 \bar{f}_6 \bar{f}_7 \\ &= f_7 + f_6 + f_5 + f_4. \end{aligned}$$

As eight-input priority encoders are available commercially, the above equations will not be implemented.

PROBLEM 17: *A 64-flag Sorter*

Design a 64-flag sorter. Implement your design using eight-flag sorters.

SOLUTION

The block diagram of a 64-flag sorter is shown in Figure (a). The 64 flags are arranged into eight groups of eight flags, each group being allocated a flag sorter. The interrupt signals from the eight flag sorters

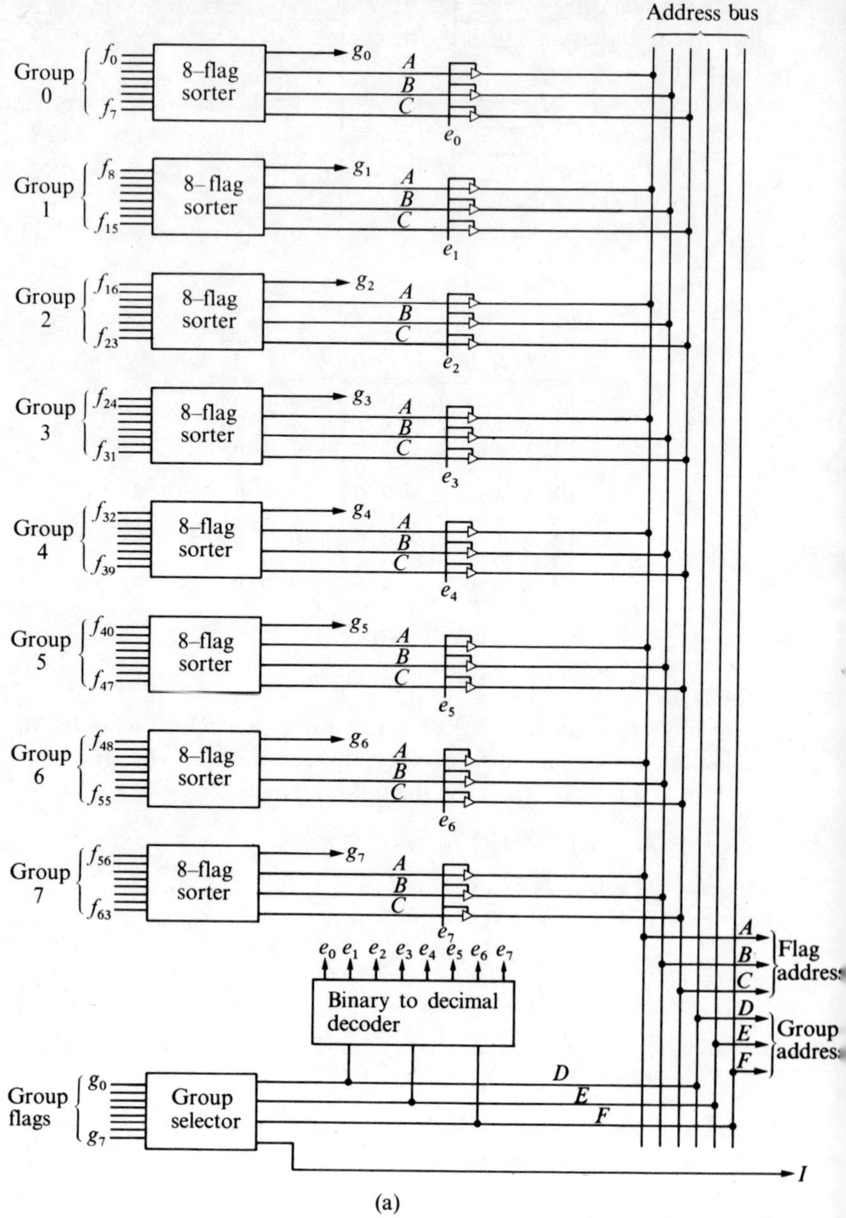

(a)

are connected to a group selector, itself an eight-flag sorter. It operates as follows.

The group selector selects a group flag that is on, generates the system interrupt signal, I, and a three-bit address DEF which identifies the selected group. Signals D, E, and F, in addition to being connected to the address bus, drive a binary-to-decimal decoder. Each of the eight outputs of the decoder drives in turn the three tristates which connect the address lines of the corresponding flag-sorter to the address bus, as shown in Figure (a).

Note that our 64-flag sorter arrangement can be used directly to accommodate less than 64 flags by simply grounding the unused flag terminals.

Clearly the modular method we used to derive a 64-flag sorter using eight-flag sorters, can be used to produce a system for handling up to 4012 flags simply by using the 64 flag sorter in Figure (a) as the module.

Appendix 1

BOOLEAN ALGEBRA

The necessary basis for the design of logic circuits is a working knowledge of Boolean Algebra. In this appendix we give a brief but complete description of those aspects of Boolean Algebra that provide such a basis.

A1.1 BASIC CONCEPTS

As in conventional algebra, so in Boolean algebra we combine variables into expressions with operators that obey certain laws. The *Boolean variables* denoted by letters of the alphabet, A, B, C, etc. may assume one of two values only, 0 or 1. These are new quantities and they are sometimes read as 'false' and 'true' respectively. They are not the 'zero' and 'one' of arithmetic. Although there exists a wide number of *Boolean operators*, such as NAND, NOR, etc., we need only consider three operators at this stage – all other operators can be expressed in terms of these three. They are:

Boolean addition (or disjunction)
Boolean multiplication (or conjunction), and
Boolean inversion (or negation).

The addition (or disjunction) operator is written as +. Sometimes it is written as ∪ or 'OR'. '$A + B$' may be read 'A or B' or 'A plus B'. '$A + B$' is true if either A is true or B is true, and false otherwise. Thus,

$$0 + 0 = 0$$
$$0 + 1 = 1$$
$$1 + 1 = 1$$
$$1 + 0 = 1.$$

The multiplication (or conjunction) operator is written as · or ×, or omitted when its factors are variables denoted by single letters (the same rule as in ordinary algebra). Sometimes it is written as ∩ or 'AND'. '$A \cdot B$' may be read 'A and B', or 'A times B'. '$A \cdot B$' is true if A and B are both true, and false otherwise. Thus,

$$0 \times 0 = 0$$
$$0 \times 1 = 0$$
$$1 \times 1 = 1$$
$$1 \times 0 = 0.$$

The inversion (or complementing or negation) operator is written as a bar over its argument or a $\neg$ in front of it. Sometimes it is written 'NOT'. Thus the inverse of A is $\bar{A}$, or $\neg A$, or 'NOT' A.

A1.2 BOOLEAN THEOREMS

Theorem 1 *Redundancy theorem*

$$A + AB = A.$$

Proof.

$$\begin{aligned} A + AB &= A(1 + B) \\ &= A \cdot 1 \\ &= A. \end{aligned}$$

This theorem states that in a sum-of-products Boolean expression, a product that contains all the factors of another product is redundant. It allows us to eliminate redundant products in a sum-of-products expression. For example, in the Boolean function $f = AB + ABC + ABD$, the products ABC and ABD can be eliminated, because each contains all the factors present in AB.

Theorem 2 *Race-hazard theorem*

$$AB + \bar{A}C = AB + \bar{A}C + BC.$$

Proof.

$$\begin{aligned} AB + \bar{A}C + BC &= AB + \bar{A}C + (A + \bar{A})BC \\ &= AB + \bar{A}C + ABC + \bar{A}BC \\ &= AB(1 + C) + \bar{A}C(1 + B) \\ &= AB + \bar{A}C \\ &= \text{L.H.S.} \end{aligned}$$

This theorem allows us to introduce optional† products into a sum-of-products expression. The optional product is the product of the coefficients of A and $\bar{A}$ in the expression $AB + \bar{A}C$. The product BC is optional so long as its parent products (AB and $\bar{A}C$) remain in the expression. Should, however, one of its parent products be eliminated (by applying Theorem 1), then such a product is no longer optional, and cannot be removed from the expression. We shall demonstrate this property by three examples.

† A Boolean product is optional if its presence in an expression does not affect the value of the function.

Example 1

In the Boolean expression $f = A + \overline{A}B$, we observe that one of the products ($A(= A \cdot 1)$) contains A, and another product ($\overline{A}B$) contains $\overline{A}$. Therefore, using Theorem 2, we can introduce the optional product $1 \cdot B = B$, thus,

$$f = A + \overline{A}B + B.$$

Now, by Theorem 1, product AB is redundant, because it contains all the factors (in this case, simply B) of the product B. Since $\overline{A}B$, one of the parent products of B, is not now present in the expression, the term B is no longer optional.

Diagrammatically, we show these steps as follows:

$$f = A + \overline{A}B$$

$\vee$

B – replaces parent product $\overline{A}B$.

$$= A + B.$$

Example 2

Consider the Boolean expression $f = AB + \overline{A}C + BCD$. Because of the presence of A in the product AB and the presence of A in the product $\overline{A}C$, we can use Theorem 2 to introduce the optional product BC. Thus,

$$f = AB + \overline{A}C + BCD + BC.$$

Now, by Theorem 1, the product BCD is redundant, since it contains all the factors of the product BC. Therefore,

$$f = AB + \overline{A}C + BC.$$

Now, because the parent products of BC, namely AB and $\overline{A}C$, are still present in the expression, the term BC is redundant, and therefore it can be eliminated, leaving

$$f = AB + \overline{A}C.$$

Diagrammatically, we show these steps as follows:

$$f = AB + \overline{A}C + BCD$$

$\vee$

BC – eliminates non-parent product BCD.

$$= AB + \overline{A}C.$$

Example 3

Consider the Boolean expression $f = A + \overline{A}B + BC$. The optional product B, generated from the first two products (namely, A and $\overline{A}B$), replaces its parent product $\overline{A}B$ and eliminates non-parent product BC. Diagrammatically, we show this process as follows:

$$f = A + \bar{A}B + BC$$

B – replaces parent product $\bar{A}B$ and eliminates non-parent product BC.

$$= A + B.$$

In summary, *an optional product can be used* (*i*) *to eliminate non-parent products, and/or* (*ii*) *to replace parent products.*

Theorem 3 *De Morgan's theorem*

The complement of a Boolean expression can be derived directly by replacing each variable by its complement in the corresponding dual expression. For example, the dual of $P = A + BC$ is

$$A \cdot (B + C).$$

Therefore, by De Morgan's theorem, the complement of P is

$$\bar{P} = \bar{A} \cdot (\bar{B} + \bar{C}).$$

Proof.

See page 9 of *Logic Design Algorithms* (Zissos, 1972).

Before inverting a given expression it is advisable (a) to reduce the expression and (b) to include all product terms in brackets. The brackets remain unaffected by the complementing process.

Example

Derive the complement of $P = A + B\bar{C} + AD$.

Suggested procedure

Given	$P = A + B\bar{C} + AD$
Reduce	$P = A + B\bar{C}$
Bracket all products	$P = A + (B\bar{C})$
Invert	$\bar{P} = \bar{A} \cdot (\bar{B} + C)$
Remove redundant brackets	$\bar{P} = \bar{A} \cdot (\bar{B} + C)$.

Theorem 4 *Fan-in theorem*

$$(H1 + T1)(\overline{H1} + T2) = H1T2 + \overline{H1}T1.$$

Proof.

$$\begin{aligned} \text{L.H.S.} &= (H1 + T1)(\overline{H1} + T2) \\ &= H1\overline{H1} + H1T2 + \overline{H1}T1 + T1T2. \end{aligned}$$

Now, $H1\overline{H1} = 0$, and $T1T2$ is redundant, by Theorem 2. Therefore,

$$\begin{aligned} \text{L.H.S.} &= H1T2 + \overline{H1}T1 \\ &= \text{R.H.S.} \end{aligned}$$

This theorem allows us to multiply out two irredundant Boolean sums, two sections of which are the complement of each other, without generating algebraically redundant products.

We shall often find it convenient, when multiplying out two Boolean sums, to refer to a section of a Boolean sum as its *head H*, and to the remaining section as its *tail T*. The partition of a Boolean sum into head and tail sections is arbitrary. For example, in the case of $A + B + C$, any of the following partitions is allowable.

Head	Tail
A	$B+C$
B	$A+C$
C	$A+B$
$A+B$	C
$A+C$	B
$B+C$	A

Theorem 4 tells us that if, when we have to multiply out two Boolean sums, we can partition them in such a way that the two heads of the sums are each the complement of the other, then we need only multiply the head of each sum with the tail of the other. For example, suppose we wish to multiply out the contents of the two brackets $(A + B + CD)(\overline{A} + E + F)$. If we choose $H1 = A$ and $H2 = \overline{A} = \overline{H1}$, we have

$$\begin{aligned} (A + B + CD)(\overline{A} + E + F) &= A(E + F) + \overline{A}(B + CD) \\ &= AE + AF + \overline{A}B + \overline{A}CD. \end{aligned}$$

If there are terms common to both of the sums to be multiplied, we can further simplify the process of multiplication by noting that such terms appear in the product in their original form (that is, not multiplied by an factor). We indicate terms common to both brackets by I. For example,

$$(A + B)(A + C) = A + BC.$$

This is obvious if we multiply out and eliminate redundant terms,

$$\begin{aligned} (A + B)(A + C) &= AA + AC + AB + BC \\ &= A + AC + AB + BC \\ &= A + BC. \end{aligned}$$

Summarizing, therefore,

if $\quad P \equiv H1 + T1 + I,$

and $\quad Q = \overline{H1} + T2 + I,$

where $H1$, $T1$, $T2$, and I are expressions such that $T1$ and $T2$ are different,

then $\quad P \cdot Q = H1 \cdot T2 + \overline{H1} \cdot T1 + I.$

However, in the case where P and Q cannot be partitioned in such a way that their heads are the complement of each other, we have

$$P = X + I,$$
$$Q = Y + I,$$

and $\quad PQ = XY + I.$

A1.3 BOOLEAN REDUCTION

A Boolean function is said to be *irredundant*, or *reduced*, if it contains no redundancies, that is products or factors whose presence does not affect the value of the function. For example, factor $\bar{A}$ in $A + \bar{A}B$ is redundant, since $A + \bar{A}B = A + B$. Redundancies in two-level Boolean expressions can be removed in three steps, using Theorems 1 and 2 of A1.2. If an expression contains more than two levels, such as $f = A + B(C + D)$, we convert it into its two-level sum-of-products form by multiplying out.

The three steps for eliminating redundancies in Boolean expressions are as follows (see Fig. A1.1).

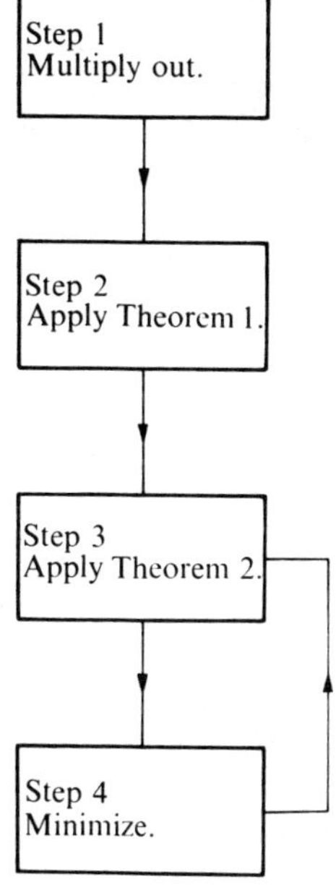

FIG. A1.1

Step 1. Multiply out

The expression to be reduced is converted into its two-level sum-of-products form by multiplying out. Products that contain both a variable and its inverse as factors are eliminated, using the identity $A \cdot \overline{A} = 0$. The repetition of a variable in a product is eliminated using the identity $A \cdot A = A$. The products are finally rearranged in ascending order of size from left to right.

Example

Consider the Boolean function $f = BC + (AB + D)\overline{D} + A$. Applying step 1, we obtain

$$\begin{aligned} f &= BC + (AB + D)\overline{D} + A \\ &= BC + ABD + D\overline{D} + A \\ &= BC + AB\overline{D} + A \\ &= A + BC + AB\overline{D}. \end{aligned}$$

Step 2. Apply Theorem 1

We eliminate redundant products, using Theorem 1, as follows. Starting with the products of the fewest factors, i.e. from the left, we take each term in succession and compare with it all products containing more factors; these will be to its right. A product that contains all the factors of the given term is eliminated.

Example

In step 1, we derived $f = A + BC + AB\overline{D}$. We start step 2 by considering the first product, in this case A. We scan the products to the right of A, looking for a product that contains A as a factor. $AB\overline{D}$ is such a product, which therefore is eliminated, resulting in $f = A + BC$. Since there are no products to the right of BC, we do not repeat the step.

Step 3. Apply Theorem 2

Here we generate optional products, using Theorem 2. In practice, we find that experience will enable us to take short cuts in the process described below. However, a complete systematic description is given, which would be used by beginners or in a computer program.

Assuming the products are arranged in ascending order of size from left to right, we proceed as follows.

(1) The first variable in the first product is selected, and the remainder of the expression is scanned for a product that contains the complement of the selected variable. When such a product is found, we form an optional product, using Theorem 2. The optional product is used to eliminate non-parent products and/or to replace parent products, as explained in Example 3, following Theorem 2. If a parent product has been replaced, we insert the optional product at the beginning of the expression, and we

repeat step 3. If the optional product has not been used, it is discarded.

Step 3 is repeated until all first-level optional products have been generated.

(2) We repeat step 3, using higher-level optional products.

We shall demonstrate the reduction steps by means of the following problems.

PROBLEM 1

Reduce the Boolean function $P = A + AB + \bar{A}C + \bar{C}D$.

SOLUTION

Step 1. No change.

Step 2. $P = A + AB + \bar{A}C + \bar{C}D$
$= A + \bar{A}C + \bar{C}D$

Step 3. $P = A + \bar{A}C + \bar{C}D$

C - replace parent product $\bar{A}C$.

$P = C + \bar{C}D + A$

D - replaces parent product $\bar{C}D$.

$= D + A + C$.

No further optional products can be generated, therefore the reduced sum of the given function is $A + C + D$ - the required result.

PROBLEM 2

Reduce the Boolean function $Q = A(\bar{A} + B) + \bar{B}C + \bar{A} + \bar{C} + ABC$.

SOLUTION

Step 1. $Q = A\bar{A} + AB + \bar{B}C + \bar{A} + \bar{C} + ABC$
$= \bar{A} + \bar{C} + AB + \bar{B}C + ABC$

Step 2. $Q = \bar{A} + \bar{C} + AB + \bar{B}C + ABC$
$= \bar{A} + \bar{C} + AB + \bar{B}C$

Step 3. $Q = \bar{A} + \bar{C} + AB + \bar{B}C$

B - replaces parent product AB.

$= B + \bar{A} + \bar{C} + \bar{B}C$

C - replaces parent product $\bar{B}C$.

$$= \underbrace{C + B + \overline{A} + \overline{C}}_{1}$$

$= 1$ - the required result.

PROBLEM 3

Reduce the Boolean function $R = \overline{A}\overline{B} + \overline{A}C + BC + AB$.

SOLUTION

Step 1. No change.

Step 2. No change.

Step 3. $R = \overline{A}C + BC + AB + \overline{A}\overline{B}$

$\overline{A}C$ and AB → BC - eliminates non-parent product BC.

BC and $\overline{A}\overline{B}$ → $\overline{A}C$ - cannot eliminate nor replace.

$= \overline{A}C + AB + \overline{A}\overline{B}$.

Since one first-level optional product only can be generated, viz. BC, the above derived form cannot be reduced. Therefore $\overline{A}C + AB + \overline{A}\overline{B}$ is the required result.

Note. An alternative reduced form $\overline{A}\overline{B} + BC + AB$ is obtained if optional product $\overline{A}C$ (generated from $\overline{A}\overline{B}$ and BC) is generated first.

PROBLEM 4

Reduce the Boolean function $S = AB + \overline{A}C + (\overline{B} + \overline{C})D$.

SOLUTION

Step 1. $S = AB + \overline{A}C + \overline{B}D + \overline{C}D$.

Step 2. No change.

Step 3. $S = AB + \overline{A}C + \overline{B}D + \overline{C}D$

AB and $\overline{A}C$ → BC

BC and $\overline{B}D$ → CD

CD and $\overline{C}D$ → D - replace parent products $\overline{B}D + \overline{C}D$.

$= D + AB + \overline{A}C$

AB and $\overline{A}C$ → BC - cannot eliminate or replace.

Since one first-level optional product only can be generated, viz. BC, the above derived form $D + AB + \overline{A}C$ is the required result.

PROBLEM 5

Reduce the Boolean function $T = \overline{A}B + A\overline{D} + A\overline{B} + \overline{C}(A + D) + \overline{A}BD.$

SOLUTION

Step 1. $T = \overline{A}B + A\overline{D} + A\overline{B} + A\overline{C} + \overline{C}D + \overline{A}BD.$

Step 2. $T = \overline{A}B + A\overline{D} + A\overline{B} + A\overline{C} + \overline{C}D + \overline{A}BD$
$= \overline{A}B + A\overline{D} + A\overline{B} + A\overline{C} + \overline{C}D.$

Step 3. $T = \overline{A}B + A\overline{D} \quad + \quad A\overline{B} + A\overline{C} + \overline{C}D$

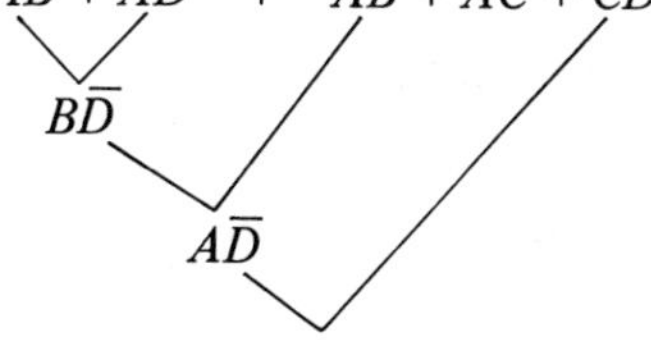

$B\overline{D}$

$A\overline{D}$

$A\overline{C}$ - eliminates non-parent product $A\overline{C}$.

$= \overline{A}B + A\overline{D} + A\overline{B} + \overline{C}D$

$A\overline{C}$

$B\overline{C}$ - neither eliminates nor replaces.

$= \overline{A}B + A\overline{D} + A\overline{B} + \overline{C}D$

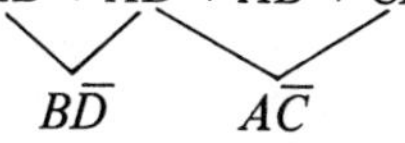

$B\overline{D} \qquad A\overline{C}$

Since no second-level optional products can be generated using $B\overline{D}$ and $A\overline{C}$, and no other first-level optional products can be generated, the above derived form cannot be reduced further. Therefore, $T = \overline{A}B + A\overline{D} + A\overline{B} + \overline{C}D$ is the required result.

PROBLEM 6

Reduce the Boolean function $U = A + \overline{A}C + B + D(\overline{B}\overline{C} + A\overline{C}).$

SOLUTION

Step 1. $U = A + B + \overline{A}C + \overline{B}\overline{C}D + A\overline{C}D.$

Step 2. $U = A + B + \overline{A}C + \overline{B}\overline{C}D + A\overline{C}D$
$= A + B + \overline{A}C + \overline{B}\overline{C}D.$

Step 3. $U = A + B + \overline{A}C + \overline{B}\overline{C}D$

C - replaces parent product $\overline{A}C$.

$$U = C + A + B + \overline{B}\overline{C}D$$

$\overline{B}D$ - replaces parent $\overline{B}\overline{C}D$.

$$= \overline{B}D + C + A + B$$

D - replaces parent $\overline{B}D$

$$= D + C + A + B.$$

Since no optional products can be generated in the above derived form, $S = D + C + A + B$ is the required result.

A1.4 BOOLEAN MINIMIZATION

Definition. A Boolean sum-of-products expression is said to be minimal if

(a) no other sum-of-products expression for the same function has fewer products, and

(b) of other sum-of-products expressions for the same function with the same number of products, none has fewer factors.

That a reduced Boolean expression is not necessarily minimal, we can prove by direct reference to the function $f = A\overline{C} + AB + \overline{A}C + \overline{A}\overline{B}$. That the function is irredundant can be proved by direct reference to Figure A1.2(a) - its Karnaugh map. That it is not minimal we can show by inspection of Figures (b) and (c), where a different looping arrangement reduces the function from a sum of four products, viz. $f = A\overline{C} + AB + \overline{A}C + \overline{A}\overline{B}$ to a sum of three products, viz. either $f = A + BC + \overline{A}\overline{B}$ or $f = AB + \overline{B}\overline{C} + \overline{A}C$. Although in this example we were able to obtain the two minimal solutions of the given function by referring to its Karnaugh map, this method becomes progressively complex, tedious, and susceptible to errors as the number of variables in an expression increases. Furthermore it is difficult to computerise.

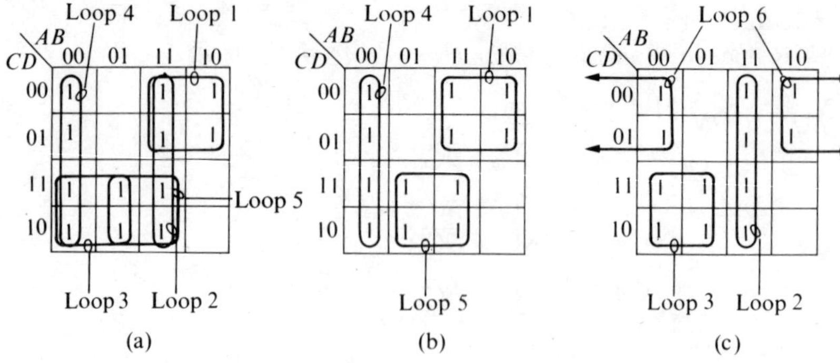

FIG .A1.2.

Note that the minimal solutions of the given function have been obtained by replacing loops 2 and 3 by a new loop, loop 5 in one instance, and by replacing loops 1 and 4 by a new loop, loop 6 in the other.

Expressed algebraically, we minimized the given irredundant expression by replacing two of the products in the original function, namely AB and $\bar{A}C$ in one case and $\bar{A}\bar{B}$ and $A\bar{C}$ in the other, by new products BC and $\bar{B}\bar{C}$ respectively. We were able to do this because the introduction of the new products generate as optional products those that they have replaced when taken with the remaining products. This constitutes the basis of our minimization process, viz. *the generation of an optional product that replaces two products present in the irredundant function.*

Let us denote by $p2$ and $p3$ the two products that are to be replaced by a new product $p23$. The introduction of $p23$ clearly must allow the generation as optional products of $p2$ and $p3$, if they are to be eliminated. Therefore, two more products, $p1$ and $p4$, must be present in the expression which, with $p23$, generate $p2$ and $p3$ as optionals. We show this diagrammatically in Figure A1.3.

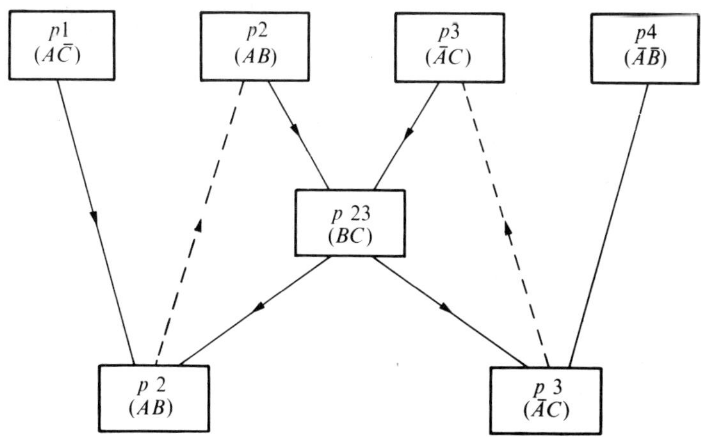

FIG. A1.3.

Now it follows that since the function is irredundant, $p23$ must be generated by $p2$ and $p3$; that is, a factor of $p2$ must be present in $p3$ in its inverted form. Let us denote these two factors by A and $\bar{A}$. Clearly each of the two products $p2$ and $p3$ must contain at least a different factor, otherwise the two products would have been replaced by their optional product in step 3. We denote these factors by B and C respectively, i.e. $p2 = A \cdot B$, $p3 = \bar{A} \cdot C$ and $p23 = B \cdot C$. Since $p23$ with $p1$ and $p4$ must generate $p2$ and $p3$ respectively, $p1 = A \cdot \bar{C}$ and $p4 = \bar{A} \cdot \bar{B}$.

It therefore follows that a necessary condition for this situation is that there should be a set of four products in which

(a) some variable, say A, appears or can be made to appear, at least twice in its true form and at least twice in its inverted form, and

(b) two other variables, say B and C, are each present at least once in their true form and at least once in their inverted form.

Clearly, none of the products may be either a single literal (since in this case the expression would not be irredundant) or a minterm (i.e. a product containing all the variables of the expression).

Steps 3 and 4 are repeated until either the size of the sum reduces to three or the minimization tree structure cannot be established. Note that we need only apply step 3 to the new product and products not used in the tree structure.

If the products can be arranged in such a manner that those to be replaced are in the second and third positions, and the other two in the first and fourth positions, then much time and effort can be conserved, since in such a case the steps will consist of simply replacing products 2 and 3 by their optional product.

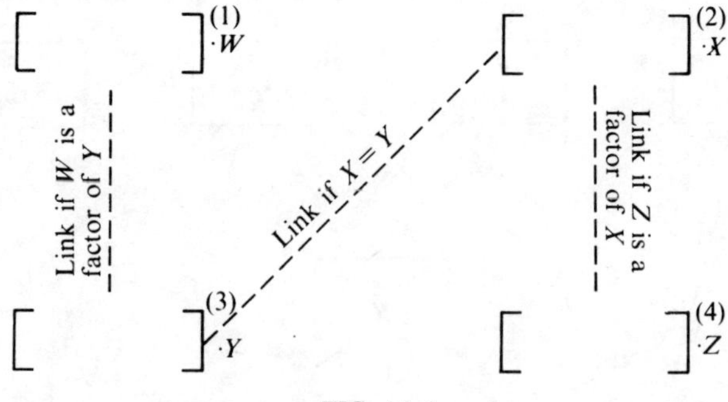

FIG. A1.4.

The criteria for this condition can be expressed by means of the diagram shown in Figure A1.4. It consists of four brackets labelled for convenience 1, 2, 3, and 4. In bracket 1 we insert a product that has as factors A and either B or $\overline{B}$. Should it contain additional factors, these are introduced outside the bracket. In bracket 2 we insert a product containing $\overline{A}$ and either $\overline{B}$ or B depending on whether B or $\overline{B}$ is present in bracket 1. Similarly in bracket 3 we insert a product containing A and either C or $\overline{C}$ depending on whether $\overline{C}$ or C is present in bracket 3.

The application of this diagram is as follows. We link bracket 2 and diagonally opposite bracket 3 if the variables outside the brackets are the same or can be made to be the same. Bracket 1 is next linked to bracket 3 if all the variables outside bracket 1 are present outside bracket 3, i.e. if W is a factor of Y. Also, a link is established between brackets 2 and 4 if the terms outside bracket 4 are all present outside brackets 2. If a diagonal and two vertical links can be established, this indicates that our conditions for replacing products 2 and 3 by their optional product are satisfied. The numbering of the brackets indicates the order in which the products are to be arranged. It is possible that further sets of a diagonal and 2 vertical links can be established. This will imply that further minimal solutions exist.

We shall demonstrate the minimization steps by means of the following problems.

PROBLEM 1

$$P = AB\overline{C}\overline{D} + \overline{B}(AC + \overline{A}\overline{C}) + A\overline{B}.$$

SOLUTION

Step 1. Multiply out

$$P = A\overline{B} + A\overline{B}C + \overline{A}\overline{B}\overline{C} + AB\overline{C}\overline{D}.$$

Step 2. Apply Theorem 1

$$\begin{aligned} P &= A\overline{B} + A\overline{B}C + \overline{A}\overline{B}\overline{C} + AB\overline{C}\overline{D} \\ &= A\overline{B} + \overline{A}\overline{B}\overline{C} + AB\overline{C}\overline{D}. \end{aligned}$$

Step 3. Apply Theorem 2

$$P = A\overline{B} + \overline{A}\overline{B}\overline{C} + AB\overline{C}\overline{D}$$

$\overline{B}\overline{C}$ – replaces parent product $\overline{A}\overline{B}\overline{C}$.

$$= \overline{B}\overline{C} + A\overline{B} + AB\overline{C}\overline{D}.$$

$$P = \overline{B}\overline{C} + A\overline{B} + AB\overline{C}\overline{D}$$

$A\overline{C}\overline{D}$ – replaces parent product $AB\overline{C}\overline{D}$.

$$= A\overline{C}\overline{D} + \overline{B}\overline{C} + A\overline{B}.$$

No more optional products can be generated, therefore the derived expression is irredundant.

Step 4. Minimize. Since the expression derived in step 3 contains less than four products, it is minimal.

PROBLEM 2

$$P = A\overline{B} + \overline{A}\overline{C} + ACD + \overline{A}BD \text{ (irredundant).}$$

SOLUTION

Because the given expression is irredundant, we leave out the first three steps.

Step 4. Minimize. The expression contains four products, therefore it may not be minimal. Furthermore, because variables A and $\bar{A}$ each appear twice, and $B, \bar{B}, C,$ and $\bar{C}$ once, the necessary conditions for drawing the minimization-tree exist (see Figure (a)).

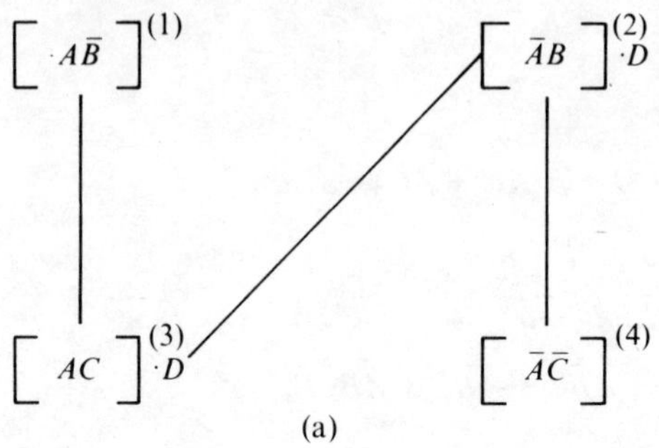

(a)

We link bracket 2 and diagonally opposite bracket 3, because the variables outside the brackets (D) are the same. Bracket 1 is linked to bracket 3, because all the variables outside bracket 1 are present outside bracket 3 (the variables are 1 and $D \cdot 1$, respectively). Similarly, bracket 4 is linked to bracket 2. Therefore, products 2 and 3 can be replaced by their optional product, namely, BCD, resulting in

$$P = A\bar{B} + BCD + \bar{A}\bar{C}.$$

Although a diagonal link can be established between brackets 1 and 4, the two vertical links cannot be drawn.

Step 3 is not repeated as all four products have been used in the minimization-tree. Since the expression now contains only three products, it is minimal.

PROBLEM 3

$$P = A\bar{C} + AB + \bar{A}C + \bar{A}\bar{B} \text{ (irredundant).}$$

SOLUTION

Because the given expression is irredundant, we leave out the first three steps.

Step 4. Minimize. The expression contains four products, therefore it may not be minimal. Further, because variables A and $\bar{A}$ each appear twice, and $B, \bar{B}, C,$ and $\bar{C}$ once, the necessary conditions for drawing the minimization-tree exist (see Figure (a)).

Two sets of a diagonal and vertical links can be established in this case, since the variables outside the four brackets are all the same. Using the first set (shown by the continuous lines), we obtain

$$P = AB + \bar{B}\bar{C} + \bar{A}C.$$

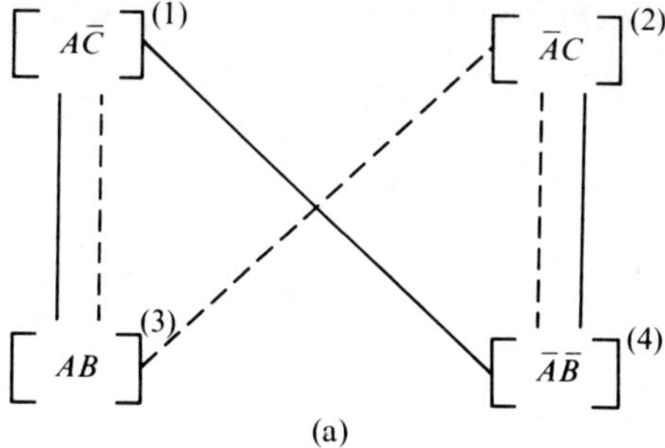

(a)

Similarly, using the second set (shown by the interrupted lines), we obtain

$$P = A\bar{C} + BC + \bar{A}\bar{B}.$$

These are the two minimal solutions obtained by reference to the Karnaugh map in Figure A1.2.

PROBLEM 4

$$P = AB + \bar{A}\bar{B} + ACD + \bar{A}\bar{C} + \bar{A}\bar{D} \text{ (irredundant).}$$

SOLUTION

As in the previous two examples, because the given expression is irredundant, we leave out steps 1, 2, and 3.

Step 4. Minimize. The expression contains five products, therefore it may not be minimal. Further, because variable A appears twice, $\bar{A}$ three times, B, $\bar{B}$, C and $\bar{C}$ once, the necessary conditions for drawing the minimization-tree exist (see Figure (a)).

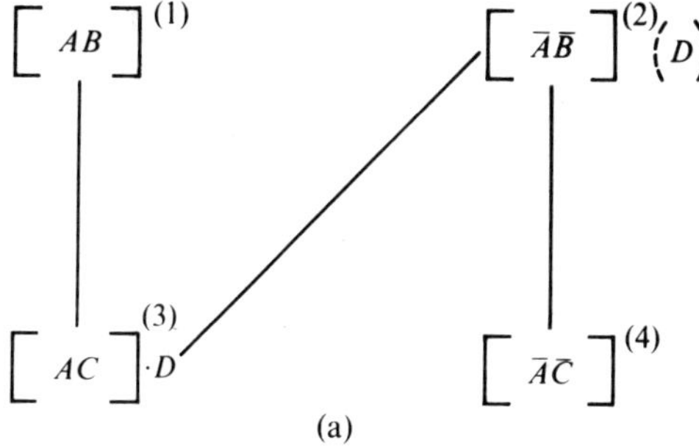

(a)

On first sight a complete set of a diagonal and two vertical links cannot be established. However, because of the presence of $\bar{A}\bar{D}$, product $\bar{A}\bar{B}$ can be modified to $\bar{A}\bar{B}D$, by Theorem 2, thus making the coefficients of brackets 2 and 3 appear the same. In this case, we obtain

$$P = AB + \bar{B}CD + \bar{A}\bar{C} + \bar{A}\bar{D}.$$

We next apply step 3 between $\bar{B}CD$ and $\bar{A}\bar{D}$.

Step 3. Apply Theorem 2.

$$P = AB + \overline{B}CD + \overline{A}\overline{D} + \overline{A}\overline{C}$$

$$\overline{A}\overline{B}C$$

$$\overline{A}\overline{B} \text{ - discard.}$$

Step 4. Minimize. The conditions for establishing the minimization-tree do not exist and cannot be made to exist, therefore,

$$P = AB + \overline{B}CD + \overline{A}\overline{C} + \overline{A}\overline{D}$$

is a minimal solution.

PROBLEM 5

$$P = ABC + ABD + \overline{A}\overline{C} + \overline{A}\overline{D} + \overline{B}\overline{D} \text{ (irredundant).}$$

SOLUTION

As in the previous three examples, because the given expression is irredundant, we leave out steps 1, 2, and 3.

Step 4. Minimize. The expression contains six products, therefore it may not be minimal. Furthermore, because variables A, $\overline{A}$, B, and $\overline{D}$ appear twice and $\overline{B}$, C, $\overline{C}$, and D once, the necessary conditions for drawing the minimization-tree exist (see Figure (a)).

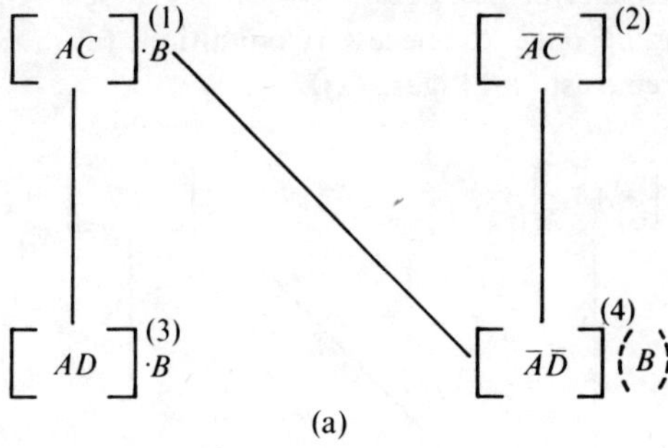

(a)

On first sight, as in the previous example, a complete set of a diagonal and two vertical links cannot be established. However, because of the presence of $\overline{B}\overline{D}$, product of $\overline{A}\overline{D}$ can be modified to $\overline{A}\overline{D}B$, by Theorem 2, thus making the variables outside brackets 1 and 4 appear the same, allowing the minimization structure to be established. In this case, we obtain

$$P = ABD + BC\overline{D} + \overline{A}\overline{C} + \overline{B}\overline{D}.$$

We next apply step 3 between $BC\overline{D}$ and $\overline{B}\overline{D}$.

Step 3. Apply Theorem 2.

$$P = ABD + BC\overline{D} + \overline{A}\,\overline{C} + \overline{B}\,\overline{D}$$

$C\overline{D}$ - replaces parent product $BC\overline{D}$.

$$= C\overline{D} + ABD + \overline{A}\,\overline{C} + \overline{B}\,\overline{D}.$$

Step 4. Minimize. The conditions for establishing the minimization-tree do not exist and cannot be made to exist, therefore,

$$P = \overline{A}\,\overline{C} + \overline{B}\,\overline{D} + C\overline{D} + ABD$$

is a minimal solution.

PROBLEM 6

$$P = AB + \overline{A}\overline{B} + AC + \overline{A}D + \overline{C}\overline{D} \text{ (irredundant).}$$

SOLUTION

Because the expression is irredundant, we leave out steps 1, 2 and 3, and proceed directly to step 4, the minimization step.

Step 4. Minimize. As the expression contains more than three products, it may not be minimal. However, our four-bracket configuration cannot be established using the products in the given expression, as the product in bracket 4 is missing from the expression. Such a product can, however, be generated from $\overline{A}D$ and $\overline{C}\overline{D}$, thus allowing us to complete the four-bracket configuration (see Figure (a)).

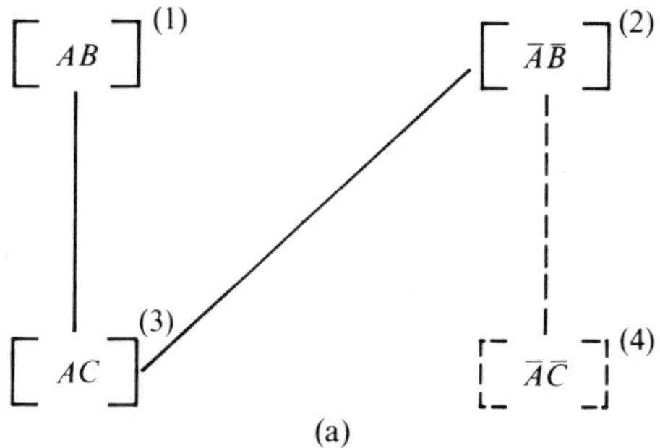

(a)

We can, therefore, replace the products in brackets 2 and 3 by $\overline{B}C$, resulting in

$$P = AB + \overline{B}C + \overline{A}D + \overline{C}\overline{D}.$$

Applying step 3 does reduce the new expression. Also, because each variable now appears only once, the new expression is minimal.

A1.5 MINTERM AND MAXTERM EXPRESSIONS

A *minterm expression* is a sum-of-products expression in which each product contains all the variables in either their true or inverted form. An example of a minterm expression is

$$P = A\bar{B}\bar{C} + AB\bar{C} + \bar{A}B\bar{C} + \bar{A}BC.$$

The minterm form of a Boolean expression is also referred to as the *standard sum* form.

To express a Boolean sum-of-products expression in minterm form we multiply each product by the sum of each missing variable and its inverse. Since the Boolean sum of a variable and its complement equals 1, the value of each expanded product is clearly not affected. For example

$$\begin{aligned} (1)\quad P &= AB + \bar{A}C \\ &= AB(C + \bar{C}) + \bar{A}C(B + \bar{B}) \\ &= ABC + AB\bar{C} + \bar{A}BC + \bar{A}\bar{B}C. \end{aligned}$$

$$\begin{aligned} (2)\quad Q &= A + \bar{B}\bar{C} \\ &= A(B + \bar{B})(C + \bar{C}) + (A + \bar{A})\bar{B}\bar{C} \\ &= ABC + AB\bar{C} + A\bar{B}C + A\bar{B}\bar{C} + A\bar{B}\bar{C} + \bar{A}\bar{B}\bar{C} \\ &= ABC + AB\bar{C} + A\bar{B}C + A\bar{B}\bar{C} + \bar{A}\bar{B}\bar{C}. \end{aligned}$$

A *maxterm expression* is a product-of-sums expression in which each sum contains all the variables in either their true or inverted forms. An example of a maxterm expression is

$$P = (A + B + C)(\bar{A} + B + C)(A + B + \bar{C}).$$

The maxterm form of a Boolean expression is also referred to as the *standard product* form.

To express a Boolean product-of-sums expression in maxterm form we replace each factor F which has a missing variable V by two factors $(F + V)(F + \bar{V})$. Since $(F + V)(F + \bar{V}) = F$, this does not affect the value of the expression. For example

$$\begin{aligned} (1)\quad P &= (A + B)(\bar{A} + C) \\ &= (A + B + C)(A + B + \bar{C})(\bar{A} + B + C)(\bar{A} + \bar{B} + C). \end{aligned}$$

$$\begin{aligned} (2)\quad Q &= (A + B)C \\ &= (A + B + C)(A + B + \bar{C})(A + C)(\bar{A} + C) \\ &= (A + B + C)(A + B + \bar{C})(A + B + C)(A + \bar{B} + C)(\bar{A} + B + C) \\ &\quad\ (\bar{A} + \bar{B} + C) \\ &= (A + B + C)(A + B + \bar{C})(A + \bar{B} + C)(\bar{A} + B + C)(\bar{A} + \bar{B} + C). \end{aligned}$$

For every maxterm expression there is a corresponding minterm expression having the same value. Conversion from minterm to maxterm form of a Boolean expression F can be accomplished in three steps:

(1) invert the function F by De Morgan's theorem,

(2) express $\bar{F}$ as a minterm expression,
(3) invert again using De Morgan's procedure.

Example

$$P = ABC + \bar{A}\bar{B}C + \bar{A}B\bar{C}.$$

$$\begin{aligned}(1)\quad \bar{P} &= (\bar{A} + \bar{B} + \bar{C})(A + B + \bar{C})(A + \bar{B} + C)\\ &= (\bar{A}B + A\bar{B} + \bar{C})(A + \bar{B} + C)\\ &= A\bar{C} + \bar{B}\bar{C} + \bar{A}BC + A\bar{B}C.\end{aligned}$$

$$\begin{aligned}(2)\quad \bar{P} &= AB\bar{C} + A\bar{B}\bar{C} + A\bar{B}\bar{C} + \bar{A}\bar{B}\bar{C} + \bar{A}BC + A\bar{B}C\\ &= AB\bar{C} + A\bar{B}\bar{C} + \bar{A}\bar{B}\bar{C} + \bar{A}BC + A\bar{B}C.\end{aligned}$$

$$(3)\quad P = (\bar{A}+\bar{B}+C)(\bar{A}+B+C)(A+B+C)(A+\bar{B}+\bar{C})(\bar{A}+B+\bar{C}).$$

The conversion from maxterm to minterm form can be accomplished by reversing the above procedure, i.e.
(1) invert the function F by De Morgan's procedure,
(2) express $\bar{F}$ as a maxterm expression,
(3) invert again using De Morgan's procedure.

A1.6. THE KARNAUGH MAP

The Karnaugh map is a device whereby the values of a Boolean function of Boolean variables for all values of these variables can be displayed in a convenient tabular form. Skeleton Karnaugh maps for functions 2, 3, 4, 5, and 6 variables are shown in Figure A1.5.

Each square corresponds to a combination of values given by the row and column headings. For example, square 14 in Figure A1.5(c) corresponds to $A = 0, B = 1, C = 1, D = 0$. Similarly, square 7 in Figure A1.5(b) corresponds to $A = 1, B = 1, C = 1$. The value of the function for the particular combination is placed in the square.

Example

For the function $P = A + BC$ we use a three-variable Karnaugh map.

For square 1, $A = 0, B = 0, C = 0$, and so $P = 0 + 0 . 0 = 0$.
For square 2, $A = 0, B = 1, C = 0$, and so $P = 0 + 1 . 0 = 0$.
For square 3, $A = 1, B = 1, C = 0$, and so $P = 1 + 1 . 0 = 1$, etc.

The result is shown in Figure A1.6.

It is important to note the succession of values given in the row and column headings i.e.

for one variable,	0 1
for two variables,	00 01 11 10;
for three variables,	000 010 110 100 101 111 011 001.

The significant feature of these sequences is that, in passing from one row

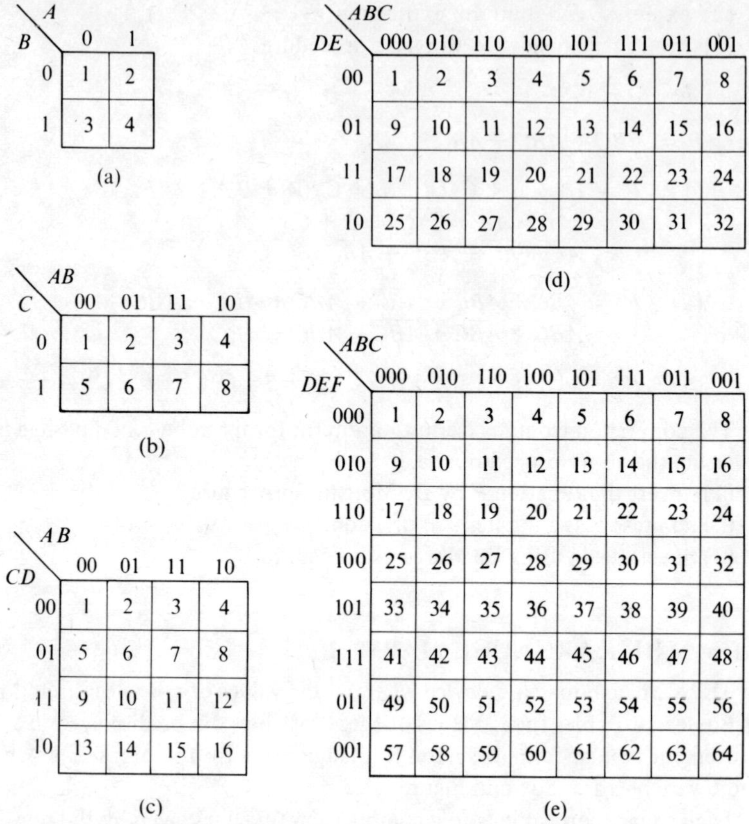

B \ A	0	1
0	1	2
1	3	4

(a)

DE \ ABC	000	010	110	100	101	111	011	001
00	1	2	3	4	5	6	7	8
01	9	10	11	12	13	14	15	16
11	17	18	19	20	21	22	23	24
10	25	26	27	28	29	30	31	32

(d)

C \ AB	00	01	11	10
0	1	2	3	4
1	5	6	7	8

(b)

CD \ AB	00	01	11	10
00	1	2	3	4
01	5	6	7	8
11	9	10	11	12
10	13	14	15	16

(c)

DEF \ ABC	000	010	110	100	101	111	011	001
000	1	2	3	4	5	6	7	8
010	9	10	11	12	13	14	15	16
110	17	18	19	20	21	22	23	24
100	25	26	27	28	29	30	31	32
101	33	34	35	36	37	38	39	40
111	41	42	43	44	45	46	47	48
011	49	50	51	52	53	54	55	56
001	57	58	59	60	61	62	63	64

(e)

FIG. A1.5. Skeleton Karnaugh maps for functions of (a) 2, (b) 3, (c) 4, (d) 5, (e) 6 variables.

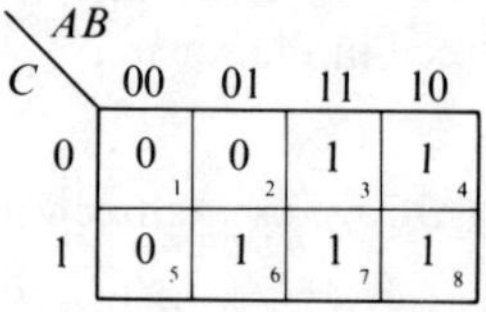

C \ AB	00	01	11	10
0	0 (1)	0 (2)	1 (3)	1 (4)
1	0 (5)	1 (6)	1 (7)	1 (8)

FIG. A1.6. Karnaugh map of $P = A + BC$.

or column to the next, the value of only one variable changes. For example, in passing from 01 to 11, A changes from 0 to 1 while B remains 1; in passing from 110 to 100, B changes from 1 to 0 while A and C remain at 1 and 0 respectively. Note also that the same applies when passing from the end of a row or column back to the beginning (10 to 00, or 001 to 000).

Other permutations may be chosen which also have this feature (for example, 00 10 11 01), but it is as well to adopt only one for each size of map and to use it consistently.

The reason for adopting such a sequence of values for the rows and columns will become clear when the applications of Karnaugh maps are discussed.

Note. Karnaugh maps are useful for displaying functions of up to 5 or 6 variables. Beyond that the map becomes complicated in use and loses its effectiveness.

Plotting Karnaugh maps

It is not necessary to compute the value of the Boolean expression for each set of values of its variables before plotting the Karnaugh map. We can usually reduce the work considerably if we realize that a term that is the product of less than all of the variables controls a group of adjacent squares. To illustrate this, consider an expression in three variables A, B, C in which ABC is a term (i.e. it is of the form $P = \ldots + ABC + \ldots$). Now if $A = B = C = 1, ABC = 1$ and so $P = 1$. Thus there is a 1 in square 7 (Figure A1.5(b)) as a consequence of the presence of the term ABC. But if we have an expression $Q = \ldots + AB + \ldots$, also in the three variables A, B, C, we have $Q = 1$ if $A = B = 1$ for both $C = 0$ and $C = 1$ (i.e. 1 in square 3 and in square 7). We can say the term ABC 'controls' square 7, the term AB controls squares 3 and 7, and, further, the term A controls squares 3, 4,, 7, 8.

In the case of a function of 4 variables (Figure A1.5(c)), a term $\overline{C}\overline{D}$ controls squares 1, 2, 3, 4, that is, in a function $F = \ldots + \overline{C}\overline{D} + \ldots$ in the four variables A, B, C, D, the presence of the term $\overline{C}\overline{D}$ implies a 1 in each of the four adjacent squares 1, 2, 3, 4.

Let us return to the example $P = A + BC$, conveniently in sum-of-products form. In such an expression, if any term is equal to 1, the whole expression is equal to 1. In terms of the map, this means that, if $A = 1$, $P = 1$ regardless of BC. We can write 1 in each of the squares 3, 4, 7, 8 for which $A = 1$. Similarly, if $BC = 1, P = 1$ regardless of A; we can write 1 in each of the squares for which $BC = 1$ - these are 6 and 7. (It happens that 7 has a 1 already.) We have now exhausted the terms of the expression; therefore we enter 0 in each of the remaining squares 1, 2, 5. The values of the variables corresponding to squares 1, 2, 5 make $P = 0$.

A similar procedure can be followed to plot an expression given as a product-of-sums. Here it is more convenient first to consider values for which the expression reduces to 0. This is because if one factor in a product is equal to 0, the whole product reduces to 0.

Consider the example

$$F = (A + \overline{B})(A + \overline{C}).$$

$F = 0$ when either $A + \overline{B} = 0$ or $A + \overline{C} = 0$, i.e. when either $A = 0$ and $B = 1$ or $A = 0$ and $C = 1$.

Now $A = 0$ and $B = 1$ specifies the adjacent squares 2 and 6 in the three-variable map. We enter 0 in these squares. Similarly, $A = 0$ and $C = 1$ specifies squares 5 and 6. There is already a 0 in square 6 so we have only to enter a further 0 in square 5. Since we have now exhausted the factors of the expression – there is no other way in which the expression can be made to take the value 0 – we enter 1 in each of the remaining squares 1, 3, 4, 7, 8 (Figure A1.7).

$C \backslash AB$	00	01	11	10
0	1 (1)	0 (2)	1 (3)	1 (4)
1	0 (5)	0 (6)	1 (7)	1 (8)

FIG. A1.7. Karnaugh map of $F = (A + \bar{B})(A + \bar{C})$.

Reading Karnaugh maps

We shall now consider the 'reading' of Karnaugh maps, that is, the translation of Karnaugh maps into equivalent Boolean expressions. Before doing so we need to clarify what is meant by the term *adjacent squares* in a Karnaugh map. Adjacent squares are squares with one side in common, for example, squares 1 and 2, squares 2 and 6 in Fig. A1.5(b). The squares at the end and beginning of a row, and the squares at the bottom and top of a column – for example, 4 and 1, and 15 and 3 in Figure A1.5(c) – are also regarded as adjacent.

An *adjacency* in a map is a set of 1 entries in adjacent squares. Adjacencies are conventionally indicated by loops drawn around them. The number of entries in an adjacency must always be a power of two (1, 2, 4, 8, 16, etc.) and the adjacency must be rectangular. Examples of adjacencies are given in Figure A1.8.

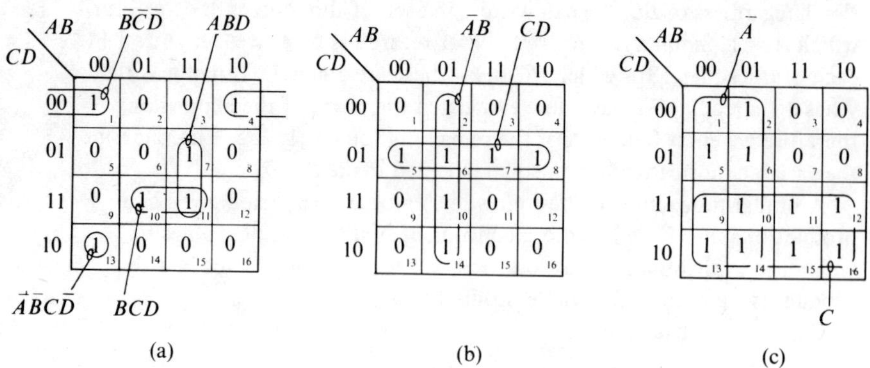

FIG. A1.8. Adjacencies in Karnaugh maps.

An adjacency of one entry stands for a term, in the sum-of-products form of the expression, which contains all the variables in the map. For example, square 13 of Figure A1.8(a) stands for $\bar{A}\bar{B}C\bar{D}$. (Check: if the expression is $P = \ldots + \bar{A}\bar{B}C\bar{D} + \ldots$, then for $A = 0, B = 0, C = 1, D = 0$, the term $\bar{A}\bar{B}C\bar{D}$, and hence P, is equal to 1.)

An adjacency of two entries always stands for a term, in the sum-of-products form of the expression, which contains one less variable than the number of variables in the map. For example, squares 10 and 11 in Figure A1.8(a) stand for BCD (10 alone stands for $\overline{A}BCD$, 11 alone stands for $ABCD$, 10 and 11 together stand for $\overline{A}BCD + ABCD = BCD$).

An adjacency of four entries always stands for a term, in the sum-of-products form of the expression, which contains two less variables than the number of variables in the map. For example, squares 2, 6, 10, 14 in Figure A1.8(b) stand for $\overline{A}B$.

(Note that squares 2, 5, 6, 7 in Figure A1.8(b) do not form an adjacency, since, although all these squares have a 1 and there are 4 of them, they do not form a rectangle.)

In general, in an m-variable map, and adjacency of 2^n entries stands for a term being a product of $(m - n)$ factors, each factor being a variable or the complement of a variable. In Figure A1.8(c), the adjacency of 8 (2^3) entries formed of squares 9–16 stands for a term that is a product of $4 - 3 = 1$ variables; this term is in fact C.

Example

Derive the minimal sum-of-products expressions for each of the Karnaugh maps in Figure A1.9.

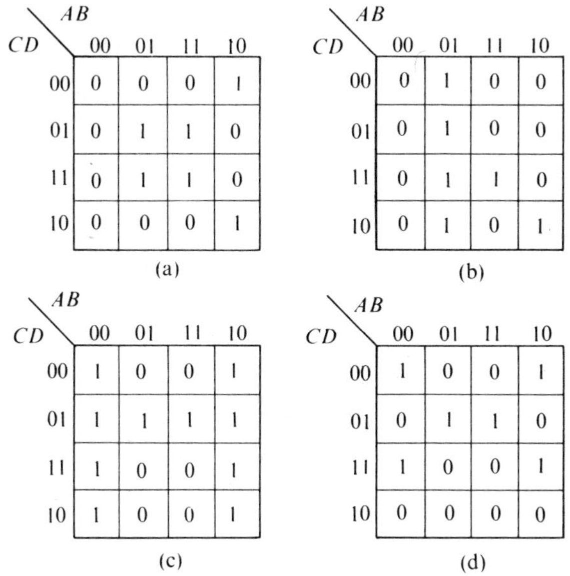

FIG. A1.9.

Answers

(a) $BD + A\overline{B}\overline{D}$, (b) $\overline{A}B + BCD + A\overline{B}C\overline{D}$, (c) $\overline{B} + \overline{C}D$, and (d) $\overline{B}\overline{C}\overline{D} + B\overline{C}D + \overline{B}CD$.

The term corresponding to an adjacency in a Karnaugh map is called a *lift set* of the expression concerned. By analogy, the term corresponding to an adjacency in the Karnaugh map of the complementary expression is called a *drop set* of the original expression.

Figure A1.10 shows a Karnaugh map with 1 and 0 entries looped. The lift sets here are $\overline{A}\overline{B}$ and AB; the drop sets are $\overline{A}B$ and $A\overline{B}$.

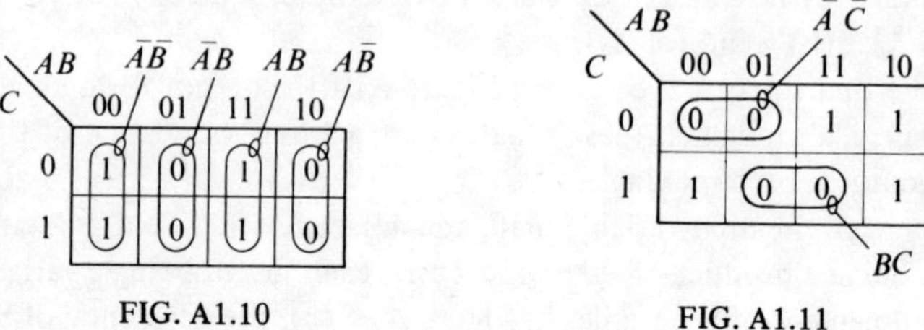

FIG. A1.10 FIG. A1.11

Clearly, a Boolean sum can be expressed as a sum of its lift sets. We can express the function in terms of lift sets $P = \overline{A}\overline{B} + AB$ and we can express its complement in terms of the drop sets $\overline{P} = \overline{A}B + A\overline{B}$.

Inverting this last equation,

$$P = (A + \overline{B})(\overline{A} + B)$$
$$= AB + \overline{A}\overline{B}.$$

Example

Derive the minimal product-of-sums expression of the function given its Karnaugh map in Figure A1.11.

Answer

$$\overline{f} = \text{sum of drop sets}$$
$$= \overline{A}\overline{C} + BC.$$

Inverting,

$$f = (A + C)(\overline{B} + \overline{C}).$$

A1.7 PROBLEMS AND ANSWERS

Boolean reduction

Reduce the Boolean functions	*Answers*
1. $A + \overline{A}B + BC$	$A + B$
2. $A + \overline{A}B + \overline{B}C$	$A + B + C$
3. $A\overline{B} + \overline{A}B + ABC\overline{C}$	$A\overline{B} + \overline{A}B + A\overline{C}$ or $A\overline{B} + \overline{A}B + B\overline{C}$
4. $A(\overline{A} + B)(\overline{B} + C)$	ABC
5. $(A + B)(\overline{A} + C)(B + C + D)$	$(A + B)(\overline{A} + C)$

	Answers
6. $(A + \bar{A}B)(\bar{A} + AC)(B\bar{C} + C\bar{D} + D)$	$(A + B)(\bar{A} + C)$
7. $AB + \bar{B}CD + \bar{A}\bar{B} + A$	$A + \bar{B}$
8. $A + \bar{A}B + AB + \bar{A}\bar{B}$	1
9. $A + B + \bar{A}\bar{B}C + \bar{C}D$	$A + B + C + D$
10. $AD + BD + CD + \bar{A}\bar{B}\bar{C}$	$D + \bar{A}\bar{B}\bar{C}$
11. $AB + AD + \bar{B}\bar{D} + A\bar{C}\bar{D}$	$A + \bar{B}\bar{D}$
12. $ABC + ABD + A\bar{C}\bar{D} + \bar{A}\bar{D}$	$AB + \bar{A}\bar{D} + \bar{C}\bar{D}$
13. $(A + B)(\bar{B} + \bar{C} + \bar{D})(A + \bar{C} + \bar{D} + \bar{E})$ $(A + B + C + D)$	$(A + B)(\bar{B} + \bar{C} + \bar{D})$
14. $(A + B + C)(\bar{A} + B + \bar{D}) + BD$	$(A + B + C)(\bar{A} + B + \bar{D})$
15. $(A + \bar{A}B + C)(\bar{A} + \bar{B} + C) + CDE$	$(A + B + C)(\bar{A} + \bar{B} + C)$
16. $(A + B + \bar{A}\bar{B}C)(\bar{A} + C + D) + (\bar{B} + \bar{D})E$	$(A + B + C)(\bar{A} + C + D)$ $+ E$
17. $(A + B + C)(A + B + D)(A + \bar{C} + \bar{D})$ $(\bar{A} + \bar{D})$	$(A + B)(\bar{A} + \bar{D})(\bar{C} + \bar{D})$
18. $(\bar{A} + B + \bar{C})(A + D)(C + D)(B + D)$	$(A + D)(C + D)(\bar{A} + B + \bar{C})$
19. $\bar{A}\bar{B} + (A + B)C + \bar{C}\bar{D} + D$	1
20. $A\bar{B} + \bar{A}CD + B + \bar{C} + \bar{D}$	1
21. $(A + B)(\bar{A}\bar{B} + C)(\bar{C} + \bar{D})\bar{D}$	$(A + B)C\bar{D}$
22. $(A + \bar{A}B + \bar{B}C)(A\bar{D} + B\bar{D} + C\bar{D} + D)$ $(E + F)$	$(A + B + C)(E + F)$
23. $(A + B + \bar{A}\bar{B}C)(\bar{A}\bar{B} + D)(C + D + E)$	$(A + B + C)(\bar{A}\bar{B} + D)$
24. $\bar{A}\bar{B}\bar{C} + (A + \bar{B})C + \bar{C}\bar{D} + \bar{B}\bar{D}$	$\bar{A}\bar{B} + AC + \bar{C}\bar{D}$

Boolean minimization

Minimize the Boolean functions	*Answers*
25. $A + B + \bar{A}\bar{B}C + D$	$A + B + C + D$
26. $A + \bar{A}\bar{B} + \bar{B}(C + DE)$	$A + \bar{B}$
27. $\bar{A}D + \bar{B}CD + A\bar{B}(C + D) + \bar{B}\bar{C}\bar{D}$	$\bar{A}D + A\bar{B}$
28. $C\bar{E} + \bar{C}\bar{D} + ABCD + ABC\bar{E}$	$ABCD + C\bar{E} + \bar{C}\bar{D}$
29. $A(\bar{B} + \bar{C}) + A\bar{B}D + ABCD$	$AD + A\bar{B} + A\bar{C}$
30. $\bar{A}D + \bar{B}CD + A\bar{B}(C + D) + \bar{B}\bar{C}\bar{D}$	$A\bar{B} + \bar{B}\bar{C} + \bar{A}D$
31. $\bar{A}\bar{B} + \bar{A}D + CD\bar{E} + E$	$\bar{A}\bar{B} + \bar{A}D + CD + E$
32. $\bar{A}\bar{B}\bar{C} + \bar{A}BC + AB\bar{C}\bar{D} + AB\bar{C}D + E$	$\bar{A}\bar{B}\bar{C} + \bar{A}BC + AB\bar{C} + E$
33. $\bar{A}\bar{B}\bar{C} + \bar{A}\bar{B}C + B\bar{C}\bar{D} + A\bar{B}\bar{C} + ABCD$	$\bar{A}\bar{B} + \bar{C}\bar{D} + \bar{B}\bar{C} + ABCD$
34. $\bar{A}BD + ABC + A\bar{B}\bar{C}\bar{D} + A\bar{B}\bar{C}D + \bar{A}\bar{B}C\bar{D}$	$ABC + \bar{A}BD + A\bar{B}\bar{C} + \bar{A}\bar{B}C\bar{D}$
35. $AB + \bar{A}\bar{B} + A\bar{C} + \bar{A}C$	$A\bar{C} + BC + \bar{A}\bar{B}$ or $AB + \bar{B}\bar{C} + \bar{A}C$
36. $A\bar{B} + \bar{A}B + AC + \bar{A}\bar{C}$	$A\bar{B} + BC + \bar{A}\bar{C}$ or $AC + \bar{B}\bar{C} + \bar{A}B$
37. $ABD + \bar{A}\bar{B}D + ACD + \bar{A}\bar{C}D$	$ABD + \bar{B}CD + \bar{A}\bar{C}D$ or $B\bar{C}D + \bar{A}\bar{B}D + ACD$
38. $(\bar{A} + B + C)(\bar{A} + \bar{B} + \bar{C})(\bar{A} + \bar{C} + D)$ $(\bar{A} + C + \bar{D})$	$(\bar{A} + B + C)(\bar{A} + \bar{B} + \bar{D})$ $(\bar{A} + \bar{C} + D)$

or $(\bar{A} + C + \bar{D})(\bar{A} + B + D)$
$(\bar{A} + \bar{B} + \bar{C})$

39. $\bar{A}\bar{B} + AC + \bar{A}\bar{C}D + ABD$ $\quad AC + B\bar{C}D + \bar{A}\bar{B}$
40. $\bar{A}BD + \bar{A}CDE + A\bar{B}DE + A\bar{C}D$ $\quad \bar{A}BD + \bar{B}CDE + A\bar{C}D$
41. $\bar{A}\bar{B}\bar{C} + \bar{A}\bar{C}D + ABD + AC$ $\quad AC + B\bar{C}D + \bar{A}\bar{B}\bar{C}$
42. $AB + AC + \bar{A}\bar{C} + \bar{A}D + A\bar{B}E$ $\quad AC + B\bar{C} + \bar{A}\bar{C} + \bar{A}D + AE$
43. $A\bar{B}D + ACD + \bar{A}B + \bar{A}\bar{C}$ $\quad A\bar{B}D + ACD + \bar{A}B + \bar{A}\bar{C}$
44. $\bar{A}B\bar{C} + \bar{A}CD + A\bar{C}D + A\bar{B}C$ $\quad \bar{A}B\bar{C} + \bar{A}CD + A\bar{C}D + A\bar{B}C$
45. $A\bar{C} + AB + \bar{A}\bar{B} + B\bar{D} + \bar{A}CD$ $\quad A\bar{C} + BC + \bar{A}\bar{B} + B\bar{D}$
46. $AC + A\bar{B} + \bar{A}\bar{C}D + \bar{A}B + A\bar{D}$ $\quad AC + \bar{B}\bar{C}D + \bar{A}B + A\bar{D}$
47. $(A + B)(\bar{A} + \bar{B})(A + \bar{D})(A + C)$ $\quad (A + C)(B + \bar{C} + D)$
$(\bar{A} + \bar{C} + D)$ $\quad (\bar{A} + \bar{B})(A + \bar{D})$
48. $(A + D)(\bar{A} + \bar{C})(\bar{A} + \bar{D})(\bar{B} + \bar{D})$ $\quad (A + D)(C + \bar{D})(\bar{A} + \bar{C})$
$(A + B + C)$ $\quad (\bar{B} + \bar{D})$

Index

Action/status devices, 54
algebra, *see* Boolean
asynchronous counters, 146
asynchronous sequential circuits, *see* unclocked sequential circuits

B-c-d counters, 153
binary codes, *see* codes
Boolcan algebra
  basic concepts, 194
  karnaugh maps, 213
  maxterms and minterms, 212
  problems and answers, 218
  redundancies, 199
Boolean minimization, 204
Boolean operations, 194
Boolean reduction, 199
Boolean theorems, 195

Circuit misoperation, 15
classification of logic circuits, 1
clock-driven circuits, *see* clocked sequential circuits
clocked flip-flops, 82
clocked (clock-driven, pulse-driven) sequential circuits
  definition, 1
  design steps, 83
  introduction, 82
  problems and solutions
    1. a pulse distributor, 90
    2. pulse frequency reduction, 91
    3. a pulse train switch, 92
    4. one-shot circuit, 94
    5. a word scanner, 95
    6. a binary string scanner, 97
    7. 4-5-6 detector, 98
    8. blank entries, 100
    9. radar control, 101
    10. a digital scanner, 104
    11. a three-pump controller, 106
    12. invalid code detection, 108
    13. a parity circuit, 110
    14. a word comparator, 111
    15. a self-locking data buffer, 113
    16. a double data buffer, 114
codes
  b-c-d, 135
  Gray, 134
  Johnson, 135
  Hamming, 135
  shift register, 86
  true binary, 134
  weighted/non-weighted, 135
combinational circuits
  definition, 2
  introduction, 170
  problems and solutions
    1. circuit reduction, 176
    2. circuit reductions, 177
    3. minimal design, 178
    4. minimal design, 179
    5. minimal design, 180
    6. race hazards, 181
    7. hazard-free design, 182
    8. a parity circuit, 183
    9. two's complement circuit, 183
    10. seven-segment display, 184
    11. encoders/decoders, 186
    12. code conversion, 186
    13. NOR circuit design, 187
    14. a two-flag sorter, 188
    15. a four-flag sorter, 189
    16. an eight-flag sorter, 190
    17. a 64-flag sorter, 191
counters
  asynchronous (ripple-through) binary, 146
  b-c-d, 153
  classification, 2
  decode, 151
  definition, 134
  design steps, 136
  Gray, 140, 143, 146
  Johnson, 154
  problems and solutions
    1. binary counters, 155
    2. programmable counters, 155
    3. a self-locking counter, 156
    4. pulse tranis
    5. Gray up/down counter, 159
    6. Gray up/down decode counter, 159
    7. b-c-d 'up' counters, 160
    8. divide-by-60 circuit, 162
    9. a 60-minute clock, 163
    10. a 12-hour clock, 164
    11. a 24-hour clock, 165
    12. an event counter, 166
    13. a digital tachometer, 167
    14. a large cycle shift register, 168
  resettable, 149
  ripple-though, 146
  synchronous binary, 136, 139
  up/down control, 144
cyclic circuits, 2, 87

Decode counters, 151

decoders, 186
definitions
  Boolean minimization, 204
  Boolean redundancies, 199
  circuit misoperation, 15
  clocked flip-flops, 82
  clocked sequential circuits, 2, 82
  combinational circuits, 2
  counters, 134
  cyclic circuits, 2, 87
  'don't care' conditions, 15
  'fan-in' restrictions, 170
  flag signals, 62
  flag sorters, 188
  race hazards, 22
  sequential circuits, 2
  weighted/non-weighted codes, 135
design factors, 35, 82
design philosophy, 1
design steps for sequential circuits, 35, 82, 117, 136
DFF (D flip-flop), 82
'don't care' conditions, 15
dummy states, 9

Encoders, 186
error-correcting codes, 135
event-driven circuits, *see* unclocked sequential circuits
external-state diagrams, 7

Fan-in restrictions, 170
fan-in theorem, 197
flag signals, 62
flag sorters, 188
flip-flops (clocked)
  DFFF, 73, 82
  JKFF, 74, 82
  SRFF, 82
  TFF, 71, 82
front end logic, 57

Gates, 3
Gray counters, 140, 143, 146

Hamming codes, 135
hazards, *see* race hazards

Internal characteristics, 35, 84, 117
internal state diagrams, 7, 8

JKFFs
  external operation, 82
  internal operation, 74
Johnson codes, 135
Johnson counters, 154

Karnaugh maps, 213

Logic design
  design philosophy, 1
  introduction, 1
logic circuits, 1

Maxterms, 212
Merging table, 171, 172
minimization (Boolean), 204
minterms, 212
misoperation of sequential circuits, 15
multi-mode circuits, 121

NAND circuits, 4
non-weighted codes, 135
NOR circuits, 4

Parity circuit, 183
priority encoders, *see* flag sorters
problems and answers, *see* Boolean algebra
problems and solutions, *see* clocked sequential circuits, combinational circuits, counters, pulse-driven circuits, unclocked sequential circuits
pulse-driven circuits, 115
  introduction, 115
  the design steps, 117
  a design problem, 118
  problems and solutions, 123
  pulse sequence detector, 123
  an electronic padlock, 125
  a motor control, 128
  up/down control of counters, 132

Races between primary signals, 15
races between primary and secondary signals, 18
races between secondary signals, 17
race-free diagrams, 10
race hazards, 22, 170, 181
redundancies, *see* Boolean
ripple-through counters, 146

Secondary signals, 9
sequential circuits
  classification, 2
  clocked (clock-driven or synchronous), 82
  cyclic, 2, 87
  definition, 1
  pulse driven, 115
  unclocked (event-driven or asynchronous), 35
sequential equations, 1, 19
shift registers, 86
signal races, 15
SRFFs, 82
state diagrams, 7
state reduction, 12
state tables, 12

state variables, 9
synchronous sequential circuits, 82

TFFs
  external operation, 82
  internal operation, 71
theorems, *see* Boolean
$33^1/_3$ per cent property, 21
transition table, 25
tristates, 7
two-wire interface, 54

Unclocked (event-driven or asynchronous) sequential circuits
  definition, 2
  design steps, 35
  introduction, 35
  problems and solutions, 37
unspecified circuit responses, 11
unused states, 11

Weighted codes, 135